The Quality System Compendium

GMP Requirements & Industry Practice

Second Edition

Tammy M. Pelnik, Technical Editor
With contributions from FDA and Industry

Association for the Advancement of Medical Instrumentation
1110 North Glebe Road, Suite 220, Arlington, VA 22201-4795
Phone 703-525-4890 / Fax 703-276-0793

Published by the
Association for the Advancement of Medical Instrumentation
1110 North Glebe Road, Suite 220
Arlington, VA 22201-4795

Printed in the United States of America

ISBN 1-57020-292-3

FOREWORD AND ACKNOWLEDGMENTS

The Association for the Advancement of Medical Instrumentation (AAMI) is an alliance of medical instrumentation entities with the common goal of increasing the understanding and effective use of medical instrumentation. As a part of its mission, AAMI offers numerous courses on various aspects of the safe design, manufacturing, and use of medical instrumentation. *The Quality System Compendium: GMP Requirements & Industry Practice* serves as the basis for AAMI's intensive course titled "GMP Requirements & Industry Practice," which presents the requirements of the Quality System regulation.

The first edition of *The Quality System Compendium: GMP Requirements & Industry Practice* was published in 1996. That edition presented the best industry practices at the time and was based on the collective wisdom of the foremost experts on the regulation from all related disciplines, including Food and Drug Administration (FDA) staff, corporate representatives, and leading industry consultants. The *Supplement to the Quality System Compendium* was published in 2004. It provided updated information on FDA's organizational structure, international Quality System standards, and new information concerning industry practices for managing electronic records and signatures, process validation, and software validation. This second edition of the *Compendium* combines the previous two books, and expands on their content. It represents current industry practice and FDA regulatory strategies, based on more than 10 years of industry and regulatory experience working with the Quality System regulation.

AAMI wishes to gratefully acknowledge the many individuals who contributed to this and the previous edition of the *Compendium* and the *Supplement*. The expert authors and technical editors have each provided immeasurable value in producing a text that is a fair and comprehensive treatment of this broad topic: the Quality System regulation and current industry practice. AAMI thanks each of the contributors to this and previous editions:

Edwin L. Bills, Bilanx Consulting
Cheryl Boyce, Boyce Regulatory & Quality Consulting
Vera A. Buffaloe, Buffaloe Consulting, Inc.
Robert Etheredge, Transport Pharmaceuticals, Inc.
William J. Feingold, Spektra Management Consultants, Inc.
Chris Flahive, Chris Flahive Associates
Annette M. Hillring, Hillring & Associates, Inc.
Wm. Fred Hooten, Hogan & Hartson
Doug Lichorwic, Northrop Grumman Information Technologies
Karen Mackison, Consultant (formerly Baxter Healthcare)
John J. Malloy, Malloy and Associates, Inc.
Edward McDonnell, Biometric Research Institute, Inc.
Dale McMullen, GMP Institute
Jane Moffitt, Consultant
M. Christine Nelson, Consultant
Philip E. Nickerson, Consultant
Daniel P. Olivier, Computer Applications Specialists

Tammy M. Pelnik, The St. Vrain Group, Inc.
Virginia Perry, Perry-D'Amico and Associates
Susan C. Reilly, Medical Device Consultants, Inc.
James W. Sandberg, Protocol Systems, Inc.
John Sawyer, Realistic Quality Solutions
Patricia B. Shrader, Becton-Dickinson and Company
Larry Spears, U.S. Food and Drug Administration
Robert Steinmeier, Abbott Laboratories
Anita Thibeault, Anita Thibeault and Associates
Kimberly A. Trautman, U.S. Food and Drug Administration
William R. Trilsch, William Trilsch and Associates
Tim Ulatowski, U.S. Food and Drug Administration
Arthur J. Ward, AJW Technology Consultants, Inc.
Jan B. Welch, U.S. Food and Drug Administration

In addition, AAMI acknowledges Ed Kimmelman, John Gagliardi, and Kimberly A. Trautman, the presenters for AAMI's online seminar, "Comparing the New Quality System Standard ANSI/AAMI/ISO 13485:2003 With the FDA Quality System Regulation." AAMI offered this seminar on December 17, 2003. Material from that presentation was adapted for this edition.

AAMI is also very grateful for the early contributions of the members of the AAMI GMP Steering Committee and the AAMI GMP Education and Training Committee, including the participation of FDA personnel. Both committees volunteered their time and considerable expertise to develop AAMI's educational program, which was originally launched in March 1997. In addition, AAMI's expert course faculty members have continued to provide assistance in updating the course content to ensure that course materials provide up-to-date industry practice guidance. AAMI's faculty has ensured that the courses are subject to continuous improvement.

AAMI acknowledges the assistance of Kathy Warye, the former AAMI staff member who initially organized and coordinated the publication of the first edition of the *Compendium*, and Judith A. Veale, who edited that text.

Finally, AAMI also acknowledges the assistance of Deborah Reuter, AAMI's vice president of government programs, who organized and coordinated the publication of the *Supplement* and publication of this second edition. Her focus on ensuring that AAMI's courses and related material continue to provide attendees with critical insight into current industry practices was vital in completing this project. Publication Professionals LLC also provided considerable assistance in copy editing this second edition.

INTRODUCTION

The Quality System Compendium: GMP Requirements & Industry Practice, second edition, provides a comprehensive explanation of the Food and Drug Administration (FDA) Quality System regulation. The *Compendium* is organized in logical "subsystems," where related aspects of the Quality System regulation are presented in sequence, to facilitate a system-based understanding of the regulatory requirements. The specific requirements are grouped into eight major subject areas: general provisions, quality management, design controls, acceptance activities, production and process controls, product controls, monitoring and feedback, and documents and records. The text presents each section of the regulation followed by a discussion of the requirements, which presents a regulatory perspective, and a review of current industry practice. This second edition provides new and seasoned professionals with a resource that helps explain the "current" implementation approaches of medical device current Good Manufacturing Practice (GMP) as defined in the Quality System regulation. This resource is based on 10 years of industry experience.

In addition, several chapters present current practice for specific regulatory areas that have matured in the years since the Quality System regulation was first published, notably electronic records and electronic signatures compliance, process validation, risk management, and software validation. A new chapter on combination products and FDA's regulatory perspective provides a summary of current practice and challenges for such products. Finally, the appendices provide a bibliography, an extensive list of relevant Internet web sites, a complete copy of the Final Rule for the Quality System, and an index.

In the October 7, 1996, issue of the *Federal Register,* FDA published the Final Rule for the Quality System regulation (see Appendix C). The Quality System regulation superseded the GMP regulation promulgated in 1978. The final rule culminated a revisions process, undertaken by FDA under the authority of the Safe Medical Devices Act (SMDA) of 1990, to amend the original medical device GMP regulation. The focus of the GMP amendment activity was incorporating preproduction design controls and implementing other Quality System requirements for consistency with applicable international standards. The standards were primarily the International Organization for Standards (ISO) 9001:1994 *Quality Systems—Model for Quality Assurance in Design, Development, Production, Installation, and Servicing,* and the ISO committee draft (CD) revision of ISO/CD 13485 *Quality Systems—Medical Devices—Supplementary Requirements to ISO 9001.* Chapters 2 and 3 provide additional information and perspective on FDA's harmonization efforts and ISO 13485.

The basic Quality System requirements remain in effect more than 10 years later, although a few technical amendments have been published in the intervening years. These amendments address issues such as title or address changes for various FDA offices specifically cited in the regulation. Furthermore, industry and FDA have adopted additional strategies for compliance since the publication of the Final Rule of the Quality System regulation. FDA's efforts to harmonize U.S. regulations with international medical device regulations, coupled with efforts by various independent standards organizations, have resulted in a better understanding and implementation of key Quality System areas.

Recognizing the critical need for expertise in interpreting and applying the Quality System regulation, the Association for the Advancement of Medical Instrumentation (AAMI) has developed an educational program for industry professionals. The primary goals of AAMI's educational program are twofold:

a. AAMI seeks to support establishment of a common body of knowledge on the Quality System regulation.

b. AAMI intends to provide a series of education courses that will be credible and beneficial to regulatory, quality, and other professionals, including staff members of medical device manufacturers, GMP consultants, and FDA staff.

AAMI offers a series of courses, domestically and internationally, to meet its educational goals, including courses on topics such as:
- GMP requirements (i.e., the Quality System regulation);
- design controls;
- process validation;
- software validation;
- corrective and preventive action;
- risk management; and
- sterilization processes.

FDA's Center for Devices and Radiological Health has actively supported the development and presentation of AAMI's public courses. AAMI envisions that its educational program will ultimately benefit all those involved in medical device manufacturing by bringing greater uniformity and consistency to the interpretation and application of the medical device GMP requirements.

ABBREVIATIONS AND ACRONYMS

§:	Section (e.g., § 820.25), used throughout the Quality System regulation
510(k):	Premarket Notification submitted under section 510(k) of the federal Food, Drug and Cosmetic Act
AAMI:	Association for the Advancement of Medical Instrumentation
ACRA:	Associate Commissioner for Regulatory Affairs
ANSI:	American National Standards Institute
AP:	Accredited Person
ASQ:	American Society for Quality (previously, ASQC: American Society for Quality Control)
ASTM:	American Society for Testing and Materials
ATE:	Automated Test Equipment
BLA:	Biologics License Application
CAB:	Conformity Assessment Body
CAPA:	Corrective and Preventive Action
CBER:	Center for Biologics Evaluation and Research
CDER:	Center for Drug Evaluation and Research
CDRH:	Center for Devices and Radiological Health
CE:	Conformité Européene (French phrase that literally means "European Conformity". CE Marking is affixing "CE" to products, indicating that the manufacturer has conformed to all European Union obligations required by EU legislation).
CEO:	Chief Executive Officer
CFR:	Code of Federal Regulations
cGMP:	current Good Manufacturing Practice
CNC:	Computerized Numerical Control
DCN:	Document Change Notice
DCO:	Document Change Order
DCR:	Document Change Request
DHF:	Design History File
DHR:	Device History Record
DMR:	Device Master Record
DSMA:	Division of Small Manufacturers Assistance (has been changed to DSMICA)

DSMICA:	Division of Small Manufacturers, International and Consumer Assistance (formerly DSMA)
EC:	European Council
ECN:	Engineering Change Notice
ECO:	Engineering Change Order
ECR:	Engineering Change Request
EIR:	Establishment Inspection Report
EPA:	Environmental Protection Agency
ESD:	Electrostatic Discharge
EtO:	Ethylene Oxide
EU:	European Union
FD&C:	Federal Food, Drug, and Cosmetic
FDA:	Food and Drug Administration
FDAMA:	Food and Drug Administration Modernization Act of 1997
FIFO:	First In, First Out
FMEA:	Failure Modes and Effects Analysis
FOI:	Freedom of Information
FTA:	Fault Tree Analysis
FY:	Fiscal Year
GAMP:	*Good Automated Manufacturing Practice Guide* (published by ISPE)
GHTF:	Global Harmonization Task Force
GLP:	Good Laboratory Practice
GMP:	Good Manufacturing Practice
HACCP:	Hazard Analysis and Critical Control Points
HCT/P:	Human cells, tissues, and cellular and tissue-based product
HEPA:	High-Efficiency Particulate Air
HIPAA:	Health Insurance Portability & Accountability Act of 1996
HR:	Human Resources
HVAC:	Heating, Ventilation, and Air Conditioning
IDE:	Investigational Device Exemption
IEC:	International Electrotechnical Commission
IEEE:	Institute of Electrical and Electronics Engineers
IQ:	Installation Qualification
ISO:	International Organization for Standardization
ISPE:	International Society of Pharmaceutical Engineering

IT:	Information Technology
IVD:	In Vitro Diagnostics
IVDD:	In Vitro Diagnostics Directive (EU IVD regulations)
MDD:	Medical Device Directive (EU medical device regulations)
MDR:	Medical Device Report
MDUFMA:	Medical Device User Fee and Modernization Act of 2002
MRA:	Mutual Recognition Agreement
MRB:	Material Review Board
MRC:	Material Review Committee
MRP:	Material Resource Planning
NAI:	No Action Indicated
NB:	Notified Body
NIST:	National Institute of Standards and Technology
OAI:	Official Action Indicated
OCP:	Office of Combination Products
ODE:	Office of Device Evaluation
OIVD:	Office of In Vitro Diagnostics
OQ:	Operational Qualification
ORA:	Office of Regulatory Affairs
OSHA:	Occupational Safety and Health Administration
OTS:	Off-the-Shelf
P&PC:	Production and Process Controls
PC:	Personal Computer
PCB:	Printed Circuit Board
PDF:	Portable Document Format (a computer data file exchange format, trademarked by Adobe Software International)
PDP:	Product Development Protocol
PERT:	Program Evaluation and Review Technique
PMA:	Premarket Approval
PQ:	Performance Qualification
QA:	Quality Assurance
QC:	Quality Control
QFD:	Quality Function Deployment
QMS:	Quality Management System
QS:	Quality System

QSIT: Quality System Inspection Technique

QSR: Quality System Record

R&D: Research and Development

R&R: Repeatability and Reproducibility

RA: Regulatory Affairs

SGML: Standard Generalized Markup Language (a computer language, portable to many different operating systems; SGML is what the web language HTML is based on)

SMDA: Safe Medical Devices Act of 1990

SOP: Standard Operating Procedure

SUD: Single-use Device

TAPPI: Technical Association of the Paper and Pulp Industry

U.S.:   United States

USC: United States Code (codification of the laws of the United States)

USP: U.S. Pharmacopeia

VAI: Voluntary Action Indicated

XML: Extensible Markup Language (a computer language, portable to many different operating systems)

SECTION I. REGULATORY OVERVIEW

CHAPTER 1. FDA'S ORGANIZATION AND REGULATORY STRATEGIES

FDA's Mission

The Food and Drug Administration Modernization Act (FDAMA) of 1997 (Public Law 105-115) affirmed the public health protection role of the Food and Drug Administration (FDA) and defined the Agency's current mission with respect to the regulation of medical devices, drugs, food, cosmetics, and radiation-emitting products. Specifically, FDAMA established FDA's mission as the following:

1. To promote the public health by promptly and efficiently reviewing clinical research, and taking appropriate action on the marketing of regulated products in a timely manner.

2. To protect the public health by ensuring that:
   - Foods are safe, wholesome, sanitary, and properly labeled;
   - Human and veterinary drugs are safe and effective;
   - Devices intended for human use have reasonable assurance of safety and effectiveness;
   - Cosmetics are safe and properly labeled; and
   - Electronic product radiation reasonably provides for public health and safety protection.

3. To participate through appropriate processes with representatives of other countries in order to reduce the burden of regulation, harmonize regulatory requirements, and achieve appropriate reciprocal arrangements.

4. As determined to be appropriate by the Secretary of Health & Human Services, to carry out the activities described above, in:
   - Consultation with experts in science, medicine, and public health; and
   - Cooperation with consumers, users, manufacturers, importers, packers, distributors and retailers of regulated products.

The Medical Device User Fee and Modernization Act (MDUFMA) of 2002 (Public Law 107-250) amended the Federal Food, Drug, and Cosmetic (FD&C) Act to provide FDA with new responsibilities, resources, and challenges. MDUFMA was originally in effect until September 30, 2007. Some of the more significant provisions included the following:
- user fees for premarket reviews,
- establishment inspections by accredited persons (third parties),
- new regulatory requirements for reprocessed single-use devices (SUDs), and
- electronic labeling for prescription devices that are intended for use in health care facilities.

MDUFMA recognized that public health would be served by increasing FDA funding to facilitate timely, high-quality product reviews. Ultimately, this increased funding should lead to more rapid introduction of safe and effective medical treatments. MDUFMA authorizes FDA to collect fees for Premarket Approval (PMA) applications, Product Development Protocols (PDPs), premarket reports for reprocessed SUDs, Biologics License Applications (BLAs), certain supplements, and 510(k)s (Premarket Notifications). The authority to collect user fees is tied to performance goals for the FDA.

MDUFMA authorized FDA to establish a third-party program for conducting inspections of certain medical device manufacturers. FDA evaluates and trains the third parties and makes the final decision about what, if any, regulatory action to take as a result of an inspection by a third party. By allowing the use of third-party inspections, FDA is able to focus internal resources on higher-risk inspections. Information regarding third-party inspections and a list of accredited third parties is available on FDA's web site under "Accredited Persons Inspection Program."

MDUFMA provided several definitions relevant to reprocessed SUDs and imposes additional requirements for labeling. Labeling must identify the particular medical device as reprocessed and provide the name of the manufacturer that reprocessed the device. Other requirements relate to premarket review of reprocessed SUDs. The premarket review of reprocessed SUDs is based on the finished device's product classification. In some cases, reprocessing validation data must accompany premarket notification and premarket approval applications.

MDUFMA authorized manufacturers to provide labeling in electronic form for certain medical devices.[1] Manufacturers of such devices must provide traditional paper labeling upon request.

The FDA performance goals established by MDUFMA were monitored and evaluated by Congress. FDA reported performance status for fiscal year (FY) 2003 and FY2006 as follows:

Percentage of Decisions Meeting Goal[2]	FY2003	FY2006
PMAs/Panel Track Decisions (Goal: 320 days)	91.7%	100.0%
Expedited PMAs (Goal: 300 days)	100.0%	0 (2 open)
180-day PMA Supplements	94.1%	98.9%
510(k) Decisions (Goal: 90 days)	76.1%	96.5%

The FDA Amendments Act of 2007 (Public Law 110-85), signed into law in September 2007, included several provisions concerning medical devices, pharmaceuticals, and food safety. Among the provisions was reauthorization and expansion of MDUFMA, extending its expiration to 2012. The expansion includes new requirements for manufacturers to:
- provide annual facility registration data electronically,
- pay annual registration fees,

---

[1] *General Program Memorandum #G03-1 (MDUFMA)*, FDA/CDRH, March 31, 2003
[2] *Quarterly Update on Progress Towards Meeting MDUFMA Performance Goals – Performance Data For FDA (Combined CBER and CDRH) – Actions through September 30, 2006*, FDA

- include a description of the potential impact of new devices on pediatric populations in premarket submissions, and
- conduct postmarket surveillance studies when directed by FDA as a condition of device clearance or approval.

In addition, medical device clinical trial sponsors must now register 510(k) and PMA pivotal trials with the National Institutes of Health, and post their study results when available.

Details on the implementation of the MDUFMA are available on the Center for Devices and Radiological Health (CDRH) web site under "Device Program Areas."

Organization of the FDA

FDA is a part of the U.S. Department of Health and Human Services. It is headed by a commissioner who is appointed by the U.S. President and confirmed by the U.S. Senate. The commissioner is typically assisted by associate commissioners, a chief counsel, and an administrative law judge, all of whom direct operations in their respective offices. The current structure of the FDA commissioner's office is available on FDA's web site under www.fda.gov/oc.

Five centers at FDA headquarters regulate substantive commodity areas including food, drugs, biologic products, medical devices, radiation-emitting electronic products, veterinary medicine products, and cosmetics. Each center is led by a director. Two centers regulate medical devices. CDRH regulates medical devices and radiation-emitting electronic products. The Center for Biologics Evaluation and Research (CBER) regulates certain *in vitro* diagnostic devices used in blood banks to test blood for disease. The center directors report directly to the FDA commissioner.

In addition to the product-specific centers, the Office of Combination Products provides support for manufacturers of combination products, such as drugs with delivery devices. Chapter 28 provides further detail on this evolving product area. The duties of this office include the following:
- assigning a primary FDA center for review of a combination product;
- ensuring timely and effective premarket review of combination products by overseeing reviews involving more than one FDA center;
- ensuring consistency and appropriateness in postmarket regulation of combination products;
- resolving disputes regarding premarket review of combination products;
- updating agreements, guidance documents, or practices specific to the assignment of combination products; and
- working with FDA centers to develop guidance or regulations to clarify regulation of combination products.

Of most direct interest to quality assurance and regulatory affairs professionals in the medical device field are the activities of FDA's Office of Regulatory Affairs (ORA) and CDRH. The field organization in ORA carries out the enforcement functions that apply to all FDA-regulated commodity areas. FDA's medical device enforcement activities are guided by ORA and CDRH. Their policies and procedures are implemented by field offices.

Office of Regulatory Affairs

ORA is headed by the associate commissioner for regulatory affairs (ACRA), who reports to the FDA commissioner. The current organizational chart for ORA is available at www.fda.gov/oc/orgcharts/ora1.pdf. In January 2007, ORA published the first *ORA Quality Manual,*[3] which describes its organizational structure and Quality Management System.

The ACRA oversees the field organization. Field personnel include consumer safety officers who are employed in the compliance and investigation branches of the district offices. Employees in the investigation branch are called *investigators*. Employees in the compliance branch are called *compliance officers*. Some investigators are trained to conduct inspections of all commodity areas that FDA regulates, but most receive specialized training in particular commodity areas (e.g., medical devices, drugs, and foods) or technologies (e.g., software-controlled devices).

Center for Devices and Radiological Health

CDRH is responsible for overseeing the safety and effectiveness of medical devices. CDRH is also charged with eliminating unnecessary human exposure to radiation emitted from medical, occupational, and consumer products. CDRH's current organization chart is maintained on its web site under "Organizational Information—Organizational Structure." Its mission is to promote and protect public health throughout the total product life cycle. CDRH accomplishes its mission by:

    a. Reviewing requests to research or market medical devices;

    b. Collecting, analyzing, and acting on information about injuries, deaths, and other experiences from the use of medical devices and radiation-emitting electronic products;

    c. Setting and enforcing GMP regulations, other regulations, and performance standards for radiation-emitting electronic products and medical devices;

    d. Participating in establishing and revising voluntary national and international standards;

    e. Monitoring compliance and surveillance programs for medical devices and radiation-emitting electronic products;

    f. Providing technical and other non-financial assistance to small manufacturers of medical devices;

    g. Participating in the Global Harmonization Task Force (GHTF) and its efforts to harmonize medical device regulations worldwide; and

    h. Training, evaluating, and monitoring third parties that perform premarket 510(k) reviews and inspections on behalf of FDA.

---

[3] *ORA Quality Manual,* January 2007, Version 1.0, Document #ORA.1.1

The GHTF and FDA's participation in GHTF activities are discussed briefly at the end of this chapter and in more detail in Chapter 27.

Division of Small Manufacturers, International and Consumer Assistance

CDRH's Division of Small Manufacturers, International, and Consumer Assistance (DSMICA) provides assistance to industry and consumers by:
- conducting workshops and teleconferences,
- participating in industry programs and conferences,
- distributing publications and information, and
- answering questions.

DSMICA was formerly the Division of Small Manufacturer's Assistance (DSMA). This division maintains an extensive web site that provides information through tutorials, with links to key guidance documents, regulations, and databases. Information is available through www.fda.gov/cdrh/industry/support/index.html and www.fda.gov/cdrh/devadvice.

FDA Compliance Program

FDA uses its compliance programs to assess whether regulated manufacturers are complying with established regulations. The *Compliance Program Guidance Manual for Inspection of Medical Device Manufacturers* describes an organized system for issuing and filing written program plans and instructions for FDA field operations. The present system was inaugurated in October 1974. Compliance programs are revised as needed.

CDRH and ORA collaborate in developing and preparing compliance programs with regard to strategy, objectives, timetables, and goals. Typically, CDRH drafts a program subject to review and input from ORA. The completed compliance program contains FDA's inspectional priorities.

Compliance programs provide:

a. Uniform guidance and specific instructions for gathering and presenting evidence needed to support regulatory enforcement initiatives by FDA,

b. Guidance for field investigators and laboratory personnel on gathering product or industry information within a specific timeframe to determine the existence or extent of a problem, and

c. A mechanism by which FDA's centers can accumulate data on known problems to identify long-range trends.

Compliance programs are one of the best sources for understanding FDA's regulatory priorities. Compliance programs may change when regulations are issued or rescinded, or when industry practices change. Compliance programs related to medical devices that define current CDRH regulatory practices include the following:
- 7382.845: Inspection of Medical Device Manufacturers,
- 7386.001: Inspection of Manufacturers of Laser Products,
- 7386.002: Field Implementation of the Sunlamp and Sunlamp Products Performance Standard as Amended,

- 7386.003: Field Compliance Testing of Diagnostic (Medical) X-Ray Equipment, and
- 7386.004: Field Compliance Testing of Cabinet X-Ray Equipment.

The compliance programs can be found at www.fda.gov/ora/cpgm/default.htm#devices. In addition to the compliance programs described above, various compliance policy guides exist to provide device-specific regulatory focus. These policy guides can be located on CDRH's web site at: www.fda.gov/ora/compliance_ref/cpg/default.htm

Compliance Program 7382.845, *Inspection of Medical Device Manufacturers*, is a comprehensive program that provides guidance for FDA field and center staff on inspection, administrative, and enforcement activities. The compliance program, published in June 2006, is effective until June 2010. It covers activities related to:
- Quality System regulation (21 CFR Part 820),
- Medical Device Reporting regulation (21 CFR Part 803),
- Medical Device Tracking regulation (21 CFR Part 821),
- Corrections and Removals regulation (21 CFR Part 806), and
- Registration and Listing regulation (21 CFR Part 807).

Compliance Program 7382.845 is organized in six parts:

a. Part I (Background) presents a brief description of the regulations covered by this program and the inspectional approach.

b. Part II (Implementation) sets forth specific program objectives for each regulation covered and provides instructions and guidance for prioritizing and scheduling inspections (i.e., compliance program management guidelines).

c. Part III (Inspectional) describes operational concerns related to conducting inspections, including definition of the three inspection levels and guidance for determining compliance with the regulations covered by the program.

d. Part IV (Analytical) specifies the interactions between the district offices and FDA's analyzing laboratories, analyses to be performed, and any special reporting requirements.

e. Part V (Regulatory/Administrative Follow-up) provides direction and guidance to the field office staff on what to do when deficiencies or violations are documented during an inspection. It describes the types of violations that warrant regulatory follow-up and the regulatory actions that the field office should take.

f. Part VI (References and Program Contacts) provides supplemental information that is important to understanding how the compliance program works and lists contacts inside the CDRH that can answer questions for inspectors and field office staff.

g. Attachments include additional information and guidance that is useful in conducting inspections.

One of the most important sections of the compliance program is Part V. District compliance officers use Part V when deciding whether regulatory action is warranted on the basis of inspection results. Regulatory professionals need to be familiar with this part. FDA inspectional approaches and inspection levels, covered in Part III of the compliance program, are discussed later in this chapter, as are foreign inspections.

Compliance Program 7382.845 is available from DSMICA or on FDA's web site at www.fda.gov/cdrh/comp/guidance/7382.845.pdfversion.html.

FDA Enforcement Authorities

If FDA determines that a manufacturer is in violation of the FD&C Act or its accompanying regulations, FDA may take any of the following enforcement actions:

a. Issue a Warning Letter telling the company to notify FDA within 15 days of the corrective actions it plans to take.

b. Order a firm to repair or replace certain devices or to provide a refund.

c. Order a firm to discontinue further distribution of certain devices and advise customers of the problems with the devices.

d. Order a firm to recall devices to the user level.

e. Disapprove or withdraw approval of a PMA.

f. Prohibit the importation of devices manufactured outside the U.S. when there is documented evidence to suggest that the foreign manufacturer is producing or is likely to produce nonconforming and/or defective devices, or the device presents a hazard to health.

g. Administratively detain or seize devices believed to be misbranded or adulterated.

h. Bring an injunction (i.e., consent decree) against an establishment that has a continuing pattern of significant deviations, despite past warnings. The purpose of the injunction is to prevent the manufacture and distribution of a device until deviations are corrected.

i. Prosecute individuals who are in violation of a regulation.

j. Impose civil monetary penalties or fines on firms that are in violation of a regulation.

Warning Letters

In most cases, Warning Letters are issued by district office directors, according to guidance provided in compliance programs. Warning Letters sent by district offices typically require the concurrence of headquarters or review by the Office of the Chief Counsel, especially when technical evaluation of complex scientific or medical data is required. The Office of Compliance in CDRH issues Warning Letters to foreign firms.

FDA issues Warning Letters only for violations of significance and generally requests a response from the manufacturer within 15 days. Warning Letters include a warning that failure to take prompt action to correct violations may result in further enforcement action. However, such letters do not commit FDA to taking enforcement action. FDA's Freedom of Information (FOI) Office keeps Warning Letters on public display and makes them available at: www.fda.gov/foi/warning.htm.

I

Criminal Prosecutions

FDA employs criminal investigators who are differentiated from investigators who conduct routine inspections. Criminal investigators receive special training in how to investigate and document knowing and willful violations of the law. The documentation is intended to support criminal prosecution. FDA works with the U.S. Department of Justice to carry out criminal prosecutions.

Civil Penalties

FDA can impose civil monetary penalties in proceedings before an administrative law judge. The maximum initial penalty FDA may impose is $15,000 per shipment or violation, not to exceed $1 million for all such violations, against each individual and company.

Traditional Enforcement Chain of Command

Typically, a recommendation for a device-related enforcement action proceeds from the district investigations branch to the compliance branch to the district office director and then to CDRH for review by the Office of Compliance. In some cases, the center director may also review recommendations. Concurrence by the Office of Chief Counsel and the ACRA may also be necessary (e.g., in the case of seizures). Criminal cases and other court actions are referred to the Department of Justice. Cases may be tried by FDA attorneys, working with lawyers from the Department of Justice who serve in the local U.S. attorney's office.

In some situations, CDRH may make a device-related recommendation, suggesting that district offices pursue a certain enforcement action. These actions require subsequent review at FDA headquarters.

Inspections

The FDA is mandated by law to inspect manufacturers of class II and class III devices at least once every 2 years[4]. In addition, all PMAs and 510(k) clearances for class III devices are contingent on completion of a satisfactory facility inspection. Inspections may also be made in connection with surveys conducted prior to issuance of new regulations, audits of clinical investigators, recalls, enforcement actions, complaints of serious problems, or significant Medical Device Reports (MDRs). FDA also conducts inspections of foreign manufacturers that distribute FDA-regulated products in the U.S.

Documentation of the inspectional findings (list of observations) for a regulated establishment is prepared on a Form FDA-483. The establishment's management receives a copy of the Form FDA-483 at the conclusion of the inspection. After conducting inspections, investigators prepare Establishment Inspection Reports (EIRs) describing the inspections.

---

[4] FD&C Act section 510(h): "*Every establishment ... engaged in the manufacture, propagation, compounding, or processing of ... a device or devices classified in class II or III shall be so inspected ... at least once in the 2-year period beginning with the date of registration of such establishment pursuant to this section and at least once in every successive 2-year period thereafter.*"

Inspections are classified as No Action Indicated (NAI), Voluntary Action Indicated (VAI), or Official Action Indicated (OAI). Compliance officers review EIRs and prepare enforcement action recommendations, if appropriate. FDA may provide EIRs to manufacturers; manufacturers may also request copies of EIRs through FOI requests.

District offices also employ consumer safety officers, and FDA employs criminal investigators. When Warning Letters or other significant compliance issues arise as the result of an inspection, a reinspection is likely to occur within 6 months.

The *Investigations Operations Manual*, published by ORA, provides a set of general policies and procedures to guide investigators and field office staff. The manual is updated regularly and is available on the ORA web site.

Quality System Inspection Technique

Starting in late 1997, CDRH established a team to reengineer the establishment inspection process in light of the Quality System regulation's system-based approach. After several open public meetings and sessions with Quality System experts, the team proposed a top-down inspection method. CDRH undertook a validation study of the new inspection method to determine whether it provided relevant and valid findings in the context of manufacturer inspections. After conducting the validation study and reviewing the data, CDRH determined that this new top-down inspection method would provide for efficient inspections that resulted in appropriate determinations of compliance. In 1999, CDRH began training investigators on the Quality System Inspection Technique (QSIT). Industry workshops in 1999 and 2000 provided opportunities for manufacturers to learn about the QSIT.

FDA began using the QSIT in January 2000 to conduct inspections of medical device manufacturers. On average, a full QSIT inspection can be completed at the manufacturer's facility within 4 days. The QSIT is described in the *Guide to Inspections of Quality Systems, Quality System Inspection Technique (QSIT)*, which is available on FDA's web site: www.fda.gov/ora/inspect_ref/igs/qsit/qsitguide.htm.

The QSIT is based on the concept that a Quality System is composed of seven subsystems:
- Management Controls,
- Design Controls,
- Corrective and Preventive Actions,
- Production and Process Controls,
- Records, Documents, and Change Controls,
- Facility and Equipment Controls, and
- Material Controls.

Figure 1.1 shows the interrelationships between the seven subsystems and related regulatory topics. From this model of seven subsystems, four major subsystems were identified as the primary focus of a QSIT inspection:
- Management Controls,
- Design Controls,
- Corrective and Preventive Actions, and
- Production and Process Controls.

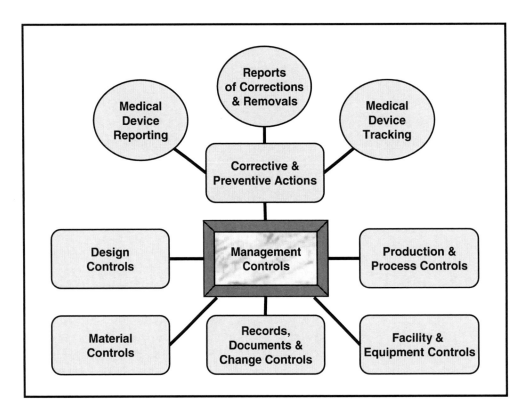

Figure 1.1. FDA's seven quality subsystems.

The *Guide to Inspections of Quality Systems* provides inspectional objectives for investigators to achieve in determining the firm's state of compliance. By evaluating compliance in four major quality subsystems using a top-down inspection approach, the investigator can assess overall compliance within a manufacturer's organization. For each of the four major subsystems, the *Guide* includes a statement of the subsystem's purpose and importance, a list of inspectional objectives, a flowchart for the inspectional objectives, and advice on conducting the inspection. The remaining three subsystems are covered through links with the four major subsystems. The section that covers the production and process controls subsystem includes guidance for evaluating sterilization processes. The *Guide* also contains guidance for evaluating compliance with the Medical Device Reporting regulation, the Corrections and Removals regulation, and the Medical Device Tracking regulation. Investigators evaluate compliance with these requirements while inspecting the Corrective and Preventive Action (CAPA) subsystem.

The QSIT is based on statistically valid sampling of records to ensure the validity of the resulting compliance assessment. The *Guide* includes sampling plans for selecting records to be reviewed.

Foreign Inspections

FDA inspects foreign manufacturers of medical devices distributed in the U.S. Foreign manufacturers that are inspected and fail to meet Quality System requirements may receive Warning Letters, with or without import detention orders. An import detention order prohibits the entry of the foreign manufacturer's medical devices into the U.S., and is used to control devices that are likely to pose a significant risk of injury to users and patients.

If a foreign manufacturer refuses to allow an FDA inspection, FDA may choose to impose an import detention order. In such cases, the presumption is that failure to allow an inspection stems from knowledge that the manufacturing facility fails to meet the Quality System regulation requirements. Devices manufactured in light of such violations are considered adulterated.

In general, FDA will lift an import detention order only after conducting a reinspection to confirm that violations have been corrected. The Office of Compliance issues Warning Letters to foreign manufacturers. As with Warning Letters to U.S. manufacturers, foreign manufacturers are requested to respond in writing within 15 days. The response should be sent to the Office of Compliance.

Types of Inspections

As stated earlier, Part III of Compliance Program 7382.845 includes descriptions of three types of inspections to be conducted: level 1, level 2, and level 3. The QSIT is the basis for level 1 and level 2 inspections.

The first type of inspection a medical device manufacturer is likely to experience, under the current Compliance Program and Quality System regulation, is a level 2 *Comprehensive* or "baseline" inspection. Inspectors follow the QSIT in covering the four major subsystems during a level 2 inspection. FDA considers the outcome of a level 2 inspection to be the baseline for determining a firm's compliance with the Quality System regulation.

The baseline inspection results may be classified as NAI, VAI, or OAI. If the baseline inspection result is satisfactory (NAI or VAI), then future inspections can be level 1 inspections, according to the compliance program. However, the compliance program stipulates that a baseline level 2 inspection should be conducted at least once every 6 years, as resources permit.

A level 1 inspection is an *Abbreviated* inspection. The QSIT is followed in covering the CAPA subsystem, as well as either the production and process control subsystem or the design control subsystem (i.e., CAPA + 1). Investigators are instructed to cover corrective and preventive actions in every inspection of the firm and to select a different second subsystem to cover each time the firm is inspected using the level 1 method.

A level 3 or *Compliance Follow-up* inspection is conducted when the previous inspection of the firm was classified as OAI. During a level 3 inspection, the investigator will determine:
- whether adequate corrections have been implemented to resolve the Quality System problems previously identified; and
- whether the violations continue to exist, if corrections were not implemented.

The investigator works closely with the district office compliance officer to document violative conditions and to collect sufficient evidence to support a recommendation for regulatory action.

At the close of any of the three types of inspections, the investigator meets with the firm's management to discuss the findings. If significant Quality System problems were observed or identified during the inspection, the investigator will issue a Form FDA-483, which lists the observations of problems. The investigator discusses each observation during the meeting with the firm's management. This discussion provides the firm's management with an important opportunity to ask the investigator for further clarification of any observations listed on the Form FDA-483.

Innovations in FDA's Inspection Approaches

In accordance with its obligations under MDUFMA, discussed earlier under "FDA's Mission," FDA has pursued a number of innovative approaches to streamline inspections. This section discusses several of those programs.

Inspections by Third Parties: Accredited Persons Program

MDUFMA gives FDA the authority to establish a third-party program for conducting inspections of medical device manufacturers and imposes a strict timetable for establishing the program. The legislation describes requirements that third parties must meet to become Accredited Persons (APs) and thus eligible to conduct inspections on behalf of FDA. FDA published criteria for AP accreditation in the spring of 2002.

The legislation also describes requirements that manufacturers must meet to be eligible to have an AP conduct an inspection of their facilities. Only those manufacturers whose last inspection was classified NAI or VAI are eligible to be inspected by APs. Additional manufacturer eligibility criteria include marketing a medical device in the U.S. and in one or more foreign countries. Medical device manufacturers in foreign countries may also have APs conduct inspections on behalf of FDA under the AP inspection program.

Manufacturers are responsible for paying fees to APs for inspection services. The CDRH Office of Compliance reviews the EIRs submitted by APs and sends Warning Letters when appropriate.

FDA issued guidance on the implementation of this program in April 2003. FDA guidance and other information on the AP inspection program can be found at: www.fda.gov/cdrh/mdufma/index.html.

Inspections by Third Parties: Multi-Purpose Audit Program

In September 2006, FDA and Health Canada announced a Pilot Multi-Purpose Audit Program, whereby a single third party authorized by both agencies' programs could perform a single compliance audit. The audit results would be used by both agencies to evaluate compliance with applicable regulations. For more information, see: www.fda.gov/cdrh/ap-inspection/pmap-qa.html.

Global Regulatory Harmonization

As required under MDUFMA, CDRH is actively pursuing various activities related to harmonization of global regulatory policies, notably through the GHTF and other pilot programs.

Global Harmonization Task Force

The GHTF is an international consortium of medical device regulatory bodies and industry representatives. It was formed in 1992 by the United States, the European Union, Australia, Canada, and Japan. The GHTF's purpose is to encourage convergence in the regulation of medical devices to promote medical device safety, effectiveness, performance, and quality. The group promotes convergence through the publication of guidance on basic regulatory practices. The guidance documents are then recognized or adopted by member regulatory agencies, including FDA.

The GHTF is organized into five specialized study groups. They are currently working on guidance in the following areas:
- Study Group 1: common regulatory operating principles, premarket submissions, and product labeling;
- Study Group 2: adverse event reporting, postmarket surveillance, and other vigilance activities;
- Study Group 3: Quality System requirements;
- Study Group 4: medical device regulatory auditing practices; and
- Study Group 5: clinical investigation and evaluation practices.

FDA actively participates in GHTF activities. When appropriate, FDA endorses GHTF guidance documents.

Japan – U.S. "Harmonization By Doing" Pilot Program

In December 2003, Japan's Pharmaceutical and Food Safety Bureau, Japan's Pharmaceutical and Medical Devices Agency, and FDA announced a pilot harmonization program related to premarket review of cardiovascular technology. This pilot program is designed to eliminate redundancies in product development efforts by establishing common investigational clinical study protocols and regulatory submissions. To further its objective, the "Harmonization By Doing" Steering Committee has established various working groups to focus on both premarket and postmarket activities. Periodic joint meetings, called "think tanks," are held to facilitate pilot program activities and to evaluate global clinical study research protocols.

CHAPTER 2. DEVELOPMENT HISTORY OF THE QUALITY SYSTEM REGULATION

The Quality System regulation, which was published by FDA as a final rule on October 7, 1996, revises the 1978 medical device GMP regulation. The Quality System regulation replaces quality assurance (QA) program requirements with Quality System requirements that include new provisions concerning the design, purchasing, and servicing of medical devices. The current regulation also codifies FDA's interpretation of the 1978 GMP regulation with regard to record-keeping requirements for device failure and complaint investigations. It also clarifies the requirements for process validation, product change control, and collection and evaluation of quality data. As part of the revision process, FDA has attempted to harmonize the Quality System regulation with International Organization for Standardization (ISO) 13485, the Quality Management System (QMS) standard for medical device manufacturers.

Historical Perspective: The 1978 GMP Regulation

The GMP requirements for medical devices (21 CFR Part 820) were authorized by the Medical Device Amendments of 1976, which are found in section 520(f) of the FD&C Act (21 USC 360j(f)). In response to the new authority provided by section 520(f), FDA issued final regulations in the *Federal Register* of July 21, 1978 (43 FR 31508), prescribing GMP requirements for the methods used in—and the facilities and controls used for—the manufacture, packing, storage, and installation of medical devices. This regulation became effective on December 18, 1978, and was codified under part 820.

In drafting the 1978 regulation, FDA recognized that the medical device industry consists of manufacturers whose devices and manufacturing processes differ significantly. Therefore, the GMP regulation was designed to specify general requirements in areas of concern that applied to all medical device manufacturers, as well as additional requirements for high-risk devices, which were termed "critical devices." This two-tier approach was intended to prevent excessive regulation of the medical device industry. Each manufacturer was expected to supply the details of an appropriate GMP program by developing for the manufacture of each device a detailed set of procedures implementing the GMP regulation. FDA would then examine these procedures to determine whether a manufacturer was complying with the regulation. This flexible, umbrella GMP philosophy is carried over into the current Quality System regulation.

The GMP Revision Process

Until the promulgation of the Quality System regulation, the medical device GMP requirements had not been revised since 1978, except for editorial changes to update organizational references and revisions to the list of critical devices that were included in the Preamble to the 1978 regulation. The Quality System regulation is the result of a revision effort begun in 1990.

An advance notice of proposed rulemaking appeared in the *Federal Register* on June 15, 1990. This notice announced FDA's intent to revise the GMP regulation. Because several studies and recall evaluations indicated that a significant number of medical device failures were caused by design defects,[5] FDA began promoting the addition of design controls to the GMP regulation. In response, the industry took a common position that FDA did not have the authority to add design controls to the regulation.

This difference of opinion between FDA and the industry became a non-issue on November 28, 1990, when Congress passed the Safe Medical Devices Act of 1990 (SMDA). The SMDA amended section 520(f) of the FD&C Act, providing FDA with the authority to add preproduction design controls to the GMP regulation. On November 30, 1990, a notice of availability of an information document intended to facilitate changes to the cGMP was printed in the *Federal Register*. Subsequently, FDA's Device Good Manufacturing Practice advisory committee held a public meeting in May 1991 to solicit comments and discuss the proposed changes to the regulation.

SMDA also included a new section 803, which encouraged FDA to work with foreign countries toward mutual recognition of GMP and other regulations. FDA had already been working for a number of years with the European Community, Australia, Canada, and Japan in an effort to harmonize requirements. The revision of the GMP regulation, including the design controls authorized by the SMDA, allowed the regulation to be consistent, where feasible, with the requirements contained in applicable international standards, specifically ISO 9001:1994, *Quality systems—Model for Quality Assurance in Design, Development, Production, Installation, and Servicing*, and ISO 13485:1996, *Quality systems—Medical devices—Particular requirements for the application of ISO 9001*.

The first proposed rule revising the GMP requirements was published in the November 23, 1993 issue of the *Federal Register*. This proposal consisted of the ISO requirements plus those requirements of the 1978 regulation that were not part of ISO 9001. Approximately 280 individuals and groups commented on the proposal.

FDA announced a second proposal in July 1995, as "Notice of Availability of a Working Draft of the CGMP Final Rule." Approximately 175 individuals and groups commented on the draft. Shortly after the release of the July 1995 Working Draft, FDA held an open public meeting and a GMP Advisory Committee meeting to solicit public comment.

The Final Rule of the Quality System regulation, published on October 7, 1996, includes in its Preamble FDA's responses to 204 summarized industry comments on the 1995 Working Draft. These comments provide insight into FDA's perspective on quality systems and its regulatory objectives for medical device manufacturers.

Key Differences between the 1978 GMP and the Quality System Regulation

As mentioned previously, the 1978 GMP regulation imposed additional requirements on "critical devices," which were defined as devices that are intended for surgical implantation into the body, or devices that are intended to support or sustain life, and whose failure to

---

[5] Specifically, FDA's January 1990 publication, *Device Recalls: A Study of Quality Problems* (HHS Publication FD 90-4235), and the 1990 Department of Health and Human Services Inspector General's study, *FDA Medical Device Regulation from Premarket Review to Recall* (HHS Publication OEI 09-90-00040)

perform when properly used according to the labeling, can reasonably be expected to result in significant injury to the user. The term "critical device" has been eliminated in the Quality System regulation. However, the regulation still allows manufacturers the flexibility to determine the amount or degree of action necessary, commensurate with the risk associated with the finished device.

The Quality System regulation incorporates new requirements for preproduction design control and supplier control. Servicing controls for manufacturers also have been added. Although it was inherent in the 1978 GMP regulation, specific language for management responsibilities, process validation, corrective and preventive action, Quality System Records (QSRs), and statistical techniques is explicit in the Quality System regulation.

Several technical amendments to the Quality System regulation have been published since 1996. These amendments and the complete text of the Final Rule for the Quality System regulation (including the Preamble) can be found in Appendix C.

CHAPTER 3. THE QUALITY SYSTEM REGULATION AND EVOLVING STANDARDS

This chapter covers the effect of evolving international Quality System standards on FDA's Quality System regulation (21 CFR Part 820) and on medical device manufacturers. It provides information that is based on changes in relevant industry standards since 1997. Specifically, the ISO 9001 and ISO 13485 Quality System standards (i.e., the general Quality Systems standard and the standard appropriate for medical device manufacturers, respectively) are discussed. The terms "Quality Management System," used in the ISO standards, and "Quality System," used in FDA regulation, are used interchangeably throughout this chapter.

Quality System Regulation and ISO 9001

This section provides information on two versions of ISO 9001 and their relationship to the Quality System regulation.

ISO 9001:1994

The ISO 9000 family of standards, first published in 1987, provides a basis for Quality Management Systems. The standards are voluntary (i.e., firms may choose to follow the standard and to obtain certification based on the standard). The standards are designed to support consistent design and manufacture of products and services that meet customer quality expectations, across a variety of industries. The use of the ISO 9000 family of standards as a basis for Quality Systems gained significant momentum in the 1990s. This was due to a number of factors, including:

a. Customers often required their suppliers of goods and services to establish a Quality System, as a criterion for selecting and approving these suppliers.

b. Requirements were placed on manufacturers of goods distributed within countries belonging to the EU to obtain Conformité Européene (CE) marks, which could be obtained more easily with registration to a Quality Management System standard.

c. Increasing evidence suggested that world-class organizations relied on strong Quality Systems to help meet their overall goals of improving efficiency, with resulting profitability.

In 1994, the ISO 9000 family of standards included three standards, which differed in terms of scope and were applied on the basis of the manufacturer's scope of operations. Firms that designed and manufactured products were subject to the requirements of ISO 9001:1994. Firms that manufactured, but did not design products were subject to ISO 9002:1994. Firms that provided products or services for which quality was assured solely by final inspection and testing were subject to ISO 9003:1994. Ancillary standards and guidelines in the ISO 9000 family provided support in the selection of an appropriate Quality Management System standard and the implementation of the manufacturer's Quality System.

ISO 9001:1994 served as a basis for ISO 13485:1996, which was developed specifically for Quality Management Systems of medical device manufacturers. Each subsection in ISO 13485:1996 refers to a related subsection of ISO 9001:1994 and adds additional requirements for medical device manufacturers where appropriate.

Harmonization of Medical Device Regulations with ISO 9001:1994 and 13485:1996

FDA's initial GMP regulation for medical devices was not based on a Quality System model. When the GMP regulation was published in 1978, Quality System standards were not typically established in manufacturing firms and Quality System standards were not generally available.

As required by the Safe Medical Devices Act of 1990, FDA pursued harmonization with existing international Quality System standards for medical devices during the development of the Quality System regulation. Harmonization meant that the regulation would have requirements that were very similar to or aligned with the requirements in those internationally recognized standards, whenever appropriate. The harmonization was pursued for a number of reasons:

a. Many medical device manufacturers produce devices for use domestically and in foreign countries. The harmonization effort supported these manufacturers by making it possible to establish a single Quality System to address U.S. and foreign regulatory requirements.

b. By aligning U.S. regulations with a commonly recognized Quality System standard, FDA was in a better position to implement agreements for relying on and exchanging manufacturer inspection reports with other regulatory bodies. Thus, alignment would not only support streamlined manufacturer operations but also potentially reduce FDA inspection efforts in foreign manufacturing facilities.

The Quality System regulation is based on a Quality System model. The regulation is harmonized with ISO 9001:1994 and ISO 13485:1996. ISO 9001:1994 contained 20 elements that work together to form a Quality System.

A comparison of FDA's Quality System regulation with FDA's 1978 GMP regulation, ISO 9001:1994 and ISO 13485:1996 is available at www.fda.gov/cdrh/dsma/133.pdf and in *The FDA and Worldwide Quality System Requirements Guidebook for Medical Devices.*

ISO 9001:2000

Updates of ISO standards are required on a periodic basis. ISO 9001 was updated and re-issued in 2000, and ISO 9001:1994 formally expired in December 2003. The 2000 version of ISO 9001 took a substantially different approach to Quality Management System organization. The 1994 version was based on a 20-element Quality System model; ISO 9001:2000 is based on a process model.

Some of the requirements in ISO 9001:2000 are not necessarily appropriate for a regulatory body to evaluate in the context of design and manufacture of safe and effective medical devices. For example:

a. ISO 9001:2000 requires assurance of customer satisfaction. Although FDA and other regulatory bodies are concerned that user needs and intended uses are considered in device design activities, other aspects of customer satisfaction do not necessarily pertain. Although device design characteristics and usability can play a significant role in customer satisfaction, other issues, such as delivery schedules or efficiency of the customer service staff, are not pertinent in determining medical device safety or effectiveness.

b. ISO 9001:2000 requires active pursuit of continuous improvement with a goal of increasing efficiency. Improvements pursued as part of a corrective and preventive action process are generally pertinent to regulatory agencies. However, a manufacturer's efficiency is not necessarily relevant to safety and effectiveness.

c. ISO 9001:2000 requires significantly less procedural documentation than ISO 9001:1994. However, FDA and many other regulatory bodies believe that clear, documented procedures help reduce nonconforming product issues and improve medical device quality.

FDA does not intend to reissue the Quality System regulation on the basis of the changes in ISO 9001:2000, nor does it intend to adopt ISO 9001:2000 in lieu of 21 CFR 820. FDA does not see a potential safety or quality benefit to having manufacturers revise the structure of their Quality System documentation to address the process model approach. Aligning the Quality System regulation with the ISO 9001:2000 standard will not necessarily improve the protection of public health and thus is not required by the FDA.

Medical device manufacturers that do not currently have registration to ISO 9001/13485 and that intend to distribute medical devices in foreign countries are faced with a decision concerning their Quality System. Some countries, such as Canada, require registration to a specific Quality System standard in order to gain approval to market a medical device in that country. In other countries, such as the EU member states, medical device manufacturers have options for obtaining registration to a recognized Quality System standard or conducting specific device testing in order to gain approval to market through CE marking.

Quality System Regulation and ISO 13485

Because ISO 13485:1996 was based on ISO 9001:1994, a revision was necessary after ISO 9001:2000 was published. Similarly, ISO 13488:1996 was based on ISO 9002:1994. ISO Technical Committee 210, which was responsible for drafting the revision to ISO 13485, sought to adopt aspects of ISO 9001:2000 that are appropriate for medical device manufacturers, while creating a single standalone standard. Making the new version of ISO 13485 a standalone standard means that it will not be affected to the same extent the next time that ISO 9001 is revised.

The revised ISO 13485 standard (13485:2003) strikes a balance between maintaining parallelism with ISO 9001:2000 and defining the appropriate scope for medical device manufacturers' Quality Systems. Also, the new standard eliminates the separate standard (i.e., ISO 13488) for manufacturers that do not design devices. ISO 13485:2003 can be used by any medical device manufacturer. By excluding sections that are not applicable, each manufacturer tailors its implementation of the Quality System standard as appropriate for its operations.

ISO 13485:2003 was published in September 2003. FDA was directly involved in efforts to revise ISO 13485 as a member of ISO Technical Committee 210. The Quality System regulation and ISO 13485:2003 have many requirements in common and are still harmonized, although the regulation is based on the 20-element Quality System model and the standard is based on a process model. Registration to this standard may be an alternative to ISO 9001:2000 registration for medical device manufacturers seeking to gain approval to market their devices in foreign markets.

In the future, FDA plans to maintain harmonization with the ISO 13485 standard and will no longer maintain the linkage with ISO 9001.

Comparison of the Quality System Regulation to ISO 13485:2003

Table 3.1 compares 21 CFR Part 820 with ISO 13485:2003. Although the Quality System regulation ("Regulation") and ISO 13485:2003 ("Standard") are generally in agreement, there are a few substantive differences between the two:

a. The Regulation requires "a quality plan", while the Standard does not.

b. The Regulation includes requirements concerning communication with FDA (e.g., availability of certain records upon request), while the Standard has none.

c. The Regulation requires the establishment of certain files (DMR, DHR, DHF, QSR, and complaint files), while the Standard requires similar records but does not require that they be kept in content-specific "files".

d. The Regulation limits the applicability of design controls to higher-risk devices on the basis of device classifications, while the Standard does not define a risk-based scope for design controls.

e. The Standard requires an explicit Quality Manual, while the Regulation does not.

f. The Standard has a broader focus of risk management than the Regulation.

Table 3.1. Comparison of 21 CFR 820 to ISO 13485:2003.		
21 CFR Part 820 Quality System Regulation Sections ("the Regulation")	**ISO 13485:2003 Clause(s) ("the Standard")**	**Similarities and Significant Differences**
820.1 Scope	0.1 Introduction, General 0.2 Process approach 0.3 Relationship with other standards 0.4 Compatibility with other management systems 1.2 Application 2 Normative references	The Regulation addresses exemptions, applicability to foreign manufacturers, and the authority under which the Regulation was promulgated. The Regulation also addresses possible conflicts between compliance with the Regulation and with other FDA regulations. Explanations of the meaning of "where appropriate" and "if appropriate" in the Standard are similar to "where appropriate" in the Regulation. The Standard addresses regulatory exclusions from design controls (based on scope of operations). The Standard explains its relationship with ISO 9001 and ISO Technical Report 14969, and references ISO 9000:2000 with regard to the fundamentals of quality systems and vocabulary. The Regulation does not reference these standards, although it does use some terms and concepts that appear in these standards. The Standard explains the process approach. The Regulation has no similar explanation. The Standard addresses compatibility with management systems for other types of activities. The Regulation does not.
820.5 Quality system	0.1 Introduction, General 4.1 Quality management system, General requirements 4.2.1 (f) – Note 1	The Regulation and the Standard specify that manufacturers or organizations have flexibility in structuring their Quality System according to their device type, needs, and situation.
820.20 Management responsibility	5.1 Management commitment 5.2 Customer focus 5.3 Quality policy 5.4.1 Quality objectives	The Regulation's focus is the provision of safe and effective medical devices. The Standard has an explicit focus on meeting customer requirements, in addition to meeting regulatory requirements.
820.20(a) Quality policy	4.2.1 Documentation requirements, General 5.1 Management commitment 5.3 Quality policy	The Regulation and the Standard require a quality policy. The Standard specifies elements to address in a quality policy.
820.20(b) Organization	4.1 Quality management system, General requirements	Requirements for the "organization" (the Regulation) and the "quality management system" (the Standard) are similar.
820.20(b)(1) Responsibility and authority	5.5.1 Responsibility and authority	No significant differences.

Table 3.1. Comparison of 21 CFR 820 to ISO 13485:2003.		
21 CFR Part 820 Quality System Regulation Sections ("the Regulation")	**ISO 13485:2003 Clause(s) ("the Standard")**	**Similarities and Significant Differences**
820.20(b)(2) Resources	5.1 Management commitment 6.1 Provision of resources	The requirements are similar. The Regulation addresses "trained personnel", while the Standard discusses "competency" of personnel.
820.20(b)(3) Management representative	5.5.2 Management representative	The requirements for appointment of and responsibilities of a management representative are similar. The Standard has an additional requirement for promotion of awareness of regulatory and customer requirements throughout the organization.
820.20(c) Management review	5.1 Management commitment 5.6 Management review	Requirements to conduct periodic management reviews are similar. The Standard addresses specific topics that should be covered during management reviews and the decisions or actions that should result from the reviews.
820.20(d) Quality planning	5.4.1 Quality objectives 5.4.2 Quality management system planning	Requirements for quality planning are similar. The Standard has more detailed requirements regarding measurable quality objectives.
820.20(e) Quality system procedures	4.2.1 Documentation requirements, General 4.2.2 Quality manual	The Regulation requires establishment of procedures and instructions, but does not require a quality manual. The Standard requires establishment of a quality manual, which can include or reference procedures.
820.22 Quality audit	8.2.2 Internal audit	Requirements for quality audits (Regulation) and internal audits (Standard) are similar.
820.25 Personnel, (a) General	6.2.1 Human resources, General	Requirements for personnel (Regulation) and human resources (Standard) are similar.
820.25(b) Training	6.2.2 Competence, awareness, and training 6.4 Work environment (c)	Requirements are similar. The Regulation has additional requirements to make personnel aware of the device defects that could result from improper job performance, and to make certain personnel aware of defects and errors they may encounter in performing their jobs. The Standard specifically addresses training for temporary personnel working in controlled environmental conditions.
820.30 Design Controls, (a) General	7.3.1 Design and development planning	The Regulation requires design and development procedures for design of Class III, Class II, and certain Class I devices. The Standard requires general procedures addressing design and development activities for all devices regardless of device class or risk.
820.30(b) Design and development planning	7.3.1 Design and development planning	No significant differences.

21 CFR Part 820 Quality System Regulation Sections ("the Regulation")	ISO 13485:2003 Clause(s) ("the Standard")	Similarities and Significant Differences
	Table 3.1. Comparison of 21 CFR 820 to ISO 13485:2003.	
820.30(c) Design input	7.3.2 Design and development inputs	The requirements for design inputs are similar. The Regulation requires that design input approval records include a dated signature. The Standard includes more detailed requirements for: • types of design inputs, and • risk management activities.
820.30(d) Design output	7.3.3 Design and development outputs	Requirements for design output are similar. The Regulation requires that design output approval records include a dated signature.
820.30(e) Design review	7.3.4 Design and development review	Requirements for design review are similar. The Regulation requires use of an independent reviewer.
820.30(f) Design verification	7.3.5 Design and development verification	Requirements for design verification are similar. The Regulation includes specific documentation requirements.
820.30(g) Design validation	7.1 Planning of product realization 7.3.6 Design and development validation	Requirements for design validation are similar. The Regulation has an additional requirement for the use of initial production units or their equivalent, and specifically includes risk analysis and software validation requirements. The Standard: • addresses risk management across the product life cycle in more detail, • does not explicitly require software validation, and • explicitly states that validation must be completed before delivery of commercial devices to customers.
820.30(h) Design transfer	7.3.1 Design and development planning - Note	The Regulation has requirements for design transfer. The Standard addresses design transfer in a note which is guidance, not a requirement.
820.30(i) Design changes	7.3.7 Control of design and development changes	Requirements for control of design changes are similar. The Standard has additional requirements regarding evaluating the effect of design changes on constituent parts and product already in distribution.
820.30(j) Design history file	4.2.3 Control of documents 4.2.4 Control of records	The Standard has a general requirement for maintaining records to demonstrate conformance, which is similar in intent to the Regulation's requirement for a design history file.
820.40 Document controls	4.2.1 Documentation requirements, General 4.2.3 Control of documents	Requirements are similar. The Standard has an additional requirement for control of documents of "external origin."

I

Table 3.1. Comparison of 21 CFR 820 to ISO 13485:2003.		
21 CFR Part 820 Quality System Regulation Sections ("the Regulation")	**ISO 13485:2003 Clause(s) ("the Standard")**	**Similarities and Significant Differences**
820.50 Purchasing controls, (a) Evaluation of suppliers, contractors and consultants	7.4.1 Purchasing process	Requirements for evaluation of suppliers are similar. The Regulation has an explicit requirement to evaluate, select, and control contractors and consultants.
820.50(b) Purchasing data	7.4.2 Purchasing information	Requirements for purchasing data (Regulation) and purchasing information (Standard) are similar. The Regulation requires that manufacturers pursue an agreement with suppliers to provide notification of any changes to the product or service.
820.60 Identification	7.5.3.1 Identification	Requirements for identification are similar. The Standard explicitly addresses identification of returned devices.
820.65 Traceability	7.4.2 Purchasing information 7.5.3.2 Traceability	The Regulation has traceability requirements for life supporting, life sustaining, and implantable devices through distribution to the initial consignee. It achieves general traceability of devices through Device History Records. The Standard explicitly requires some degree of traceability for all devices and greater traceability for active implantable and implantable medical devices, including traceability beyond distributors.
820.70 Production and Process Controls (a) General, (b) Production and process changes	7.1 Planning of product realization 7.5.1 Control of production and service provision 7.5.1.1 General requirements	Requirements for developing, controlling and monitoring production processes are similar. The Regulation explicitly requires verification or validation of changes to specifications, methods, processes and procedures.
820.70(c) Environmental control, (d) Personnel, and (e) Contamination control	6.3 Infrastructure 6.4 Work environment	No significant differences.
820.70(f) Buildings	6.3 Infrastructure	Requirements for buildings (Regulation) and infrastructure (Standard) are similar.
820.70(g) Equipment	6.3 Infrastructure	Requirements for equipment (Regulation) and infrastructure (Standard) are similar. The Regulation has additional requirements for periodic inspections to ensure adherence to maintenance schedules, and making equipment adjustment limitations readily available. The Standard has an additional requirement pertaining to supporting services such as communication systems.
820.70(h) Manufacturing material	7.5.1.2.1 Cleanliness of product and contamination control	Requirements for manufacturing materials (Regulation) and cleanliness of product (Standard) are similar.

I

Table 3.1. Comparison of 21 CFR 820 to ISO 13485:2003.		
21 CFR Part 820 Quality System Regulation Sections ("the Regulation")	ISO 13485:2003 Clause(s) ("the Standard")	Similarities and Significant Differences
820.70(i) Automated processes	7.5.2 Validation of processes for production and service provision	Requirements are similar. The Regulation includes specific documentation requirements.
820.72 Inspection, measuring and test equipment	7.6 Control of monitoring and measuring devices	Requirements for inspection, measuring and test equipment (Regulation) and control of monitoring and measuring devices (Standard) are similar. The Standard has more detailed requirements for assessing the impact of out-of-calibration equipment on product in distribution, and addresses software capability requirements when used in monitoring and measurement applications.
820.75 Process validation	7.5.2 Validation of processes for production and service provision 7.5.2.1 General requirements	Requirements for process validation are similar. The Regulation has additional explicit requirements for monitoring, controlling, and documenting validated processes during routine production and having qualified operators perform validated processes.
820.80 Receiving, in-process, and finished device acceptance (a) General, (b) Receiving acceptance activities, (c) In-process acceptance activities, (d) Final acceptance activities	7.1 Planning of product realization 7.4.3 Verification of purchased product 7.5.4 Customer property 8.2.4.1 Monitoring and measurement of product, General requirements	Requirements are similar. The Regulation requires devices to be controlled or quarantined until release. The Standard explicitly requires satisfactory completion of all planned arrangements before product release and service delivery. The Standard also specifically addresses the care and control of customer property; the Regulation has no corresponding requirement.
820.80(e) Acceptance records	7.1 Planning of product realization	Requirements are similar. The Regulation includes more detailed requirements pertaining to information to include in acceptance records.
820.86 Acceptance status	7.5.3.3 Status identification	Requirements for acceptance status (Regulation) and status identification (Standard) are similar.
820.90 Nonconforming product	8.3 Control of nonconforming product	Requirements for nonconforming product are similar. The Regulation requires determination of the need for an investigation, and a signature whenever concessions are approved for use. The Standard specifically addresses nonconformity in delivered devices.
820.100 Corrective and preventive action.	8.4 Analysis of data 8.5.2 Corrective action 8.5.3 Preventive action	Requirements for corrective and preventive action are similar. The Regulation includes specific procedural requirements. The Standard treats corrective action and preventive action separately.

I

Table 3.1. Comparison of 21 CFR 820 to ISO 13485:2003.		
21 CFR Part 820 Quality System Regulation Sections ("the Regulation")	**ISO 13485:2003 Clause(s) ("the Standard")**	**Similarities and Significant Differences**
820.120 Device labeling	7.5.1 Control of production and service provision 7.5.1.1 Control of product and service provision, General requirements	The Regulation has requirements for label integrity, inspection, storage, operations, and control numbers which are more explicit and detailed than the Standard. The Regulation requires a specific, documented label release prior to use of the label.
820.130 Device packaging	7.5.1.1 Control of product and service provision, General requirements 7.5.5 Preservation of product	The Regulation requires that packaging and shipping containers be designed to protect devices. The Standard only has a general requirement for packaging operations and ensuring that product conformity is preserved during shipping.
820.140 Handling, 820.150 Storage	7.5.5 Preservation of product	Requirements for handling and storage (Regulation) and preservation of product (Standard) are similar. The Regulation specifically addresses stock rotation for product that may deteriorate over time.
820.160 Distribution	7.2.1 Determination of requirements related to the product 7.2.2 Review of requirements related to the product 7.5.3.2.2 Particular requirements for active implantable medical devices and implantable medical devices	The Regulation requires distribution procedures and records of distribution. The Standard only requires distribution records for implantable and active implantable devices. Under the Regulation, contract review is required before release of devices for distribution. Under the Standard contract review is required when orders are received.
820.170 Installation	7.5.1.2.2 Installation activities	No significant differences.
820.180 Records, General requirements	None	The Regulation specifically requires back up of records stored in data processing systems. The Regulation also requires manufacturers to make records available to company officials and FDA employees. The Standard has no corresponding requirement.
820.180(a) Confidentiality	None	The Regulation has a provision for manufacturers to mark records during an inspection to identify those containing confidential information. The Standard has no corresponding provision.
820.180(b) Record retention period	4.2.3 Control of documents 4.2.4 Control of records	Requirements for retention of documents and records are similar.
820.180(c) Exceptions	None	The Regulation exempts reports of internal audits, supplier audits, and management reviews from review during FDA inspections. The Standard has no comparable exemptions.

Table 3.1. Comparison of 21 CFR 820 to ISO 13485:2003.		
21 CFR Part 820 Quality System Regulation Sections ("the Regulation")	**ISO 13485:2003 Clause(s) ("the Standard")**	**Similarities and Significant Differences**
820.181 Device master record	4.2.1 Documentation requirements, General 7.1 Planning of product realization	Requirements are similar for maintaining a record or file for each type or model of device which includes specifications and production processes. The Regulation has additional requirements for specifications and processes for packaging, labeling, and quality assurance. Only the Regulation assigns the name "Device Master Record" to these records/files.
820.184 Device history record	7.5.1.1 Control of production and service provision, General requirements	The Regulation and the Standard have similar requirements for maintaining records of production history. The Regulation assigns the name "Device History Record" to these records. In addition, the Standard includes explicit requirements for documenting sterilization processes. The Regulation has no comparable explicit requirement; however, the expectation is that sterilization processes will be documented.
820.186 Quality system record	None	The Standard does not require a Quality System Record (QSR) but does require the types of records and documents that could be kept in the QSR.
820.198 Complaint files	8.2.1 Feedback 8.5.1 Improvement, General	The requirements for complaint handling activities are similar. In addition the Regulation requires that certain complaints be investigated and that complaints reportable under 21 CFR Part 803 be identified. The Regulation's record-keeping requirements are more stringent.
820.200 Servicing	7.5.1.2.3 Servicing activities	Requirements are similar. In addition the Regulation requires servicing data to be analyzed and maintained, and has more detailed requirements for information to be included in service records.
820.250 Statistical techniques	8.1 Measurement, analysis, and improvement, General	Requirements are similar. In addition, the Regulation requires establishing procedures for using statistical techniques and sampling methods, and for basing sampling plans on valid statistical rationale.

I

NOTES:

"The reason we don't have time to fix it today is that we didn't take the time to do it right yesterday."
H.J. Harrington, *The Improvement Process: How America's Leading Companies Improve*, 1987

CHAPTER 4. GENERAL PROVISIONS (SUBPART A) OF 21 CFR PART 820[6]

820.1 Scope

820.1(a) Applicability

The Requirement

820.1 Scope.
(a) Applicability.
(1) Current good manufacturing practice (CGMP) requirements are set forth in this quality system regulation. The requirements in this part govern the methods used in, and the facilities and controls used for, the design, manufacture, packaging, labeling, storage, installation, and servicing of all finished devices intended for human use. The requirements in this part are intended to ensure that finished devices will be safe and effective and otherwise in compliance with the Federal Food, Drug, and Cosmetic Act (the act). This part establishes basic requirements applicable to manufacturers of finished medical devices. If a manufacturer engages in only some operations subject to the requirements in this part, and not in others, that manufacturer need only comply with those requirements applicable to the operations in which it is engaged. With respect to class I devices, design controls apply only to those devices listed in § 820.30(a)(2). This regulation does not apply to manufacturers of components or parts of finished devices, but such manufacturers are encouraged to use appropriate provisions of this regulation as guidance. Manufacturers of human blood and blood components are not subject to this part, but are subject to part 606 of this chapter. Manufacturers of human cells, tissues, and cellular and tissue-based products (HCT/Ps), as defined in § 1271.3(d) of this chapter, that are medical devices (subject to premarket review or notification, or exempt from notification, under an application submitted under the device provisions of the act or under a biological product license application under section 351 of the Public Health Service Act) are subject to this part and are also subject to the donor-eligibility procedures set forth in part 1271 subpart C of this chapter and applicable current good tissue practice procedures in part 1271 subpart D of this chapter. In the event of a conflict between applicable regulations in part 1271 and in other parts of this chapter, the regulation specifically applicable to the device in question shall supersede the more general.
(2) The provisions of this part shall be applicable to any finished device as defined in this part, intended for human use, that is manufactured, imported, or offered for import in any State or Territory of the United States, the District of Columbia, or the Commonwealth of Puerto Rico.
(3) In this regulation the term ``where appropriate'' is used several times. When a requirement is qualified by ``where appropriate,'' it is deemed to be ``appropriate'' unless the manufacturer can document justification otherwise. A requirement is ``appropriate'' if nonimplementation could reasonably be expected to result in the product not meeting its specified requirements or the manufacturer not being able to carry out any necessary corrective action.

---

[6] Quality System regulation text as published by the U.S. Government Printing Office, from the Code of Federal Regulations, Title 21, Volume 8, revised as of April 2007.

Discussion of the Requirement

The requirements of the Quality System regulation are generally harmonized with current international Quality System standards for medical devices. The regulation provides an outline of basic requirements for a manufacturer to use when establishing a Quality System.

The good manufacturing practice (GMP) requirements of the Quality System regulation apply to manufacturers of finished medical devices that are intended for human use. Component manufacturers are not required to comply with the regulation, but are encouraged to use the regulation as guidance. Manufacturers of human blood and blood components are not subject to 21 CFR 820, but rather to 21 CFR 606, "Current Good Manufacturing Practice for Blood and Blood Components."

820.1(b) Limitations

The Requirement

> ***820.1(b) Limitations.*** *The quality system regulation in this part supplements regulations in other parts of this chapter except where explicitly stated otherwise. In the event of a conflict between applicable regulations in this part and in other parts of this chapter, the regulations specifically applicable to the device in question shall supersede any other generally applicable requirements.*

Discussion of the Requirement

The Quality System regulation applies to all medical devices unless specifically stated otherwise in other 21 CFR regulations that apply to medical devices. For example, the classification regulations exempt certain class I devices from GMP requirements (except complaint handling and records requirements). If, because of conflicting requirements, it is impossible to comply with all of the applicable regulations, the regulation that specifically applies to the device in question takes precedence.

820.1(c) Authority

The Requirement

> ***820.1(c) Authority.*** *Part 820 is established and issued under authority of sections 501, 502, 510, 513, 514, 515, 518, 519, 520, 522, 701, 704, 801, 803 of the act (21 U.S.C. 351, 352, 360, 360c, 360d, 360e, 360h, 360i, 360j, 360l, 371, 374, 381, 383). The failure to comply with any applicable provision in this part renders a device adulterated under section 501(h) of the act. Such a device, as well as any person responsible for the failure to comply, is subject to regulatory action.*

Discussion of the Requirement

This section states the legal authority under which the GMP requirements are written. For example, part 520 provides the Food and Drug Administration (FDA) with the authority to require the records mandated by the Quality System regulation. Also, this section defines the consequences of failing to comply with the regulation. Failure to comply with *any* GMP requirement may render the finished device *adulterated* and subject to the adulteration penalties of the Federal Food, Drug, and Cosmetic (FD&C) Act.

820.1(d) Foreign Manufacturers

The Requirement

> ***820.1(d) Foreign manufacturers.*** *If a manufacturer who offers devices for import into the United States refuses to permit or allow the completion of a Food and Drug Administration (FDA) inspection of the foreign facility for the purpose of determining compliance with this part, it shall appear for purposes of section 801(a) of the act, that the methods used in, and the facilities and controls used for, the design, manufacture, packaging, labeling, storage, installation, or servicing of any devices produced at such facility that are offered for import into the United States do not conform to the requirements of section 520(f) of the act and this part and that the devices manufactured at that facility are adulterated under section 501(h) of the act.*

Discussion of the Requirement

FDA has no authority outside the United States and must obtain permission from the manufacturers to audit foreign establishments. If a foreign manufacturer refuses to allow an FDA audit, the manufacturer's devices will be considered adulterated and will not be allowed to be distributed in the United States. This requirement resulted from refusals by certain foreign manufacturers to allow FDA inspections and from delays in allowing such inspections.

820.1(e) Exemptions or Variances

The Requirement

> ***820.1(e) Exemptions or variances.***
> *(1) Any person who wishes to petition for an exemption or variance from any device quality system requirement is subject to the requirements of section 520(f)(2) of the act. Petitions for an exemption or variance shall be submitted according to the procedures set forth in § 10.30 of this chapter, the FDA's administrative procedures. Guidance is available from the Center for Devices and Radiological Health, Division of Small Manufacturers, International and Consumer Assistance (HFZ-220), 1350 Piccard Dr., Rockville, MD 20850, U.S.A., telephone 1-800-638-2041 or 240-276-3150, FAX 240-276-3151.*
> *(2) FDA may initiate and grant a variance from any device quality system requirement when the agency determines that such variance is in the best interest of the public health. Such variance will remain in effect only so long as there remains a public health need for the device and the device would not likely be made sufficiently available without the variance.*

Discussion of the Requirement

Anyone may petition for an exemption or variance from all or part of the Quality System regulation and may even propose entirely different Quality System requirements. An exemption means that a manufacturer is not required to comply. A variance is permission to substitute a control for one required by the regulation. To date, FDA has received fewer than 100 petitions for variances and exemptions. All of those approved have been petitions for removal from the critical device list under the original 1978 GMP regulation. In general, because of the flexibility of this regulation, exemptions and variances have not been justified.

Guidance for the submission of petitions for exemptions or variances is available from FDA's Division of Small Manufacturers, International and Consumer Assistance (DSMICA). The agency may not process a petition while FDA inspections are ongoing.

820.3 Definitions

820.3(a) Act *means the Federal Food, Drug, and Cosmetic Act, as amended (secs. 201-903, 52 Stat. 1040 et seq., as amended (21 U.S.C. 321-394)). All definitions in section 201 of the act shall apply to the regulations in this part.*

Discussion: Section 201 of the FD&C Act contains a number of definitions, including the definition of "device":

> *... an instrument, apparatus, implement, machine, contrivance, implant, in vitro reagent, or other similar or related article, including any component, part, or accessory, which is—*
> *(1) recognized in the official National Formulary, or the United States Pharmacopeia, or any supplement to them,*
> *(2) intended for use in the diagnosis of disease or other conditions, or in the cure, mitigation, treatment, or prevention of disease, in man or other animals, or*
> *(3) intended to affect the structure or any function of the body of man or other animals, and which does not achieve its primary intended purposes through chemical action within or on the body of man or other animals and which is not dependent upon being metabolized for the achievement of its primary intended purposes.*

In general, a medical device does not have a metabolic effect on the patient's body.

820.3(b) Complaint *means any written, electronic, or oral communication that alleges deficiencies related to the identity, quality, durability, reliability, safety, effectiveness, or performance of a device after it is released for distribution.*

Discussion: A complaint can be from any source, but it is only considered a complaint when the communication alleges a deficiency related to the characteristics identified above. However, one condition defined in the regulation must be considered to be a complaint, even if there are no allegations of a deficiency: the requirement under section 820.200(c) that all events meeting the medical device reporting criteria (per 21 CFR 803) must be considered complaints and investigated as complaints, per section 820.198. However, the fact that an event may not meet the complaint definition does not mean that an investigation should not be made and corrective action taken, when necessary. All quality problems must be identified, evaluated, and resolved under section 820.100, "Corrective and preventive action."

820.3(c) Component *means any raw material, substance, piece, part, software, firmware, labeling, or assembly which is intended to be included as part of the finished, packaged, and labeled device.*

Discussion: All materials, as specified in this definition, are subject to component controls. Those controls include the requirements of section 820.80(b), "Receiving acceptance activities," and section 820.86, "Acceptance status."

> ***820.3(d) Control number*** *means any distinctive symbols, such as a distinctive combination of letters or numbers, or both, from which the history of the manufacturing, packaging, labeling, and distribution of a unit, lot, or batch of finished devices can be determined.*

II

Discussion: When traceability is required, the manufacturer's system and methods must ensure that a history of the finished device can be reproduced, to the degree necessary to allow the investigation of quality problems, effective recalls, and corrective action. The level of detail required should be based on the nature, complexity, risk, and use of the finished device.

> ***820.3(e) Design history file (DHF)*** *means a compilation of records which describes the design history of a finished device.*

Discussion: The design history file (DHF) is intended to act as a repository for the data and records necessary to provide evidence that the design plan was followed. The file must contain or reference the records necessary to show that the design plan and applicable design control requirements were met. The DHF for each type of device should include, for example, the design and development plan, design inputs, design specifications, design review results, design verification results, and design validation results.

> ***820.3(f) Design input*** *means the physical and performance requirements of a device that are used as a basis for device design.*

Discussion: Design input includes information obtained on needs and requirements, such as intended use, performance, safety, user interface, compatibility, reliability, labeling, and packaging. Input requirements should be established in measurable terms, including acceptable ranges and limits. Design input requirements provide context and scope to focus design activities.

> ***820.3(g) Design output*** *means the results of a design effort at each design phase and at the end of the total design effort. The finished design output is the basis for the device master record. The total finished design output consists of the device, its packaging and labeling, and the device master record.*

Discussion: Design output consists of the results of each design phase, including documentation, data, and records. Design output should meet design input requirements, as confirmed through design validation and verification, and as ensured during design review. Design output includes the specifications, blueprints, test procedures, environmental requirements, and so forth that are finalized at the end of the design process and translated into manufacturing specifications, methods, and procedures. Final design output includes the finished device, its packaging and labeling, and the device master record (DMR).

820.3(h) Design review means a documented, comprehensive, systematic examination of a design to evaluate the adequacy of the design requirements, to evaluate the capability of the design to meet these requirements, and to identify problems.

Discussion: Design reviews are conducted across the development lifecycle, and may involve different parties at different phases. Each design review must be comprehensive for the design phase being reviewed. All aspects of the design process should be reviewed when the design is transferred.

820.3(i) Device history record (DHR) means a compilation of records containing the production history of a finished device.

Discussion: The device history record (DHR) is a collection of records that objectively demonstrates that a finished device was made in accordance with its DMR.

820.3(j) Device master record (DMR) means a compilation of records containing the procedures and specifications for a finished device.

Discussion: The types and extent of documents that make up a manufacturer's DMR vary greatly. Key elements that a DMR must contain include:
- device specifications,
- component specifications,
- product process specifications,
- quality assurance procedures and specifications,
- packaging and labeling specifications and methods, and
- installation, maintenance, and servicing procedures and methods, if applicable.

820.3(k) Establish means define, document (in writing or electronically), and implement.

Discussion: Wherever the term "establish" appears, it means that adequate written documentation, either hardcopy or electronic, must be in place. The term also means that the documents must be properly implemented, such that employees have been trained and are following the documented process.

820.3(l) Finished device means any device or accessory to any device that is suitable for use or capable of functioning, whether or not it is packaged, labeled, or sterilized.

Discussion: The Quality System regulation only applies to finished device manufacturers. Therefore, the definition of a "finished device" must be broad enough so that the Quality System will be applied to the degree necessary to ensure that the device is safe and effective. The GMP requirements cannot be applied merely after a device is finished except for, say, sterilization, polishing, or testing. The definition states that a finished device is "suitable for use or capable of functioning." "Capable of functioning" is not necessarily the same as "suitable for use." For example, an implantable pacemaker may be capable of functioning, but it is not suitable for use until it has been sterilized. However, it is considered a finished device for purposes of the Quality System regulation, as soon as it is capable of functioning.

820.3(m) Lot or batch means one or more components or finished devices that consist of a single type, model, class, size, composition, or software version that are manufactured under essentially the same conditions and that are intended to have uniform characteristics and quality within specified limits.

Discussion: The term "lot" is often used for distinct physical units of product, whereas "batch" often relates to a volume of a liquid or solid that has been formulated. A lot or batch may comprise only one finished device or component. It is the manufacturer's responsibility to determine the appropriate size of a lot or batch, on the basis of the device and associated manufacturing processes.

820.3(n) Management with executive responsibility means those senior employees of a manufacturer who have the authority to establish or make changes to the manufacturer's quality policy and quality system.

Discussion: The term "management with executive responsibility" is intended to apply only to management that has the *authority* to bring about change in the Quality System and in the management of that system. Management with executive responsibility may be the chief executive officer (CEO), or the CEO may delegate the *authority* to other top-level executives to carry out the requirements of 21 CFR 820.20, "Management responsibility." Upper management may not delegate the *responsibility* for ensuring that the requirements are met.

820.3(o) Manufacturer means any person who designs, manufactures, fabricates, assembles, or processes a finished device. Manufacturer includes but is not limited to those who perform the functions of contract sterilization, installation, relabeling, remanufacturing, repacking, or specification development, and initial distributors of foreign entities performing these functions.

Discussion: Entities meeting the definition of a "finished device manufacturer" are subject to 21 CFR 820 for the sections that apply to the scope of their activities. Those entities include manufacturers of finished devices and accessories to finished devices, as well as manufacturers that perform the specific functions cited in the requirement. Accessories are packaged and labeled for commercial distribution, for a particular health-related purpose, to be used in conjunction with a finished device. The Registration and Listing regulation, 21 CFR 807, defines further requirements for finished device manufacturers, including accessory manufacturers.

Although FDA believes that persons who perform servicing and refurbishing activities outside the control of the original equipment manufacturer meet the definition of "manufacturer," the terms "servicer" and "refurbisher" are not included in the Quality System regulation.

"Remanufacturer" is included in this definition because remanufacturing changes a finished device's specifications or intended use. Contract sterilizers, installers, specification developers, repackagers, relabelers, and initial distributors that perform one or more of the functions described in the definition are also considered manufacturers because those activities may have an effect on the safety and effectiveness of the finished device.

820.3(p) Manufacturing material means any material or substance used in or used to facilitate the manufacturing process, a concomitant constituent, or a byproduct constituent produced during the manufacturing process, which is present in or on the finished device as a residue or impurity not by design or intent of the manufacturer.

Discussion: Many manufacturing processes need a manufacturing material to facilitate the process. Examples include isopropyl alcohol, which is used to wipe down the exterior of a part before assembly; mold release, which is used to help plastic parts release from the mold; and cutting oil, which is used in metal machining operations.

"Concomitant constituent" is included in this definition because of FDA's experiences with medical gloves. It is intended to address materials such as natural rubber latex, which may contain naturally occurring allergenic proteins that should be reduced or removed to a level at which they do not adversely affect the safety of the finished device.

Byproduct constituents may also be a concern. A byproduct constituent may include residue that is present in product packaging after ethylene oxide (EtO) sterilization. Such byproduct constituents must be reduced to safe levels before the product is released for distribution.

820.3(q) Nonconformity means the nonfulfillment of a specified requirement.

Discussion: FDA emphasizes that a nonconformity may not always constitute a product defect or failure, but a product defect or failure is typically a nonconformity. This definition applies to products before and after distribution.

820.3(r) Product means components, manufacturing materials, in- process devices, finished devices, and returned devices.

Discussion: As used in the Quality System regulation, the term "product" is consistent with the definitions given in ISO 8402:1994 and ISO 9000:2005. It is intended to avoid repetition of "components, manufacturing materials, in-process devices, finished devices, and returned devices" throughout the regulation.

820.3(s) Quality means the totality of features and characteristics that bear on the ability of a device to satisfy fitness-for-use, including safety and performance.

Discussion: This definition is a compromise between the desire to harmonize with ISO 8402:1994 and the need to include safety and effectiveness as necessary elements of fitness for use.

820.3(t) Quality audit means a systematic, independent examination of a manufacturer's quality system that is performed at defined intervals and at sufficient frequency to determine whether both quality system activities and the results of such activities comply with quality system procedures, that these procedures are implemented effectively, and that these procedures are suitable to achieve quality system objectives.

Discussion: Quality audits may be conducted in phases. It is not necessary for each audit to address the entire Quality System, provided that the manufacturer examines the entire system at defined, regular intervals. Those intervals should be sufficient to detect, correct, and prevent major problems.

II

820.3(u) Quality policy means the overall intentions and direction of an organization with respect to quality, as established by management with executive responsibility.

Discussion: The definition of "quality policy" is compatible with the definitions in ISO 8402:1994 and ISO 9000:2005. This definition clearly shows that FDA requires the quality policy to be implemented and enforced by top management.

820.3(v) Quality system means the organizational structure, responsibilities, procedures, processes, and resources for implementing quality management.

Discussion: This definition is harmonized with the definition in ISO 8402:1994. "Quality management" refers to the overall management activities and functions that determine and implement the quality policy, objectives, and responsibilities.

820.3(w) Remanufacturer means any person who processes, conditions, renovates, repackages, restores, or does any other act to a finished device that significantly changes the finished device's performance or safety specifications, or intended use.

Discussion: Anyone who changes the specifications of a finished device is considered to be a manufacturer because that person or entity has direct responsibility for device safety and effectiveness. This definition is consistent with 510(k) provisions and premarket approval application and supplement requirements.

820.3(x) Rework means action taken on a nonconforming product so that it will fulfill the specified DMR requirements before it is released for distribution.

Discussion: The definition of "rework" applies to devices or components before distribution and relates to the requirements of section 820.90(b)(2), "Nonconformity review and disposition." Rework should be performed according to specified DMR requirements.

820.3(y) Specification means any requirement with which a product, process, service, or other activity must conform.

Discussion: This definition applies to the documented requirements for a product, process, service, or other activity, as defined by the manufacturer.

820.3(z) Validation *means confirmation by examination and provision of objective evidence that the particular requirements for a specific intended use can be consistently fulfilled.*

Discussion: FDA adopted the ISO 8402:1994 definition of "validation." This definition is also consistent with the definition in ISO 9000:2005. FDA has emphasized that validation ensures that user needs and intended uses can be met *consistently*.

820.3(z)(1) Process validation *means establishing by objective evidence that a process consistently produces a result or product meeting its predetermined specifications.*

Discussion: Process validation ensures that the process consistently produces conforming results and products when it is controlled appropriately. Validation of the process results in establishing and confirming adequate process control methods on the basis of scientifically valid rationale.

820.3(z)(2) Design validation *means establishing by objective evidence that device specifications conform with user needs and intended use(s).*

Discussion: Design validation ensures that the finished device meets the users' needs and the requirements for its intended use. Design validation follows successful design verification.

820.3(aa) Verification *means confirmation by examination and provision of objective evidence that specified requirements have been fulfilled.*

Discussion: FDA adopted the ISO 8402:1994 definition of "verification." This definition is also consistent with the definition in ISO 9000:2005. Verification ensures that outputs for a particular device or activity meet the specified input requirements. Examples of verification are software module testing, component material testing, and subassembly material testing.

NOTES:

"A quality system is built on a foundation of fact."
S. George, *The Baldrige Quality System: The Do-It-Yourself Way to Transform Your Business*, 1992

NOTES:

II

"Quality is not an abstraction; it's a measurable, manageable business issue."
J. Guaspari, *The Customer Connection: Quality for the Rest of Us*, 1988

SECTION III. QUALITY MANAGEMENT

CHAPTER 5. QUALITY SYSTEM (SUBPART A)

820.5 Quality System

The Requirement

> **820.5 Quality system.** *Each manufacturer shall establish and maintain a quality system that is appropriate for the specific medical device(s) designed or manufactured, and that meets the requirements of this part.*

Discussion of the Requirement

The general requirements of section 820.5 are the basis on which the specific requirements of the Quality System regulation are built. Each manufacturer is required to define, implement, and maintain an appropriate Quality System, including instructions and procedures, to meet the requirements of the regulation. By meeting the requirements of the Quality System regulation, the manufacturer is ensuring, as required by section 820.1(a), the safety and effectiveness of the particular devices produced. If the manufacturer does not fully implement and maintain the Quality System, the safety and effectiveness of the finished device may come into question.

Industry Practice

Manufacturers use a variety of terms to describe their approach to satisfying the documentation requirements of the Quality System regulation. Some of the most common terms include "Quality System," "Quality Management System," and "Good Manufacturing Principles System." Note that "Quality Management System" is the term used by the ISO 13485:2003 standard and therefore is often used by firms that are registered to that standard. Regardless of the title of the manufacturer's system, it must meet the expectations of the Quality System regulation, as well as any other requirements levied by other regulatory authorities that govern the manufacturer's operations.

The focus of the Quality System regulation is on ensuring that manufacturers design, produce, and distribute finished devices that are safe and effective. The regulation provides a flexible framework within which each manufacturer must establish a Quality System suitable to its operations. The regulation emphasizes a quality assurance model as opposed to a quality control approach. Whereas quality control focuses on ensuring product quality through adequate inspection and test activities, quality assurance has a broader perspective. Quality assurance proactively considers each aspect of the product life cycle and plans appropriate controls that can influence the outcomes of each stage of the life cycle. Quality assurance spans the life cycle from early design activities through finished device release, with planned controls at all appropriate stages.

Design of the Quality System

A Quality System encompasses the prescribed approaches (i.e., policies, procedures, instructions) for completing activities such as design and production of a medical device, as well as the organizational elements specific to the manufacturer's operations. Organizational elements include organizational structure, staff, and other resources needed to carry out the prescribed operations and the responsibility and authority assignments of particular staff. Each manufacturer establishes a Quality System by creating its own procedures and by incorporating its unique organizational elements.

In general, smaller manufacturers typically have simplified Quality Systems, which have fewer procedures and instructions than larger firms. To determine the extent of documentation appropriate to fulfill Quality System regulation and other requirements, manufacturers typically consider a variety of factors:
- extent of the activities to be carried out (e.g., manufacture only, design and manufacture, contract manufacture);
- risk associated with and complexity of the products manufactured;
- size of the organization;
- activities that are outsourced versus those carried out internally;
- number and location of facilities; and
- general skill levels and language capabilities of staff.

The initial design of the Quality System is often one of the first quality planning activities a manufacturer carries out. Quality planning is discussed further in Chapter 6, "Quality System Requirements."

Because the factors cited above can and often do change over time, each manufacturer should treat its Quality System as a dynamic entity. Particular aspects of the system should be evaluated routinely for effectiveness and updated or changed whenever appropriate. Requirements for routine evaluation of the effectiveness of the Quality System are discussed further in Chapter 6, "Quality System Requirements."

The "continuous improvement" mindset is consistent with the Quality System regulation and also with relevant industry standards such as ISO 13485:2003. Figure 5.1 illustrates a Quality System continuous improvement cycle. Note, however, that the Quality System regulation *does not require* continuous improvement, only effective corrective and preventive action.

In most firms that have a global market presence, the Quality System is designed to meet all applicable regulatory requirements for all products. In other words, manufacturers typically design a Quality System that meets a superset of the national and regional requirements for medical devices. Some of the most common additional requirements that U.S. manufacturers must meet include: the European Council (EC) Medical Device Directive (MDD), the EC In Vitro Diagnostic Directive (IVDD), or the Canadian Medical Devices Regulations.

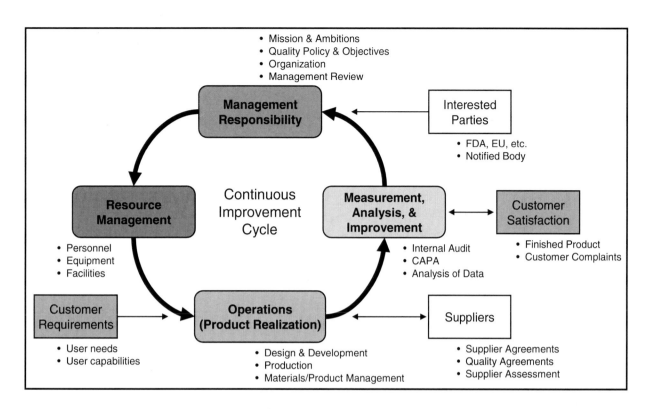

Figure 5.1. Continuous improvement model for Quality Systems (modified from ANSI/AAMI/ISO 13485:2003).

Documenting the Quality System

The Quality System regulation does not require the establishment of a Quality Manual. However, many manufacturers are also registered to ISO 13485:2003, which does require a Quality Manual. Therefore, manufacturers often establish a high-level Quality Manual that summarizes the approaches and policies implemented in various procedures.

Because the regulation does not prescribe the structure of a firm's documentation, each firm must define its own structure that suits its particular needs. Many manufacturers use a hierarchical documentation structure, where high-level procedures described "what" is required, and instructions define "how" to meet the requirements. The need for both procedures and detailed instructions is highly dependent on the manufacturer's operations, device complexity and associated risk, and staff capabilities. In some cases a high-level procedure may be sufficient, in others substantial, detailed instructions may be necessary.

Most manufacturers treat records as a part of their documentation structure. Standards such as ISO 13485:2003 use the term "record" to specifically indicate a particular type of document that contains objective evidence of an activity or work operation. The Quality System regulation does not carry the same distinction for the term "record". For example, the "Device Master Record" is a set of controlled documents that define how to manufacture a device. In contrast, the "Device History Record" is a set of completed forms and other objective evidence related to the production of a particular lot, batch, or serialized unit of finished devices.

Figure 5.2 illustrates one common documentation structure used by medical device manufacturers. Other options are possible. The approach used must be suitable and appropriate for the manufacturer's particular operations and types of medical devices produced.

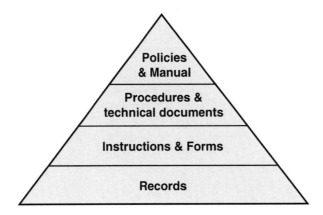

Figure 5.2. Typical documentation structure.

In considering the documentation structure illustrated in Figure 5.2, note that the term "records" is specific and consistent with the ISO 13485 standard (i.e., records serve as objective evidence). Regardless of the particular document structure used, the policies, procedures, and instructions that define a manufacturer's Quality System requirements are subject to document control procedures, which are discussed further in Chapter 22, "Document Controls". The documents that provide objective evidence of completed activities are subject to general record controls (see Chapter 23, "Records").

CHAPTER 6. QUALITY SYSTEM REQUIREMENTS (SUBPART B)

820.20 Management Responsibility

820.20(a) Quality Policy

The Requirement

820.20(a) Quality policy. Management with executive responsibility shall establish its policy and objectives for, and commitment to, quality. Management with executive responsibility shall ensure that the quality policy is understood, implemented, and maintained at all levels of the organization.

Discussion of the Requirement

Section 820.3(u) of the regulation defines "quality policy" as "the overall quality intentions and direction of an organization with respect to quality, as formally expressed by management with executive responsibility." Section 820.3(n) defines "management with executive responsibility" as "those senior employees of a manufacturer who have the authority to establish or make changes to the manufacturer's quality policy and quality system."

This section of the regulation requires a manufacturer to establish a quality policy and objectives. Management with executive responsibility is required to define this policy and to communicate it to all employees. Although the establishment of quality objectives, the development of methods and procedures based on these objectives, and the implementation of the Quality System may be delegated, it is the responsibility of top management to establish the quality policy and to ensure that it is followed.

The Food and Drug Administration (FDA) believes that it is, without question, the responsibility of executive management to ensure that employees understand the quality policy and objectives. Furthermore, FDA believes that understanding is a learning process achieved through education and reinforcement. Management with executive responsibility reinforces understanding of the quality policy by demonstrating a commitment to the Quality System, visibly and actively, on a continuous basis.

The Quality System Inspection Technique (QSIT) includes Management Controls as one of the four major subsystems addressed during a baseline facility inspection. QSIT Management Controls objectives cover each of the subparts under 21 CFR 820.20, "Management responsibility," and 21 CFR 820.22, "Quality audit." Chapter 1, "FDA's Organization and Regulatory Strategies," provides more details on the QSIT.

Industry Practice

During the past decade, the medical device industry has become more sophisticated in implementing quality programs that are based on both internal and external factors. Internally, companies have customers who demand quality products and services. Externally, competition pressures companies to improve quality while controlling costs. Companies have established quality programs based on concepts such as Total Quality

Management and Quality Leadership and on recognized quality standards such as the ISO 9001/13485. Within these quality programs, establishing a quality policy is a requirement.

Management with executive responsibility sets the quality policy and attitude for the company, regardless of the size of the company. Ensuring that the company quality policy is understood by all personnel involves formal education and training.

The following are some examples of quality policies:

III

Company A

"It is our Quality Policy to:
   a) Strive to achieve total quality performance, by understanding who the Company's customers are and what their requirements are regarding product and services;
   b) Ensure, by internal quality audits and third party assessment, that the appropriate quality level is achieved, thus assuring that our goods and services are safe and effective for their intended use and that the specifications for these goods and services are consistently achieved;
   c) Continuously strive to improve the quality of the Company's products; and,
   d) Work at all times in the manner defined in the Company's documented Quality System, thus ensuring that the standards defined in 21 CFR 820 and ISO 9001 are being maintained."

Company B

"Our ongoing objective is to provide the most technologically advanced, high performance and high quality products, as well as the most advanced customer service. We are committed to meeting the needs of our worldwide customers, both internal and external to the company, and continuing to strive for excellence in everything we do as a company.

"The well-being of patients throughout the world depends on the performance of our products; therefore, quality and reliability are critical. It is essential that we do our utmost to ensure that quality is an integral part of every function of this company.

"Our Total Quality Program has been designed to provide an effective means of maximizing quality and assuring that manufactured products fulfill their intended purpose with regard to safety, performance, reliability, appearance, and customer satisfaction. The Vice President of RA/QA is responsible to the President for the overall administration of this Total Quality Program and for assuring that annual management reviews and resultant actions shall be documented and provided to all appropriate levels of management"

Company C

"To consistently provide products and services which meet or exceed the quality requirements of our customers through continuous improvement."

Many firms prominently display their quality policy in common meeting areas as a visible reminder to personnel and visitors that management is committed to quality.

820.20(b) Organization

The Requirement

(b) Organization. Each manufacturer shall establish and maintain an adequate organizational structure to ensure that devices are designed and produced in accordance with the requirements of this part.

> **(1) Responsibility and authority.** Each manufacturer shall establish the appropriate responsibility, authority, and interrelation of all personnel who manage, perform, and assess work affecting quality, and provide the independence and authority necessary to perform these tasks.
>
> **(2) Resources.** Each manufacturer shall provide adequate resources, including the assignment of trained personnel, for management, performance of work, and assessment activities, including internal quality audits, to meet the requirements of this part.
>
> **(3) Management representative.** Management with executive responsibility shall appoint, and document such appointment of, a member of management who, irrespective of other responsibilities, shall have established authority over and responsibility for:
>
> > **(i)** Ensuring that quality system requirements are effectively established and effectively maintained in accordance with this part; and
> >
> > **(ii)** Reporting on the performance of the quality system to management with executive responsibility for review.

Discussion of the Requirement

It is a manufacturer's responsibility to create an organizational structure adequate to ensure that activities are performed in accordance with the manufacturer's Quality System and with the Good Manufacturing Practice (GMP) requirements. FDA has clearly indicated that an adequate organizational structure is necessary not only to ensure compliance, but also to ensure a manufacturer's ability to consistently produce safe and effective medical devices. The type of organizational structure established will be determined by the volume and type of devices produced, the manufacturer's organizational goals, and the expectations and needs of customers.

Section 820.20(b) of the regulation requires each manufacturer to ensure that responsibility, authority, and organizational independence is provided to personnel who manage, perform, and verify work affecting quality. Section 820.20(b)(2) requires each manufacturer to provide adequate resources for meeting the requirements of the Quality System. These resources include monetary commitment, as well as adequate personnel and appropriate infrastructure (e.g., facilities, equipment, and tools).

Management with executive responsibility is required to appoint a member of management who has established authority and responsibility for ensuring that the Quality System requirements are defined, documented, implemented, and maintained in accordance with GMP requirements. The management representative must have the independence to ensure that the Quality System is not compromised, and the management representative is responsible for reporting to management with executive responsibility on the performance of the Quality System.

III

Industry Practice

A specific organizational structure for executing a quality assurance (QA) program is not prescribed by the Quality System regulation. Past practices dictated that, where possible, a designated individual not having direct responsibility for the performance of a manufacturing operation be responsible for the QA program. However, FDA and industry are more concerned with the adequacy and appropriateness of QA activities than with organizational structure. With the downsizing and streamlining typical in industry, it is not always possible, practical, or efficient to have a separate QA function.

When a separate QA organization is in place, a manufacturer should not operate on the basis that this function has primary and direct responsibility for the quality of the finished device. To do so means those quality problems may not be solved in a timely manner because attention is directed toward the wrong organization. Rather, the QA organization should be responsible for ensuring that attention is directed toward the correct department, if a quality problem arises.

Manufacturers design their Quality Systems to fit their specific needs. Many manufacturers have developed their own quality practices to be used on a day-to-day basis. Many have also become registered to ISO 9001/13485, and their quality practices are codified in the quality policy and Quality Manual. The quality policy and Quality Manual are developed to assist manufacturers in carrying out their daily quality responsibilities.

The Quality System is a set of checks and double-checks on the product from design through distribution. Through company organization, structure, and compliance with ISO quality standards and the Quality System regulation, manufacturers have developed controls to ensure that their devices are produced to be safe and effective. Management provides resources for the Quality System by establishing written procedures and by directing personnel and funds toward this effort.

Manufacturers that have appointed a management representative often designate a member of the quality organization. Documenting this appointment does not need to be elaborate; it is often noted on an organizational chart, referenced in the Quality Manual, or included in a job description.

820.20(c) Management Review

The Requirement

> ***820.20(c) Management review.*** *Management with executive responsibility shall review the suitability and effectiveness of the quality system at defined intervals and with sufficient frequency according to established procedures to ensure that the quality system satisfies the requirements of this part and the manufacturer's established quality policy and objectives. The dates and results of quality system reviews shall be documented.*

Discussion of the Requirement

The aim of the management review is for management with executive responsibility to conduct a broad review of the organization as a whole to determine whether its quality policy is implemented and the quality objectives are being met. The review is also intended to ensure the continued adequacy and effectiveness of the Quality System. All parts of the Quality System are to be reviewed, but different areas may be reviewed at different times. The frequency of reviews should be defined and linked to the quality policy and objectives. A documented system that defines how management intends to review the Quality System is required. The regulation clearly requires establishment of written procedures to ensure the consistency and completeness of required reviews.

Although the regulation requires documentation of the management review results, FDA has decided not to request to inspect and copy the reports during routine inspections. This decision was intended to help ensure that the reviews are complete, candid, and of maximum use to the manufacturer. FDA may require management with executive responsibility to certify in writing that the requirements of section 820.20(c) have been met. In addition, the written procedure for management review will be subject to inspection and copying.

Industry Practice

Management review is an opportunity for executive management to evaluate the effectiveness of the Quality System with actual data. Gathering and presenting the information for management review is a responsibility often assigned by the Management Representative to the QA or regulatory affairs (RA) groups, which have day-to-day experience with Quality Systems and quality data.

The management review may include an evaluation of the organizational structure; the adequacy of staffing and resources; the achieved quality of the finished device relative to the quality objectives; and other information, including customer feedback (e.g., complaints or recalls), process and product performance, servicing information, audit results (internal, third-party, or supplier), and any corrective or preventive actions taken.

It is up to a manufacturer to determine what constitutes a "sufficient frequency" for management reviews. The Management Representative and management with executive responsibility should review the appropriateness of the review frequency on the basis of the findings of previous reviews. For established and compliant firms, an annual or semi-annual review may be sufficient. If there are known problems or if the Quality System is not yet proven, "sufficient frequency" may mean "fairly frequent."

A typical management review practice in industry is to convene a gathering of executive management. For ease of review, information may be presented in tabular or graphic form. Comparisons may be drawn to similar data in previous years to show improvement (or lack of improvement) relative to quality indicators. During the management review, representatives discuss the information they have obtained and determine whether additional resources, programs, or systems are appropriate to address any quality concerns. Both the review and the recommendations should be documented in the minutes of the meeting or a separate review record.

III

The formal management review may also take the form of a written report on the Quality System, which is circulated among top-level management. The written report, which may be prepared and reviewed as necessary, includes the same type of information on important quality indicators as is presented at a management review meeting. Written sign-offs, indicating that the report has been reviewed and understood, may be required as a means of documentation. Individual comments on the contents of the report may also be requested. This type of management review may be more efficient in terms of time, particularly in a large corporation, but it lacks the opportunity for discussion and exchange of ideas that a meeting presents.

In addition to meeting the requirement for documented management review of Quality Systems, the vast majority of organizations hold periodic management meetings in which, among other issues, quality indicators are reviewed and discussed. Although not a part of the formal management review, these types of meetings are quite valuable in providing timely information and feedback to executive management regarding quality issues and quality progress.

The effectiveness of management review as a tool for quality review and improvement depends, of course, on the commitment of top-level management to Quality Systems and products. FDA understands this concept well and sees it in practice often. Even though FDA will not routinely ask for information from management reviews, just as it does not routinely request audit reports, the effectiveness and adequacy of management review can be judged by reviewing other required quality records, including inspection and testing results for incoming, in-process, and finished devices; complaint files; and service reports. For this reason, a critical part of management review is to assess the information that FDA will see in terms of the quality policy and objectives and to ensure that appropriate preventive and corrective actions are under way when problems occur.

820.20(d) Quality Planning

The Requirement

> **820.20(d) Quality planning.** *Each manufacturer shall establish a quality plan which defines the quality practices, resources, and activities relevant to devices that are designed and manufactured. The manufacturer shall establish how the requirements for quality will be met.*

Discussion of the Requirement

The Quality System documentation must define the objectives and requirements for quality, including such elements as fitness for use, performance, safety, and reliability. A quality plan may be an independent document defining how the quality requirements will be met, or it may simply reference the device master record (DMR) and other elements that make up the manufacturer's Quality System.

Industry Practice

A quality plan shows how the Quality System requirements are applied to a device or device type to ensure that it meets specifications and quality requirements. The purpose of a quality plan is to communicate the requirements and controls necessary to manufacture, test, and release devices that meet customer needs. The quality plan covers all quality practices, resources, and activities at all stages of manufacturing, including design, procurement, production, and—when applicable—installation and service.

Many manufacturers do not have documents clearly identified as "quality plans." FDA has not mandated a specific format for such plans. If a manufacturer chooses to create separate quality plans, those documents should be consistent and appropriately cross-referenced with other documents relating to the device. If the individual documents are appropriately and adequately structured, it is possible to achieve the application of the Quality System elements or establishment of the quality plan through the DMR. If the DMR is used, the manufacturer's Quality Manual or other top-level procedure typically defines how the DMR meets the requirements of section 820.20(d).

Some manufacturers establish explicit quality plans as a result of strategic planning initiatives. Others use quality plans to document substantial Quality System improvement efforts.

III

820.20(e) Quality System Procedures

The Requirement

> *820.20(e) Quality system procedures. Each manufacturer shall establish quality system procedures and instructions. An outline of the structure of the documentation used in the quality system shall be established where appropriate.*

Discussion of the Requirement

Manufacturers are required to develop and maintain effective Quality System procedures for compliance with each aspect of the Quality System regulation. The complexity and structure of these instructions depends on the manufacturer, its organization, and the device being produced. The Quality System procedures must be designed to ensure the safety and effectiveness of the finished device. When appropriate and when required to define the Quality System, the documentation structure should be summarized (see section 820.186, "Quality System Record").

Industry Practice

This section of the regulation requires manufacturers to define and document the procedures and instructions used to establish and implement the Quality System. Manufacturers that have a Quality System that meets the requirements of an ISO 9001/13485 standard typically have documented systems that include an outline of the procedures, often in the form of a Quality Manual.

Although the regulation does not require a one, a Quality Manual provides a concise description of the Quality System and the policies and procedures that implement it. The importance of a Quality Manual depends on the size of the company and the complexity of its documentation structure. The requirements of this section of the regulation can be easily met by a small manufacturer through one tier of documentation. For larger manufacturers, multiple tiers of documentation, including a top-level Quality Manual, are appropriate for compliance with the GMP requirements and for effective operation of the Quality System.

The Quality Manual shows how each Quality System requirement is met. It is common for a Quality Manual to include the manufacturer's quality policy, a description of the organization, and a summary of the Quality System procedures with appropriate cross-references to more detailed documentation. Quality System procedures encompass system-related procedures as well as device-specific procedures for processes that help ensure that the quality objectives are met. The Quality Manual can be one document supported by several tiers of documents, with each tier becoming progressively more detailed; together, they define the Quality System.

820.22 Quality Audit

The Requirement

> ***820.22 Quality audit.*** *Each manufacturer shall establish procedures for quality audits and conduct such audits to assure that the quality system is in compliance with the established quality system requirements and to determine the effectiveness of the quality system. Quality audits shall be conducted by individuals who do not have direct responsibility for the matters being audited. Corrective action(s), including a reaudit of deficient matters, shall be taken when necessary. A report of the results of each quality audit, and reaudit(s) where taken, shall be made and such reports shall be reviewed by management having responsibility for the matters audited. The dates and results of quality audits and reaudits shall be documented.*

Discussion of the Requirement

This section requires each manufacturer to conduct a periodic internal evaluation of the Quality System to verify its effectiveness and its compliance with the Quality System regulation. A manufacturer must review all procedures to ensure adequacy and compliance with the regulation and to determine whether the procedures are being effectively implemented at all times. This review applies to all activities relating to the Quality System and areas of the company in which the Quality System is implemented.

Manufacturers are required to establish written procedures for conducting quality audits. The procedures should detail the specific requirements for conducting quality audits and should explain key aspects of the quality audit system. System requirements should include identification of areas and elements to be audited; scheduling of audits; standards to be used to conduct audits; auditor or audit team requirements and qualification; and audit preparation, records, reporting, corrective action, and closure.

Qualified individuals must be designated to conduct the quality audits. FDA expects auditors to be independent of the function or element being audited. Independence needs to be maintained so that the auditor is objective enough to identify deficiencies within the function or element being audited and to assess whether corrective actions, if required, are adequate and have been implemented. The failure to have an independent auditor could result in an ineffective audit.

It is up to the manufacturer to decide when and how often audits should be conducted. Audits may be conducted at one time or in stages. The decision should be based on the performance of the Quality System activity, the difficulty of the activity, and the compliance history. It is expected that audits will be conducted at least annually. Regardless, the frequency of audits should be planned, and such plans should be documented. Audits are required to cover all of a manufacturer's operations and all applicable elements of the regulation.

The results of quality audits, whether or not deficiencies are observed, must be documented. FDA expects that executive management will review audit results as part of the management review activities specified in section 820.20(c). Management is expected to identify and provide the resources needed to implement and follow up on corrective actions so that the recurrence of problems observed can be prevented and the safety, reliability, and effectiveness of the finished device ensured.

FDA also expects that audit results will be provided to the individuals responsible for the operations that are audited and that these individuals will respond, when necessary, with a corrective action plan. When corrective action is identified, it is expected that such action will be taken in a timely manner and that a reaudit will be conducted to verify that the action has been taken and is effective. Such verification should be documented.

As indicated in section 820.180(c), it is FDA policy not to review audit results and audit reports. However, manufacturers are required to maintain records documenting audits and reaudits to demonstrate that audits have been completed as planned.

FDA's Compliance Program 7382.845, *Inspection of Medical Device Manufacturers*, instructs investigators to review audit procedures, the content of which should include at least the following elements: objectives, assignment of responsibilities, audit scope, evaluation criteria, and audit scheduling.

Industry Practice

Audits address compliance with company policy, procedures, and specifications, as well as compliance with the Quality System regulation and the overall effectiveness of the Quality System. Audit programs within industry vary from facility to facility, depending in part on the resources available to conduct a successful audit.

Auditors should have management support to conduct audits and report observations objectively. Such support is often attained by having the auditor report directly to the Management Representative. Another option is to assign the auditor direct or dotted-line responsibility to the president or Chief Executive Officer (CEO).

Auditors can be quality assurance personnel, personnel from other areas within the company, or consultants. Some small companies use consultants to address the concern about independence. Larger manufacturers sometimes use consultants to obtain an outside verification of adequacy of compliance. Audits are usually conducted by one auditor, but some companies, particularly those that are seeking or have obtained ISO certification/CE marking, have gone to a team approach, using two or more auditors.

Some device manufacturers do the minimum; they audit the entire Quality System only once a year. Other manufacturers have implemented comprehensive audit schedules with a more frequent audit interval.

Systems for documenting and formally reporting audit findings vary from company to company and may take the form of audit checklists, audit records, or audit reports. In almost all instances, a summary cover letter will be generated with the observations attached or included as part of the formal audit report. For FDA review purposes, manufacturers typically maintain records to demonstrate compliance with the audit requirements of the Quality System regulation. These records often take the form of an audit log or a certification letter. Such records include the audit dates, the names of the auditors who conducted the audit, the scope of the audit, and the date the audit was closed. Audit records are typically maintained as a part of the Quality System Record (QSR).

As a practical matter, almost all audit observations require corrective action. The level of corrective action varies according to circumstances. When an observation is made, the procedures should ensure that corrective action is requested from the management representative of the audited area within a reasonable time. As with any nonconformity, an investigation into the cause of the noncompliance is conducted before corrective action is defined and initiated. At the time corrective action is implemented, or shortly afterward, the auditor returns to verify that corrective action has been taken and is effective. In some instances, implementation of corrective action may be verified by review of revised released documentation.

There are numerous ways to design and implement an effective audit program. Many manufacturers have found the following items to be useful elements of the audit procedure:

a. *Scope.* The scope defines which facilities and which functions or activities are affected by the procedure.

b. *Audit Plan and Schedule.* This part of the procedure describes how the plan and schedule are determined and approved. It also specifies the frequency of audits. When determining the audit frequency, the manufacturer should consider the amount and seriousness of past audit observations. If no previous audits have been conducted, the manufacturer should identify, on the basis of management review activities, potential problem areas or areas of major quality impact and focus on those areas first.

c. *Responsibilities.* This part defines responsibilities for executing the audit system:
   • developing the audit plan,
   • assigning auditors,
   • developing and implementing corrective action plans,
   • recording and communicating audit findings, and
   • review of findings by management.

d. *Auditor Requirements.* This part of the procedure defines the required training, experience, independence, and composition of the audit team (where teams are used) and addresses the use of consultants. Independence is crucial to the effectiveness of a successful audit program. To maintain auditor independence, auditors should not audit any areas or functions for which they have functional responsibility.

e.   *Audit Standards.* Guidance is provided on the standards to be used by auditors in conducting audits (e.g., the Quality System regulation, ISO 13485, company policies and procedures, and the DMR).

f.   *Audit Process.* The details of the audit process are described (e.g., interviewing, observing, tracing, taking notes, using checklists, reporting audit findings, debriefing on a daily or other specified basis, and opening and closing meetings). The procedure should identify any checklists to be used and how these checklists are to be approved. Checklists are a series of questions that review the function being audited to determine the effectiveness and compliance of that function. A checklist acts as a guide to the auditors to ensure that all aspects of the Quality System are assessed. Notes and observations indicating compliance or noncompliance are recorded on the checklist. Some manufacturers rate observations based on a defined scale (e.g., major or minor), depending on the risk associated with the noncompliance raised.

g.   *Results and Reports.* This part of the procedure describes the method of recording audit findings (forms, checklists, reports); preparing the final report; and issuing the report to responsible parties, including management. The procedure should identify the timeframes that responsible individuals have to provide a response and implement corrective actions. Audit reports should be part of management review activities. Any assistance required by executive management to implement corrective action should be documented.

h.   *Corrective Action.* This part of the procedure describes the steps for requesting, implementing, and verifying the corrective action, and it addresses responsibilities and timeliness. Corrective action should encompass the following:
   • identification of the root cause of the problem,
   • the action to correct the specific problem,
   • the action to correct the root cause,
   • identification of other areas or products affected by the problem, and
   • the action to correct any problems with other areas or products.

i.   *Follow-Up.* This part should address how follow-up audits are to be conducted and documented. The procedure should explain when a follow-up audit is required. During follow-up audits, it is necessary to evaluate and verify the implementation and effectiveness of corrective actions taken to remedy audit observations.

j.   *Audit Closure.* This part of the procedure describes the methods for determining that the audit loop has been completed (e.g., verification of corrective actions, completion of any logs, and certification and maintenance of audit files). Audit closure typically includes a final audit record entry or notation, to facilitate on-going assessment of audit program effectiveness.

820.25 Personnel

The Requirement

820.25 Personnel.
(a) General. Each manufacturer shall have sufficient personnel with the necessary education, background, training, and experience to assure that all activities required by this part are correctly performed.

(b) Training. Each manufacturer shall establish procedures for identifying training needs and ensure that all personnel are trained to adequately perform their assigned responsibilities. Training shall be documented.

    (1) As part of their training, personnel shall be made aware of device defects which may occur from the improper performance of their specific jobs.

    (2) Personnel who perform verification and validation activities shall be made aware of defects and errors that may be encountered as part of their job functions.

Discussion of the Requirement

This section requires each manufacturer to employ sufficient qualified personnel, as determined by the requirements of the company's Quality System; to establish procedures to identify training needs; to provide appropriate training for personnel; and to maintain records of training.

It is up to the manufacturer to determine what constitutes "sufficient" personnel with the necessary qualifications to perform their functions. The manufacturer must ensure that personnel assigned to particular functions are properly equipped and that they have the necessary education, background, training, and experience to perform their functions correctly. Ensuring that personnel are qualified supports compliance with the manufacturer's Quality System and ultimately helps to ensure that finished devices are produced according to specifications.

For the Quality System to function as planned, all personnel are required to be properly trained. Each function, not only those affecting quality, must be viewed as integral to all other functions. All personnel must be trained in the functions and procedures that they will encounter while performing their assigned jobs.

A manufacturer must have an established procedure that includes the identification of training needs. The training program must ensure that each employee understands both the job function itself and the GMP requirements pertaining to that particular job function, including how the job relates to the overall Quality System. In addition, employee training is required to cover the consequences of improper performance so that employees are aware of defects that they should look for and of the effect their actions can have on the safety and effectiveness of the finished device.

Industry Practice

No matter how effective quality and production systems are as concepts, people still play the major role in producing a quality product. Training is more than an administrative function; it should be continuous and appropriate for each employee's job function.

The first step in meeting the requirements of section 820.25 is to select and employ appropriate personnel. There is no documented guidance from FDA concerning the exact education, background, and experience needed to satisfy the intent of the regulation. In Compliance Program 7382.845, *Inspection of Medical Device Manufacturers,* FDA instructs investigators to look for situations in which personnel failed to perform a job or performed it inadequately because of insufficient training. By extension, FDA investigators may look for instances in which inadequate personnel education, background, or experience adversely affected device safety and efficacy.

Although prior GMP experience is preferred for certain positions, it is not mandated by the regulation. Personnel should, however, have the necessary education and skills to perform the tasks required of the position. Upper and middle levels of management are often exempt from job-specific training requirements. These individuals usually possess the required education or experience when hired. They are subject to general training programs (e.g., GMP requirements and orientation) that are considered to be company-wide. If an individual is hired who does not possess the required background for a given position, as noted in the job description for that position, it is the company's responsibility to make sure that training is provided and documented in a reasonable time period.

III

A manufacturer's written training program typically addresses the following:
- responsibility for training programs;
- methods of documenting job descriptions;
- methods of identifying training needs and qualifications of personnel, both at initial employment and in light of Quality System changes;
- identification of those jobs that require formal skills or knowledge training and GMP requirements training;
- methods of determining success of training (e.g., testing or documented follow-up);
- methods of documenting training activities and maintaining the documentation; and
- retraining requirements.

Medical device manufacturers routinely provide general GMP training to all employees. Such training is provided at the time the employee is hired and then annually or as needed thereafter. In addition, depending on the job skills required, specialized training may be provided for specific job functions. The degree of training required, including GMP training, will depend on the employee capabilities, on the complexity of the position, and on the risks inherent in the devices that are produced. These requirements should be established and documented.

Lack of training, as reflected in instances of negligence, poor operating techniques, or the inability of employees to perform their functions properly, can lead to defective products and sometimes to regulatory or liability issues. Management should be diligent in looking for factors that indicate a need for employee training. Evidence of personnel problems or training problems might include the following:
- an excessive number of in-process rejects and failures,
- employees' lack of knowledge of pertinent documentation,
- high rates of "employee retraining" as corrective action, or
- an excessive number of complaints.

Implementing a successful training program depends on thorough identification of training needs, appropriate to each job function. Once a training program is established, manufacturers must be diligent in carrying out the training, including creation of clear training records. Training must be an on-going activity with periodic retraining as needed.

Developing a Firm-Specific Training System

Documented training programs assure that consideration is given to training the manufacturer's permanent and temporary personnel, including contractors and

III

consultants. This approach is especially helpful if no department is specifically responsible for training and if training is implemented by various people, such as departmental supervisors. A consistent list of requirements is established for each job function, and the applicability is determined. For example, a training program checklist might include the following elements:

- orientation to the company's product lines and quality policy,
- general GMP requirements training,
- specific GMP requirements training,
- documentation and record-keeping requirements,
- standard operating procedures,
- equipment considerations,
- personnel safety and first aid,
- applicable techniques for ensuring product safety and efficacy,
- security,
- hazardous materials awareness and response to exposure,
- specific skills required (current and updates as needed),
- hygiene,
- required certifications (current and updates as needed),
- literature references,
- task practice exercises, and
- potential defects and ramifications.

When the applicable areas of the checklist have been determined for each job function, a training manual is developed to include those requirements.

Training programs must cover contract and temporary personnel. The extent of training versus supervision depends primarily on the length of time the employee will be working and the job function that the employee is performing. All contract and temporary employees should receive basic GMP and company orientation training. The company procedure should define a contract employee versus a temporary employee. Because contract employees are often long-term employees, they may require the same level of training as permanent employees receive. Constant, direct supervision and basic task-related instructions should suffice for temporary employees.

Identifying Training Needs

Job titles may be used to identify the general training topics required. Specific training requirements may be listed by department, facility work area, and job function. For example, training on GMP requirements as well as a general facility and production overview would be required for all job titles. Departmental breakdowns would identify the specific training required for personnel working in the manufacturing department versus the QA department, for example.

More specialized training may be required in particular work areas. For example, training in aseptic practices or specific safety precautions might be needed for specific jobs. Job function training would include task-specific instructions, such as how to use a particulate analyzer or a pH meter. All such requirements should be documented. Additional expectations related to operators of validated processes must also be considered, as described in Chapter 15, "Process Validation."

Implementing Training

Training is implemented as outlined in the training program. A schedule is developed to allow for personnel replacement, if necessary; for budget considerations; and for scheduling of outside training resources, if required. Ensuring that personnel are appropriately trained prior to performing work that could impact product quality is common industry practice. Some manufacturers formally assess effectiveness of training through testing or skill certification programs.

Maintaining Records

III

Various methods are used to maintain employee training records. Depending on the approach used (electronic or manual), records may be maintained by cross-referencing to a specific procedure, task, facility area, training session, or other category. Records may also be referenced to each employee or department.

In large companies, maintenance of training records may be a joint responsibility of the human resources (HR) and operating departments. For instance, educational accomplishments, external training, prior training, job descriptions, orientation records, and general ongoing training (e.g., basic GMP requirements) may be maintained by the HR department. Records of internal job responsibilities, ongoing job-related training, and training related to a specific task may be maintained by the operating department supervisor or manager. In smaller firms, one department typically maintains all training records.

Because training records are routinely audited by internal auditors and external regulatory agencies, most manufacturers maintain training records separately from performance appraisal and other personnel records. This approach helps maintain confidentiality of personnel matters, while facilitating audits.

A manufacturer's requirements for content of particular training records usually include:
- employee's name and signature;
- training subject (e.g., document or program used for training);
- name and signature of the trainer; and
- date of training.

Training systems typically also provide a means for capturing externally provided training records, such as employee attendance at seminars and workshops.

Training Updates

The Quality System regulation requires that manufacturers make certain that all personnel are adequately trained. Therefore, training should be updated as needed. To meet part of this requirement, many manufacturers provide periodic retraining in basic GMP requirements and the application of the regulation. A "periodic" interval typically translates to annual retraining. Retraining requirements should be specified in the company's training procedure.

There is no specific GMP requirement for retraining when a new procedure is written or when an existing procedure has been changed or updated. Document control requirements (21 CFR 820.40), however, do require notification of changes to affected personnel. Many manufacturers routinely retrain the affected personnel or make a notation in the change order explaining why retraining is not necessary. There are other methods of acceptable training (e.g., baseline and job skills training) that would not require retraining with each revision. Retraining may be required as part of a corrective action when, for example, procedures are being performed improperly or an excessive number of product defects are occurring.

III

NOTES:

III

"If top management does not function as a cohesive team, this presents a serious barrier to implementing a quality approach because the rest of the organization reflects top management."
D. Hutton, *The Change Agents' Handbook*, 1994

NOTES:

III

"If quality is not inspected in but is built in, if quality is integral to the product or service, then quality is a function of management."
                    R. Aguayo, *Dr. Deming: The American Who Taught the Japanese About Quality*, 1991

SECTION IV. DESIGN CONTROLS

CHAPTER 7. DESIGN CONTROLS (SUBPART C)

820.30 Design Controls

The Requirement

> **820.30 Design Controls.**
> **(a) General.**
> **(1)** *Each manufacturer of any class III or class II device, and the class I devices listed in paragraph (a)(2) of this section, shall establish and maintain procedures to control the design of the device in order to ensure that specified design requirements are met.*
> **(2)** *The following class I devices are subject to design controls:*
>   **(i)** *Devices automated with computer software; and*
>   **(ii)** *The devices listed in the following chart.*

Section	Device
868.6810	Catheter, Tracheobronchial, Suction
878.4460	Glove, Surgeon
880.6760	Restraint, Protective
892.5650	System, Applicator, Radionuclide, Manual
892.5740	Source, Radionuclide, Teletherapy

Discussion of the Requirement

Design control is the process of controlling and monitoring the design activities for a medical device to ensure that specified design requirements are met. The objective of the application of design controls is industry-wide improvements in safety and effectiveness of medical devices. The design control requirements of the Quality System regulation apply to all class II and class III devices, including accessories. The design control requirements also apply to selected class I devices, as outlined in section 820.30(a)(2)(ii), and to class I devices automated with computer software. Software accessories to class I devices also must be developed according to design controls even though the parent class I device may be exempt.

Design control requirements are not intended to apply during the research phase (i.e., to the development of concepts or to feasibility studies). After it is decided that a design will be developed, a plan must be generated for establishing the adequacy of the design requirements and for ensuring the design that will eventually be released to production meets the approved requirements. Design controls also apply to investigational device exemption (IDE) devices (i.e., medical devices used in human clinical trials). The IDE regulation (21 CFR 812) in paragraph 812.1 (Scope) exempts manufacturers from most medical device regulations with the exception of design controls to ensure the safety of human subjects.

Although section 820.30 does not require manufacturers to apply such requirements to legacy devices that were distributed before the Quality System regulation was in effect, the design control requirements do apply to changes affecting such distributed devices. Design change control is discussed later.

The Quality System Inspection Technique (QSIT) includes Design Controls as one of the four major subsystems addressed during a baseline facility inspection. The objectives for QSIT Design Controls cover each subpart under 21 CFR 820.30. Chapter 1, "FDA's Organization and Regulatory Strategies," provides more details on the QSIT.

Industry Practice

The concept of quality has evolved from quality control (inspect and test) to quality assurance (with the implementation of a Quality System), in which quality is designed into a device and the focus is on the customer. Global regulatory requirements for medical devices have become more focused on Quality Systems as one aspect of ensuring safe and effective finished devices.

As the sophistication of medical devices increases, the benefits associated with the application of design controls become more apparent. Many manufacturers have established robust product development approaches, including formal "phases" of a product development life cycle, to ensure that all projects follow an effective, repeatable, and compliant development approach. Figure 7.1 illustrates the interrelationships of key design controls elements.

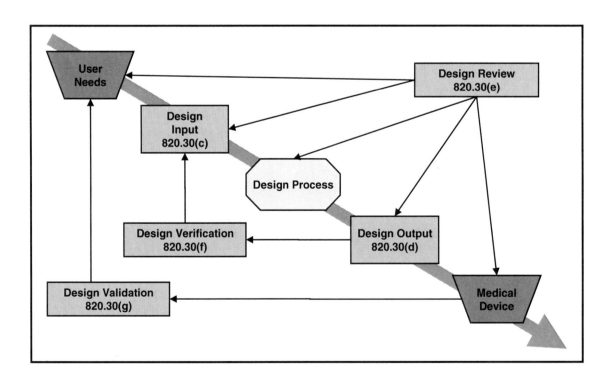

Figure 7.1. Interrelationships of key design controls elements.

As a part of establishing a product development life cycle model, manufacturers often incorporate design controls, risk management programs, human factors engineering, and business management methods into a single integrated system. The Food and Drug Administration's (FDA's) *Medical Device Use Safety: Incorporating Human Factors Engineering into Risk Management* provides advice on establishing an integrated product development model focused on product safety.

Unsafe and ineffective devices have often been the result of informal development that did not ensure the proper establishment of design requirements or did not provide for proper assessment of the device performance. Clear requirements provide a solid basis on which a device development project can build. Adequate planning, independent review, thorough design verification, and robust design validation are necessary to develop a medical device with the proper level of safety and effectiveness for the intended use of the device and the needs of the user.

820.30(b) Design and Development Planning

IV

The Requirement

> ***820.30(b) Design and development planning.*** *Each manufacturer shall establish and maintain plans that describe or reference the design and development activities and define responsibility for implementation. The plans shall identify and describe the interfaces with different groups or activities that provide, or result in, input to the design and development process. The plans shall be reviewed, updated, and approved as design and development evolves.*

Discussion of the Requirement

This section of the Quality System regulation clearly delineates the need for applying design controls in a prospective manner. The design activities must be addressed in a plan prepared before the formal development process proceeds. The design and development plan may exist across multiple documents. For example, separate plans for hardware and software development may exist. The plan should describe the development process that the manufacturer intends to follow, and it should be specific to the organization and to the complexity of the device. The plan should include or reference any relevant standard operating procedures, thereby addressing the following elements of the design and development process:
- key tasks and responsibilities for completion;
- minimum design reviews for each phase;
- development practices;
- quality practices and verification methodology, when known;
- coding guidelines for software, if applicable;
- record-keeping and documentation;
- resources (e.g., people, tools, and facilities);
- risk analysis methods; and
- schedule.

FDA requires manufacturers to establish the appropriate responsibility for activities affecting quality. FDA also emphasizes that the assignment of specific responsibilities is important to the success of the design control program and to achieving compliance with the regulation. Establishing appropriate responsibility includes assigning qualified personnel for activities having a direct impact on the quality of the device design.

In any design process, additional information on system capabilities and evolving customer requirements will mandate changes. If the process changes from the originally planned approach, the design and development plan must be updated to reflect those changes, especially when activities related to the verification and validation of the device are affected. FDA recognizes that changes to the plan may be necessary and expects such changes to be implemented in a formal manner (i.e., reviewed and approved).

Industry Practice

Historically, many manufacturers did not develop new products according to a formal design and development plan. However, critical schedule demands and time-to-market objectives have increased awareness of the benefits of formal planning. Today, the most successful manufacturers in new development invest time up front, to systematically plan the activities and resources required to build quality into new developmental products. Increasing device complexity and evolving customer expectations have dictated the need for more sophisticated development practices that are based on formal, proactive planning.

Design and development plans vary from simple to complex, depending on the technologies that are incorporated in the device, the size of the development team, and the relative effort involved. Key development tasks in the plan may relate to hardware, electronics, software, sterility, biocompatibility of materials, and interfaces or interaction with other products. Plans often also incorporate various product risk management activities and human factors engineering. Development milestones usually trigger the performance of design reviews, which are also specified in the design and development plan.

Successful, timely development projects often rely on contributions from many different areas of the organization (e.g., engineering, research and development (R&D), manufacturing, marketing, quality assurance (QA), regulatory affairs, and service). Manufacturers are often plagued by inadequate communication between engineering, R&D, and other departments. This problem can be reduced to a great extent by describing in the design and development plan the responsibilities of all affected departments, including the information and data that are received and transmitted. The regulation refers to this as "interfaces with different groups or activities." In addition to describing those internal interfaces, external interfaces (such as relationships with partners or use of suppliers to accomplish design tasks) should also be included in the plan.

Schedules may be developed and maintained by manufacturers with the help of tools, such as program evaluation review technique (PERT) and Gantt charts. Those tools aid in planning projects, evaluating the effect of deviations on development schedules, determining the probability of meeting deadlines, managing resources, and identifying bottlenecks. For simpler projects, spreadsheets and flowcharts can often be more useful.

As complex or lengthy development projects proceed, designers often encounter new information that invalidates some of the assumptions that affected the initial planning process. Some manufacturers require that development plans be reviewed and re-approved as criteria for moving between design life cycle phases. Other manufacturers establish guidelines for deciding when such changes are sufficient to require plan update and re-approval. Examples of changes that might require re-planning include:

- changes in project resources or responsibilities,
- shifts to using external resources,
- schedule slippage or milestone changes,
- adoption of new or different technology used in the device,
- identification of new tasks, or
- changes in task dependencies.

820.30(c) Design Input

The Requirement

820.30(c) Design input. *Each manufacturer shall establish and maintain procedures to ensure that the design requirements relating to a device are appropriate and address the intended use of the device, including the needs of the user and patient. The procedures shall include a mechanism for addressing incomplete, ambiguous, or conflicting requirements. The design input requirements shall be documented and shall be reviewed and approved by a designated individual(s). The approval, including the date and signature of the individual(s) approving the requirements, shall be documented.*

Discussion of the Requirement

Section 820.3(f) defines "design input" as "the physical and performance requirements of a device that are used as a basis for device design." The design input defines device performance, safety and reliability characteristics, environmental limits, physical attributes, compatibility with other devices, applicable standards, regulatory requirements, packaging specifications, and labeling. The intended use of the device must address the needs of users and patients, and it must be explicit in the labeling claims.

Some manufacturers have other regulations to consider, which present additional technical requirements for their devices. For example, laser- or radiation-emitting products must meet additional requirements imposed both by FDA and by other federal agencies. Similarly, for manufacturers of products that maintain electronic patient records, regulations based on the Health Insurance Portability and Accountability Act of 1996 (HIPAA), such as 45 CFR 160 and 164, may be a source of additional requirements related to security and privacy of the patient data.

The design input must be captured as a set of formal, testable requirements, which are reviewed and approved by the authorized personnel. When changes are made to the design input, the changes to requirements must be formally reviewed and evaluated, and related documents must also be revised to reflect those changes. All affected parties should be notified to ensure that the needs of the user and patient will continue to be met, and that any potential adverse consequences are considered.

FDA recognizes the design input as the basis of the design verification and design validation program. Failure to have an accurate and complete design input results in failure to demonstrate design adequacy. If the tests cannot be mapped to the requirements, simply providing a large number of test procedures and results does not constitute adequate evidence of device performance or safety. Thus, the design input should be testable, should completely define the system functions to be implemented, should be consistent in terminology and requirements, and should be understandable by the target audience. That audience includes groups or departments responsible for defining user needs, developing and verifying the device design, developing production processes, creating labeling, and performing other tasks necessary to complete the design process.

Section 820.30(c) requires the manufacturer to ensure that the design input requirements are appropriate (i.e., that the device will perform its intended use and meet the needs of the user). In doing so, the manufacturer must assess and set the proper level of safety and effectiveness commensurate with the intended use of the finished device.

Industry Practice

The design input phase is also known as the "requirements phase" in a traditional engineering development model.

Successful design and development manufacturers realize that using marketing objectives alone as the basis for design is not sufficient. Testable formal requirements that completely define the system are necessary to ensure finished device completeness and acceptance. Failure to define requirements results in the inability to effectively determine the completeness and adequacy of the resulting design through design verification and design validation.

One of the tools used by manufacturers to translate the user needs into design input requirements is Quality Function Deployment (QFD). QFD is the systematic determination of the design requirements that best satisfy users' needs and the intended use of the finished device. A cross-functional team translates customer preferences into design requirements. Usually, the project manager leads this activity. Other tools used by the industry are brainstorming, Pareto charts, and affinity diagrams to categorize the design input and to reach agreement on the performance and safety specifications of the device.

Relevant information for design input may come from customer complaints, sales and service data, focus groups, customer surveys, R&D, or marketing. Customer complaints, including Medical Device Reports (MDRs), form a quality feedback loop for distributed devices that drives continuous quality improvements and supports design activities. Quality data trend analyses for existing marketed devices can help define performance and safety requirements for both product improvements and new product development. Data from service reports help determine reliability and the possible need for design changes. Marketing is often the voice of the customer, and marketing tools for soliciting customer ideas include focus groups and customer surveys.

Considering the intended markets for the product may also result in design inputs. For example, in some global markets the device's materials of construction are significant if the device is disposed after use. Disposal methods may be regulated in some areas, and consideration of those methods may be included in premarket applications for some global markets. Consensus standards, such as ISO 14001 (i.e., environmental management systems), may provide additional guidance on handling end-of-life issues for devices that will be marketed in regions where disposal is regulated.

Many manufacturers use human factors engineering during product design. The human factors engineering discipline focuses on designing medical devices that are easier and safer to use. FDA has emphasized the importance of human factors engineering since the publication of its *Do It By Design* guidance in 1996, *Medical Device Use Safety: Incorporating Human Factors Engineering into Risk Management* guidance in 2000 and by establishing a formal Human Factors Program within CDRH. By evaluating and designing devices for a typical user's cognitive abilities and memory, manual dexterity, strength, and reading skills, manufacturers can have a substantial effect on the usability and safety of their device. Thus, during the establishment of design input, many manufacturers initiate human factors engineering activities to ensure that requirements are responsive to user needs.

Risk Management activities typically begin during the design input stage by establishing the intended use of the finished device. A review of field experience with previous marketed devices through complaints, clinical literature, and MDR data on competitor products can be used as an input to an initial hazard analysis. These activities often support preliminary assessments of product risk (i.e., risks that could be presented to users and patients), and serve as a source of safety requirements. Chapter 30, "Risk Management for Medical Devices", provides more details on assessing, controlling, and monitoring risk.

IV

The industry often uses a team approach to perform design reviews. Designs are reviewed and evaluated by all disciplines necessary to ensure that the design input requirements are appropriate and adequately address the intended use of the finished device, as well as user and patient needs. Thus, the first design review on a project is often a review focused on the adequacy of the documented design inputs. This review can also serve as a mechanism for identifying incomplete, ambiguous, or conflicting requirements so that those inconsistencies can be resolved or tracked for future resolution.

820.30(d) Design Output

The Requirement

> ***820.30(d) Design output.*** *Each manufacturer shall establish and maintain procedures for defining and documenting design output in terms that allow an adequate evaluation of conformance to design input requirements. Design output procedures shall contain or make reference to acceptance criteria and shall ensure that those design outputs that are essential for the proper functioning of the device are identified. Design output shall be documented, reviewed, and approved before release. The approval, including the date and signature of the individual(s) approving the output, shall be documented.*

Discussion of the Requirement

"Design output" is defined in section 820.3(g) as "the results of a design effort at each design phase and at the end of the total design effort. The finished design output is the basis for the device master record. The total finished device output consists of the finished device, its packaging and labeling, and the device master record." This section of the Quality System regulation requires a manufacturer to define and document design output and to ensure that the output meets the approved design input requirements.

Design output occurs throughout the design process. Therefore, this GMP requirement applies to all phases of design. The total finished design output includes the device itself, device and component specifications, packaging, labeling, production specifications and drawings, and quality assurance specifications and procedures. Design output documents serve as the foundation for the device master record (DMR). In accordance with quality record-keeping practices, all design outputs must be reviewed and approved before release.

Industry Practice

Design output is not just a design phase. Rather, design output is the documentation of all activities performed during the design process to verify correct implementation of design input requirements and to support final design specifications. Design output culminates with the completion of the final design documentation and the formal release of the DMR. Release of the DMR is an aspect of design transfer and is discussed later in this chapter.

Some examples of design output generated during the design process include:
- drawings,
- schematics,
- test procedures,
- laboratory notebook entries,
- hardware configuration specifications,
- software specifications,
- design review records,
- risk analysis data,
- technical reports,
- component qualifications,
- performance test plans and reports, and
- validation and verification plans and reports.

Final design output includes labeling, specifications (such as device, subassemblies, components, software, and packaging), production procedures, installation and service procedures (if applicable), and quality procedures and criteria. Those final design output elements make up the device's DMR.

The industry varies widely in the definition and documentation of essential outputs. The Quality System regulation requires manufacturers to identify outputs *essential* for proper functioning of the device. Essential outputs include device features, functions, components, etc., as well as manufacturing processes. Some manufacturers use risk analysis techniques for the product and the processes prospectively to identify essential outputs. Others derive essential outputs from design verification tests or from acceptance tests in the DMR. Similarly, many different approaches exist for documenting those essential outputs. Possibilities include maintaining a separate document in the DMR, embedding the information in the Risk Management Report, incorporating the information in acceptance specifications, and including the information in purchasing specifications.

The extent of design output documentation established varies depending on device complexity and size. For large systems, multiple layers of design documentation and descriptions that define separate subsystem specifications and functionality may be appropriate. Manufacturers have learned that design documentation is essential to capture

IV

the investment spent on the development of new medical devices. Until a design is documented, it belongs more to the designer than to the company. The cost of production-era changes and maintenance is increased substantially for products that fail to have adequate design documentation.

820.30(e) Design Review

The Requirement

> ***820.30(e) Design review.*** *Each manufacturer shall establish and maintain procedures to ensure that formal documented reviews of the design results are planned and conducted at appropriate stages of the device's design development. The procedures shall ensure that participants at each design review include representatives of all functions concerned with the design stage being reviewed and an individual(s) who does not have direct responsibility for the design stage being reviewed, as well as any specialists needed. The results of a design review, including identification of the design, the date, and the individual(s) performing the review, shall be documented in the design history file (the DHF).*

Discussion of the Requirement

The purpose of conducting design reviews during the design process is to ensure that the design satisfies the design input requirements for the intended use of the device and the needs of the user. Design reviews include:

- confirming that design inputs are complete and internally consistent;
- reviewing design verification activities to determine whether the design output meets functional and operational requirements;
- ensuring that the design is compatible with components and other accessories;
- confirming that safety, reliability, service, and maintenance requirements are met; and
- determining whether labeling and other regulatory requirements are satisfied.

Section 820.3(h) defines "design review" as "a documented, comprehensive, systematic examination of a design to evaluate the adequacy of the design requirements, to evaluate the capability of the design to meet these requirements, and to identify problems." Early aspects of the design output may not be subjected to testing and are often best evaluated through review techniques and analyses. The essence of design controls is the formal review of the specifications to support the detection and remedy of errors as early as possible in the design process.

Formal reviews are conducted at "appropriate stages" (e.g., major decision points) of the design process. The manufacturer has the ultimate responsibility for defining when reviews are to be conducted. The number of reviews should be based on the size and complexity of the design and on the length of time expended on the development effort. Design reviews should be included in the design and development plan.

An independent party who is not directly responsible for the aspect of the design under review is required to participate in design reviews. The level of independence required for the reviewer is up to the manufacturer. In all cases, the reviewer should have adequate expertise to perform a valid technical review effectively. The review activities should focus

IV

on identification of design errors (i.e., failures to meet user or patient needs and intended uses).

All design review activities should be documented with a list of the participants, identification of the independent reviewer, a description of the design aspects, topics, or issues discussed, and the checklists used for evaluation (as applicable). Documentation, including meeting minutes from design reviews, agendas for proposed design review meetings, lists of action items, and follow-up reports, is to be included in the design history file (DHF) to provide evidence of design reviews.

Industry Practice

Industry-leading companies recognize the benefits of formal design reviews and frequently provide training to personnel on effective review techniques. In addition, the most successful manufacturers track review effectiveness and use the errors found in reviews as the basis for identifying process improvement activities. When errors are found during reviews, attempts are made to define changes to the design process that might lead to preventing the errors in future development efforts.

Documents and other items essential to a design review meeting include a meeting agenda, all applicable specifications, drawings, manuals, test data, results of special studies, mock-ups, breadboards, in-process hardware, finished hardware, and test methods. Participants often find design reviews most effective and productive when they are given adequate preparation time to evaluate design documentation before the meeting.

Design reviews vary widely in the industry and may include a system requirements review, system design review, software specification review, preliminary design review, critical design review, and test readiness review. The usual participants include members of the project team, as appropriate, and at least one independent reviewer. Possible participants include manufacturing, QA, regulatory, engineering, marketing, servicing, purchasing, R&D, preclinical, and clinical personnel. Depending on the aspect of the design being reviewed, manufacturing or servicing personnel may be particularly effective as independent reviewers.

Review results should be documented in meeting minutes. Outcomes and any associated actions items from the design review meeting are typically documented and filed in the DHF. Many firms establish a standard design review minutes template to ensure that records are consistent. Identified action items are tracked to conclusion, often by means of forms or databases. Action items are frequently part of the agenda of the next design review.

820.30(f) Design Verification and 820.30(g) Design Validation

The Requirement

> **820.30(f) Design verification.** Each manufacturer shall establish and maintain procedures for verifying the device design. Design verification shall confirm that the design output meets the design input requirements. The results of the design verification, including identification

of the design, method(s), the date, and the individual(s) performing the verification, shall be documented in the DHF.

820.30(g) Design validation. *Each manufacturer shall establish and maintain procedures for validating the device design. Design validation shall be performed under defined operating conditions on initial production units, lots, or batches, or their equivalents. Design validation shall ensure that devices conform to defined user needs and intended uses and shall include testing of production units under actual or simulated use conditions. Design validation shall include software validation and risk analysis, where appropriate. The results of the design validation, including identification of the design, method(s), the date, and the individual(s) performing the validation, shall be documented in the DHF.*

Discussion of the Requirement

"Verification" is defined in section 820.3(aa) as "confirmation by examination and provision of objective evidence that specified requirements have been fulfilled." Section 820.3(z) defines "validation" as "confirmation by examination and provision of objective evidence that the particular requirements for a specific intended use can be consistently fulfilled." In section 820.3(z)(2), "design validation" is defined as "establishing by objective evidence that device specifications conform with user needs and intended use(s)."

Verification consists of specific activities performed during the design and development process that ensure that the defined process is being followed correctly and that the design inputs are met. Typical verification activities are documented inspections, tests, analyses, and objective evaluations.

Design validation follows successful design verification. Design verification is not a substitute for design validation. Design validation should be performed under defined operating conditions and on multiple initial production lots or batches. Design validation may also be carried out in earlier stages before initial production. It may be necessary to perform multiple validations if there are different intended uses.

Production units must be included in the design validation and tested under conditions similar to those that are expected to be experienced in the user environment. Tests in this phase of design control are simulated-use tests, use tests, or clinical studies, depending on the technology and intended use. Design validation may require coordination with process validation activities, as defined in section 820.75 of the Quality System regulation.

It is inappropriate to assume that merely testing for satisfaction of requirements can provide adequate confidence in the correctness of a design. Testing must certainly address the defined requirements and target the actual use environment. When an actual use environment is not possible or impractical, an environment that simulates the actual use conditions may be substituted. The validation tests also should address use by intended users because the actual use of a medical device often does not directly coincide with that envisioned by the designers. Users may attempt to use a medical device in ways that were not anticipated during the development process. Stress testing by those unfamiliar with the design is a valuable technique of identifying potential error conditions or unanticipated product risks.

Design validation requirements include product software validation and completion of risk analysis. The Quality System regulation requires the manufacturer to conduct a risk assessment that identifies potential safety risks, their severity, and the probability of their occurrence. The techniques that are most widely recognized for the performance of risk analyses include hazard analysis, fault tree analysis (FTA) and failure modes and effects analysis (FMEA). Refer to Chapter 30 for more information on risk management.

Software that is a part or component of, or an accessory to, a medical device must be validated. Similarly, any software product that is treated as a medical device is subject to validation requirements.

Results of design validation and design verification testing must be archived in the DHF.

Industry Practice

The approach for design verification and design validation is determined by the product characteristics, predicate product knowledge, and regulatory plan. For a device that will undergo Premarket Approval (PMA) to demonstrate safety and effectiveness, more extensive testing will usually be necessary than for a device that will be cleared through a 510(k) premarket notification. For a PMA, the manufacturer often conducts a clinical trial to establish safety and effectiveness. For 510(k) clearance, testing helps to establish equivalency to a device already on the market (i.e., a "predicate device").

Verification testing usually begins with working prototypes or breadboards and may be repeated as design changes are made. Typical verification tests include, where applicable:
- comparative tests with a proven design,
- simulated use in the laboratory,
- animal model tests,
- biocompatibility tests,
- material and device compatibility tests,
- functional tests after sterilization,
- reliability tests,
- performance tests,
- tests of compatibility with other devices, and
- environmental emissions and susceptibility tests.

For software, typical verification activities include code reviews, schematic reviews, unit and component tests, integration tests, and alternate calculation demonstrations. FDA's *Guidance for the Content of Premarket Submissions for Software Contained in Medical Devices*, issued in May 1998, describes expected software-specific submissions documentation based on risk presented or mitigated by the software. Various software guidance documents are discussed in further detail in Chapter 29, "New Directions in Software Validation."

A manufacturer can use many standards and guidelines to identify expected design verification tests and results. Product-specific guidance documents are available from FDA's Division of Small Manufacturers, International and Consumer Assistance (DSMICA) and on CDRH's web site. Product performance standards are also available from publishing organizations, such as the American Society for Testing and Materials (ASTM), American National Standards Institute (ANSI), International Electrotechnical Commission (IEC), Association for the Advancement of Medical Instrumentation (AAMI), and International

Organization for Standardization (ISO). See Appendix B for web site links to these organizations.

Many standards that address product safety and effectiveness have been developed with participation from CDRH staff. CDRH formally recognizes relevant national and international standards and maintains a database of those recognized consensus standards. Manufacturers may find a review of the consensus standards database helpful when planning the design verification activities. Furthermore, conformance with FDA-recognized consensus standards may help streamline Office of Device Evaluation (ODE) or Office of In Vitro Diagnostics (OIVD) activities with respect to 510(k) or PMA applications.

One recognized practice for formally documenting the results of design verification activities is as follows:

    a. Record discrete test values or measurements in the results documentation, where appropriate, rather than merely placing a check mark to signify the completion of a test step.

    b. Complete all required spaces on the test procedure forms or document the spaces as not applicable.

    c. Address all deviations from defined test protocols in a test report addendum.

    d. Review and approve protocols and results.

Design validation confirms that devices representative of those produced under typical production conditions meet the manufacturer's defined intended uses for typical users and patients. Early in the design project many assumptions are made relating to user needs and capabilities. Starting with the definition of design input, designers translate "user needs" into measurable, testable requirements, which form the basis for the design. Design validation demonstrates (or refutes) that the designer's assumptions were appropriate and that the resulting device, labeling, and packaging are adequate for the users and patients.

The design validation activities, when completed, should demonstrate that the device can be used *safely* by the users it was designed for. The validation under "actual or simulated use conditions" helps to evaluate typical users interacting with the device as they would on a day-to-day basis. Therefore, the design validation protocols should ensure that the use environment (e.g., space, lighting, and noise level) and range of user abilities are adequately represented and evaluated. For example, design validation for surgical devices often starts with confirming the users are able to open the packaged device in the sterile environment while maintaining device sterility.

For any complex device—and particularly for consumer-use products—the format and content of the labeling (e.g., instructions for use) can have a substantial effect on usability and, therefore, on finished device safety and effectiveness. FDA's *Guidance on Medical Device Patient Labeling*, published in 2000, provides support for the design of effective labeling as one aspect of a robust human factors approach to device design. The design validation activities often include evaluation of labels and labeling to ensure that they are understandable and useful for typical users.

Some manufacturers formalize the relationship between design validation and process validation. To obtain "initial production units ... or their equivalents," those firms require that design validation devices are produced during performance qualification builds. Figure 7.2 illustrates a possible optimized approach to these interrelated activities. Although not a regulatory requirement, this approach can help to streamline the development schedule.

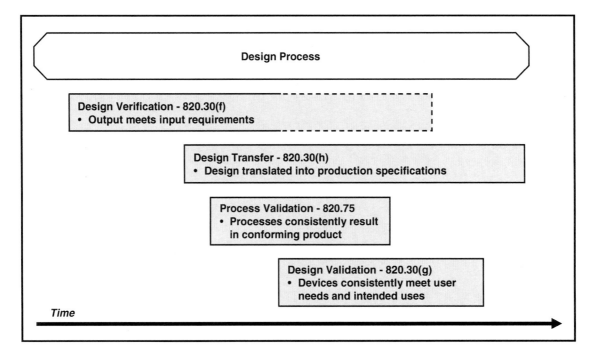

Figure 7.2. Optimized relationship between process validation and design validation.

Achieving design validation means that the finished device has been proven to meet users' needs and its intended use. Completing process validation means that the process will consistently produce a product that meets specifications (discussed further in Chapters 15 and 27).

During design verification, design validation, and process validation activities, assessing product risk and confirming that known risks are adequately controlled is paramount. Many manufacturers have established a comprehensive risk management program, which is often based on industry standards such as ISO 14971. A variety of tools and methods are available to support risk analysis. Most tools are particularly useful at a given maturity level of the design or to evaluate a particular class of risks (e.g., use-related risks). Risk management starts by following a systematic procedure to evaluate potential design inadequacies and to quantify the risk to adversely affect safety and performance. Manufacturers often conduct risk analysis method training for project teams in advance of applying the method to ensure that the analysis is conducted in a thorough, defensible manner.

Potential risks are typically analyzed for normal use and misuse conditions. If any risk is judged unacceptable, it should be reduced to acceptable levels by appropriate means, such as redesign or warnings. When risk analysis is conducted after changes are implemented, some techniques also provide a means of verifying corrective actions. Assessing potential risk conditions associated with a device is no longer just an FDA regulatory requirement; it is now recognized as a key business strategy to prevent possible injury and to document due diligence in the design and development process. Risk management is discussed in more detail in Chapter 30, "Risk Management for Medical Devices."

820.30(h) Design Transfer

The Requirement

> *820.30(h) Design transfer. Each manufacturer shall establish and maintain procedures to ensure that the device design is correctly translated into production specifications.*

Discussion of the Requirement

Except for design validation with initial production units, the completion of design transfer is the final phase of product development and is the bridge between product design and product manufacturing. It is a transfer of knowledge in the form of documentation from product development to the manufacturing function. The released DMR is part of design output and is the basis for any additional documentation produced by other departments. Section 820.30(h) requires that a formal process be established to ensure that the transfer of the design is effectively carried out.

FDA has heightened attention to manufacturing processes and the adequacy of acceptance activities. Tests performed on manufactured products should be related to key safety and effectiveness requirements identified during development. Identification of essential outputs during the design process supports this linkage.

FDA does not intend for this section to prohibit manufacturers from beginning production until all design activities are completed. The intent of the requirement is to ensure that all design specifications released to production have been approved and verified or validated before they are implemented as part of the production process. Furthermore, by recognizing that production processes may need to be developed and qualified or validated, this requirement helps ensure that *all* required development activities are successfully completed during the design transfer. See Chapter 15 for a detailed discussion of the GMP requirements for manufacturing process validation.

Industry Practice

For successful design transfer to occur, manufacturers find that communication between manufacturing and design personnel needs to be initiated during the early development phases and continued throughout the product's life cycle. In addition, whenever changes in the device design are proposed, the implications for manufacturing need to be considered.

Historically, the interface between design and manufacturing has not been very effective. Development groups have often simply released specifications to manufacturing and have failed to ensure that the specifications are well understood or effectively implemented. The results of this ad hoc process have been increased manufacturing costs, inefficient and redundant testing during manufacturing, and finished device field failures. The best practices today include coordination with manufacturing personnel early in the design process to ensure that design decisions take into consideration manufacturability and an overall test strategy that identifies component, subsystem, and final acceptance test procedures.

Industry practices include the following:

a. Manufacturing personnel participate in the design process up front to ensure that appropriate built-in test functions are defined and that adequate device access is available to examine performance parameters.

b. Manufacturability is considered in design decisions, including cost of production equipment, effect on manufacturing processes, use of off-the-shelf components, and commonality of processes and parts with existing and projected product lines.

c. A total test strategy is defined for the product. The test strategy, which may be derived from the design verification protocols, addresses appropriate test points that verify that the manufacturing operation has produced parts or products that meet specifications. The test strategy should encompass activities from component-level inspection to final acceptance testing of the finished device.

In the design transfer phase, preproduction specifications and documentation are transferred to manufacturing and production control by formally releasing them through the document control process. The transfer may not include the whole device at one point in time. Some parts may be released sooner than others. The team approach is more efficient and effective than a hand-off from design to manufacturing. A design transfer team that includes design, manufacturing, engineering, document control, purchasing, quality assurance, and technical support may be quite helpful. Release of documentation requires the completion of design validation and design verification activities.

As part of the design transfer, process control procedures, quality control procedures, sampling plans, testing and inspection instructions, equipment maintenance, calibration, cleaning procedures, and training plans are usually developed. Personnel training typically occurs before initial production and is continued thereafter as needed. A product-specific design transfer checklist is often developed to ensure all design transfer activities are considered and completed efficiently. Many manufacturers conduct a final device design review near the end of the design transfer activities to ensure that the transfer was effective and complete.

820.30(i) Design Changes

The Requirement

820.30(i) Design changes. Each manufacturer shall establish and maintain procedures for the identification, documentation, validation or where appropriate verification, review, and approval of design changes before their implementation.

Discussion of the Requirement

Design change control requirements apply during design control and continue after design transfer. However, the extent of control may vary significantly between design-era changes and production changes. It is not the intent of the Quality System regulation to mandate that all design changes be documented and evaluated to the same extent, although they must all be documented and evaluated. The level of documentation and evaluation should be in direct proportion to the significance of the change.

Manufacturers are required to have procedures to ensure that, after design input requirements are established and approved, changes to the design inputs are also reviewed, validated, and approved. Design output documentation consists of the final design specifications, which are often subject to changes during the development process. Changes to design specifications, once validated and accepted, must be subject to a formal change control process. Any changes to specifications must be subject to the same level of controls and reviews as applied to the initial development effort. Such controls include review and approval by individuals in the same functions and organizations as those who signed off originally.

When changes are made after design validation is accomplished, the validation tests that were developed for the initial release must be re-executed unless a rationale can be provided to support execution of only a limited subset of the test cases or no tests at all.

Design changes that could potentially have significant effects on safety or performance must be reviewed to determine if a new 510(k) or a supplement to a PMA application will be required.

Industry Practice

It is important to note that the design change provision of the regulation applies to all changes in design inputs and design outputs, which includes the finished device, its packaging and labeling, and the DMR (including production specifications). Design change control also applies both during design activities and after design transfer. However, the change control system can be implemented differently pre- and post-transfer at the manufacturer's discretion. Many manufacturers establish a simplified change control process for pre-transfer design changes. With this approach, manufacturers often use distinct revision nomenclature to distinguish whether a document or specification has been formally released (e.g., alphabetic revisions versus numeric revisions). This approach can be helpful if the formal change control system requires numerous approvals or takes significant time to process a given change.

Not all changes are subject to the same level of design controls and validation or verification. A systematic evaluation process can help to determine the level of effort that is necessary in controlling a change. Some considerations involved in determining the extent to which changes should be selected for design control—and when—are as follows:

   a. The initial design inputs need to be under control after they are approved, particularly in the case of complex designs.

   b. Change control is needed for devices undergoing clinical trials. A significant change in the design after the clinical devices are produced may invalidate the clinical data.

   c. After an element of a design is validated or verified and accepted, later changes need to be controlled, including re-verification and re-validation (as appropriate).

d. A specification change that affects the finished device's overall risk needs careful assessment and planning of verification and validation to ensure that device safety is still acceptable.

e. Change control requirements apply to any change to a device, its labeling, or its packaging after it is released for production.

f. Manufacturing processes, quality assurance procedures, and other elements of the DMR are also subject to design change control requirements.

g. The level of verification and validation to be performed for subcontractor changes is based on the complexity and safety implications of the proposed change as well as on the internal quality assurance activities of the subcontractor. In all cases, configuration management and control of changes is essential.

After design transfer, formal change control programs are essential to manage the complexity of most devices. Many manufacturers control revisions with an automated system to track which changes are implemented in which manufacturing lots. Manufacturing resource planning (MRP) systems are very effective in tracking subsystem and component revisions for specific products. Automated software configuration management systems are also very effective in tracking what changes are introduced into which software program releases.

One change control process, if properly structured, can deal with all types of changes efficiently (e.g., minor, major, or temporary changes to any element of the DMR). As a part of the change control process, manufacturers should always evaluate the proposed change for possible regulatory approval requirements before implementing the change. Two FDA guidance documents provide support for determining whether a new 510(k) or a PMA supplement is required: *Deciding When to Submit a 510(k) for a Change to an Existing Device* (January 1997) and *Modifications to Devices Subject to Premarket Approval (PMA)* (March 2007). Careful planning is essential for changes to FDA-cleared or approved medical devices.

820.30(j) Design History File

The Requirement

> ***820.30(j) Design history file.*** *Each manufacturer shall establish and maintain a DHF for each type of device. The DHF shall contain or reference the records necessary to demonstrate that the design was developed in accordance with the approved design plan and the requirements of this part.*

Discussion of the Requirement

Section 820.3(e) defines the "design history file" as "a compilation of records which describes the design history of a finished device." The DHF is intended to act as a repository for the documents and data necessary to show compliance with the design plan, design control procedures, and section 820.30, Design controls. The DHF provides a complete design history of the finished device. Furthermore, the DHF must provide specific documentation showing the actions taken with regard to each device design. For a device family, the same DHF may be used for minor variations in a design, such as size differences.

The DHF is subject to general record requirements under section 820.180, including record retention.

Industry Practice

The level of formality with which companies maintain design documentation for new development efforts varies greatly. The benefits of documenting the device design and design process include:
- assurance that mistakes made in initial prototypes will not be repeated;
- availability of information relating to design decisions made during development that helps in evaluating the impact of design changes after transfer;
- establishment of a baseline for evaluating quality throughout the design process and for designing the next generation of products; and
- evidence of compliance with procedures for liability and regulatory purposes.

One approach to organizing a DHF is to provide the documentation in parallel with the requirements of 820.30:
- *design and development plan* (including revisions)—documented, reviewed, and approved by team;
- *design input* (sometimes called the "requirements")—information on intended use, performance, labeling, and environment;
- *design output*—specifications, top-level drawings, major subassemblies, and development of the DMR;
- *design review*—minutes, assignments, and tracking of issues;
- *design verification and design validation*—protocols, results of all tests;
- *design transfer*—plan for moving into production and evidence related to following the plan; and
- *design changes*—for changes to the design before design transfer.

A DHF may physically contain all the documents and records, or may simply refer to each item's actual location. A DHF may be maintained for each design and development activity by device family or type or by individual catalog number. A manufacturer may choose whether to correlate the DHF directly with a 510(k) submission or PMA application. The organization of the DHF should facilitate efficient retrieval of any particular document throughout the life of the device. To ensure completion of the record demonstrating that the development plan was followed, manufacturers commonly conduct an internal audit of the DHF before the design transfer is complete.

Design control procedures often define the requirements for the DHF, such as:
- responsibility for maintaining the DHF during design and after transfer;
- process for adding new information into the DHF;
- organization of the DHF;
- storage methods (paper, electronic, or both);
- responsibility and frequency of DHF audits; and
- mechanisms for providing personnel access to the DHF.

NOTES:

IV

"There is nothing magical about capturing your customers' *Whats*; you simply ask them."
L. Guinta and N. Praizler, *The QFD Book: The Team Approach to Solving Problems and Satisfying Customers Through Quality Functional Deployment*, 1993

NOTES:

"As much as we can adapt to new configurations of technology, we retain our psychological expectation of how things work—or are supposed to work."
H. Petroski, *Small Things Considered: Why There is No Perfect Design*, 2003

NOTES:

IV

"No incentive is quite so effective as the prospect of having to live with the results of one's work."
M. Hammer & J. Champy, *Reengineering the Corporation: A Manifesto for Business Revolution*, 1994

SECTION V. ACCEPTANCE ACTIVITIES

CHAPTER 8. PURCHASING CONTROLS (SUBPART E)

820.50 Purchasing Controls

The Requirement

> ***820.50 Purchasing controls.*** *Each manufacturer shall establish and maintain procedures to ensure that all purchased or otherwise received product and services conform to specified requirements.*

Discussion of the Requirement

The requirements of this section are intended to ensure that purchased, subcontracted, or otherwise received product and services conform to specified requirements and any applicable regulatory requirements. Section 820.3(r) of the regulation defines "product" as "components, manufacturing materials, in-process devices, finished devices, and returned devices." The requirements for purchasing controls apply to all product received from an outside source by the finished device manufacturer, including product or services that a manufacturer receives from a "sister facility" or other corporate or financial affiliates.

The manufacturer is expected to establish and maintain documented controls for planning and performing purchasing activities. Controls are required that are appropriate to the product or service and to the effect of the product or service on the quality, safety, and effectiveness of the finished device.

Industry Practice

Study Group 4 of the Global Harmonization Task Force (GHTF), which focuses on auditing practices, has established guidance that highlights that organization's perspective on the importance of purchasing controls. The *Guidelines for Regulatory Auditing of Quality Management Systems of Medical Device Manufacturers, Part 2 – Regulatory Audit Strategy* (June 2006) establishes auditing strategies that are based on a Quality System model with eight subsystems. This GHTF model treats purchasing controls as a separate subsystem, in the same way as other subsystems such as documentation and records or customer-related processes. Depending on the proportion and importance of outsourced activities, the guidance recommends spending between 5% and 20% of on-site audit time on purchasing controls.

Manufacturers use various types of procurement quality programs to help ensure that product and contract services, such as testing, calibration, validation, processing, pest control, sterilization, and consulting, conform to their specified requirements. The most effective purchasing programs promote good working relationships and feedback systems between the supplier and the device manufacturer. An effective purchasing program addresses purchasing requirements and specifications, selection of acceptable suppliers, verification and inspection activities, and required quality records.

820.50(a) Evaluation of Suppliers, Contractors, and Consultants

The Requirement

(a) Evaluation of suppliers, contractors, and consultants. Each manufacturer shall establish and maintain the requirements, including quality requirements, that must be met by suppliers, contractors, and consultants. Each manufacturer shall:

> *(1) Evaluate and select potential suppliers, contractors, and consultants on the basis of their ability to meet specified requirements, including quality requirements. The evaluation shall be documented.*
>
> *(2) Define the type and extent of control to be exercised over the product, services, suppliers, contractors, and consultants, based on the evaluation results.*
>
> *(3) Establish and maintain records of acceptable suppliers, contractors, and consultants.*

Discussion of the Requirement

The Quality System regulation requires manufacturers to ensure the acceptability of purchased, contracted, or otherwise received products and services. This requirement can be accomplished through a combination of documented supplier-implemented quality programs and in-house controls. Supplier controls should include the establishment of supplier evaluation criteria, quality requirements, and other requirements, that must be met by the supplier.

Suppliers, including contractors and consultants, must demonstrate that they are able to provide products and services that meet these requirements. After a manufacturer selects a supplier, the supplier's performance must be periodically monitored, consistent with the significance of the product or service in question.

Although the GMP requirements allow flexibility in determining the degree of assessment and evaluation necessary, manufacturers are required to define the type and extent of control to be exercised over their suppliers. The degree of supplier assurance required varies with the difficulty of the service, the supplier's capabilities, the significance of the product or service, and its potential effect on the performance of the finished device.

The manufacturer must maintain adequate records of supplier, contractor, and consultant evaluation. These records must demonstrate the capability of suppliers as well as compliance with the requirements of this section. The Food and Drug Administration (FDA) will not review records such as supplier audit reports and findings, during routine inspections (per section 820.180(c)). For more information, see Chapter 23, "Records – Exceptions".

Industry Practice

Manufacturers use various methods to ensure proper evaluation, selection, and control of their suppliers. Purchasing control systems commonly focus on the selection, qualification, certification, and approval of suppliers.

Evaluating a supplier's capabilities before using the supplier is an important element of any manufacturer's quality program. Evaluation methods vary depending on the complexity and significance of the product or service supplied and its possible effect on the safety or effectiveness of the finished device. In general, manufacturers have written procedures in place to describe how supplier evaluation is conducted, and how product and service specifications are defined and communicated to suppliers. The procedures typically define such items as:

- methods of supplier evaluation, selection, and control;
- supplier performance monitoring;
- responsibilities and authority of the manufacturer and supplier;
- required documentation and data;
- control and maintenance of documentation and data;
- communication methods; and
- the mechanism for controlling changes to materials, processes, specifications, or services.

Procedures for developing purchasing documents usually provide a list of characteristics and requirements that may be relevant when describing products and services.

In most instances, manufacturers develop documented specifications for components, packaging, labeling, and the finished device, and release these as part of design transfer. These documents usually take the form of material specification sheets, drawings, or both. For well-established or catalog items, the trade name of the product is often sufficient to describe the material needed. For other items or services, specific written specifications may be necessary to ensure that requirements for the item or service desired are communicated clearly to the supplier.

Supplier Evaluation Criteria

Approaches to evaluating potential suppliers vary. One approach is to develop a checklist or matrix that covers quality requirements, design information, documentation system procedures, delivery history, manufacturing process details, part functionality, service availability, reliability, and cost considerations for a given product or service. The firm may identify an interdisciplinary supplier selection team to establish these qualifying criteria, to review the available data, and to agree on the supplier. The selection team may include representatives from various departments, such as manufacturing, quality assurance, purchasing, and development.

Evaluation criteria for quality requirements may be based on applicable sections of the Quality System regulation or other industry standards. Criteria may include controls related to design and development, facilities and equipment, materials and components, operations (process capability), finished device, policies and procedures, record-keeping, personnel (education, training, experience), and auditing, depending on the product or service to be supplied. Other minimum requirements that all suppliers are required to meet, such as financial stability and delivery arrangements, also may be determined by the selection team.

The next step is to establish how potential suppliers and contractors will be evaluated. When possible, the supplier's past history in supplying a similar product or service may be considered. Techniques such as on-site audits or mailed surveys are often used to assess the supplier's Quality System and overall capabilities. The evaluation may consider the

V

supplier's test and inspection results, validation data, first-article or pilot-run data, performance history, and references, as well as the results of any third-party audits or inspections. For contractors or consultants, a review of curricula vita and discussions with professional references (e.g., previous clients) may be conducted.

Although manufacturers may use an existing Quality System registration to ISO 9001/13485 or a similar standard as a criterion in supplier evaluation and selection, they may not necessarily rely on certification as evidence that a supplier can provide acceptable products or services. Depending on the product or service, an initial assessment or evaluation is typically performed to verify that an adequate quality assurance program is indeed in place.

Where applicable, the supplier often provides component samples or first articles to the manufacturer, so that conformance to specifications can be physically verified. Depending on the significance of the purchased item, the evaluation of samples may be coupled with a supplier qualification program, which can span over a designated time period or delivery quantity. The inspection results from the samples or first articles factor heavily into whether the supplier is considered further. For suppliers of major or significant components, initial approval may be followed by an on-site audit of the supplier's facilities. The purpose of the audit is to establish the supplier's ability to conform to the established criteria.

When suppliers that meet the evaluation criteria are approved, manufacturers may purchase and receive products or services. Most manufacturers maintain a list of approved suppliers or equivalent documentation. In addition, they implement documented systems to ensure that supplier status is verified when orders are placed.

Supplier Relations

After a supplier is chosen and approved, the supplier may be invited to tour the device manufacturer's facility to better understand the end use of the medical device and to review the specification requirements. The manufacturer's ultimate goal is to treat the supplier as an extension of the manufacturer.

Even with a supplier selection program and adequate acceptance activities, manufacturers commonly rely on additional methods of ensuring a supplier's ability to continue to provide an acceptable product or service. The objective is to find the appropriate mixture of assessment tools and incoming inspections and tests necessary for proper control.

Manufacturers often review key product and service suppliers every year and less significant suppliers every 2 to 3 years. Follow-up audits are scheduled as needed, depending on the product or service supplied. When an audit is not feasible or appropriate, the manufacturer may rely on other effective means of ensuring product or service acceptability. Mailed surveys in conjunction with monitoring of the quality of products or services received are often sufficient. All supplier reaudit, survey, and monitoring results are documented and reviewed by the supplier selection team.

Supplier monitoring activities often include:
- statistical analysis of incoming acceptance results,
- independent confirmation of certificate of conformance data,

- consideration of the supplier's responses to requests for corrective action, and
- evaluation of the supplier's routine performance for on-time delivery.

As industry increases reliance on suppliers for both components and key processes, manufacturers need to focus considerable effort on effective monitoring of supplier performance. The extent of monitoring should be commensurate with the overall risk of the finished device, the complexity of the supplier's product or service, and the maturity of the supplier's Quality System. Periodic monitoring of ISO-registered suppliers may not include on-site assessments or audits, provided that the product or service received continues to meet specified requirements.

Some manufacturers extend their supplier evaluation and selection programs to include certification. This process is often the final goal in establishing good working relations with a supplier. Achieving certification can mean reduced incoming acceptance activities or more favorable business terms for the supplier.

820.50(b) Purchasing Data

The Requirement

> ***820.50(b) Purchasing data.*** *Each manufacturer shall establish and maintain data that clearly describe or reference the specified requirements, including quality requirements, for purchased or otherwise received product and services. Purchasing documents shall include, where possible, an agreement that the suppliers, contractors, and consultants agree to notify the manufacturer of changes in the product or service so that manufacturers may determine whether the changes may affect the quality of a finished device. Purchasing data shall be approved in accordance with § 820.40.*

Discussion of the Requirement

Under the requirements of this section, manufacturers are expected to develop purchasing documents that define specific requirements, including quality requirements, for purchased components, finished devices, packaging materials, labeling materials, manufacturing materials, and contract services. Purchasing specifications for components and product-specific materials are part of the device master record (DMR). The term "quality requirements" refers to those requirements necessary to ensure that the product or service is adequate for its intended use. The amount of detail required in the purchasing documents relates to the nature of the product or service purchased, taking into account the effect that the product or service has on the safety, effectiveness, and performance of the finished device.

Purchasing data is typically provided to suppliers in documents such as, but not limited to, specification sheets, drawings, contracts, or purchase orders. Documentation may be in a written or electronic media form; however, to ensure that specified requirements are clearly described, manufacturers are required to establish a system for review and approval of data used to purchase a product or service. The manufacturer is also expected to develop procedures to ensure that requirements are clearly communicated to and understood by the supplier.

It is expected that a manufacturer's purchasing documents will include a statement that addresses notification of changes in the supplier's product, process, or service that may affect the performance of the finished device. If the supplier refuses to provide such notification, the manufacturer must implement a system of control to ensure that any such changes are identified upon receipt of the material.

Industry Practice

Manufacturers use various methods to describe or reference specifications and quality requirements for their suppliers. Purchasing data can take such forms as standard identification, process instructions, test instructions, and technical information (such as engineering drawings). The information is often communicated to suppliers by means of purchase specifications or purchase orders.

Essential design outputs should receive close scrutiny when establishing supplier requirements. Outputs that are essential for the proper function of the medical device should be the focus of increased controls to ensure safety and efficacy. By defining specific outputs as "essential" the manufacturer is elevating the criticality of the product or service, and should levy increased performance requirements on the supplier.

Purchasing Specifications

Purchasing specifications may be described in a single document or a series of documents. Some manufacturers establish general specifications for components in defined "categories", as well as part-specific documents.   The important aspect is that the purchasing specifications clearly communicate the requirements to the supplier. Specifications often include:
- description of the product (e.g., type, grade, class);
- requirements for material composition and configuration;
- process instructions and limitations (when applicable);
- performance characteristics and requirements (including references to standards);
- inspection and test plans;
- part numbers and versions;
- requirements for packaging and marking by the supplier;
- storage and shipping conditions (when required);
- certifications (e.g., certificates of analysis);
- requirements for compliance with quality standards (e.g., GMP requirements, ISO standards); and
- acceptance criteria.

Specifications for services often also include reference to regulations and standards. Commonly referenced regulations include the Quality System regulation, the regulation for Good Laboratory Practice for Nonclinical Laboratory Studies (the GLP), and the regulations of the Environmental Protection Agency (EPA) and the Occupational Safety and Health Administration (OSHA). Commonly referenced standards include those of the Association for the Advancement of Medical Instrumentation (AAMI), International Standard Organization (ISO), American Society for Testing and Materials (ASTM), Institute of Electrical and Electronics Engineers (IEEE), U.S. Pharmacopeia (USP), National Institute for Standards and Technology (NIST), and Technical Association of the Paper and Pulp

Industry (TAPPI). Alternatively, the manufacturer may provide a custom test method or other internally developed requirement.

If specific process parameters, equipment, tools, or supplies are used in the supplier's product or service (e.g., contract sterilization or contract calibration), they are typically documented in a detailed process specification. This process specification becomes part of, or is referenced by number in, the manufacturer's contract or purchase order.

Purchasing documents are usually established and maintained under a documentation control system to ensure that requirements have been approved and that subsequent changes are evaluated and approved. The document control system typically identifies the individuals who are required to approve documents, describes the records required to demonstrate approval, and defines the distribution, retrieval, and change control system.

Supplier Agreements

Manufacturers typically review the specification requirements with the supplier to ensure that the supplier can provide the product and understands its use in the manufacturer's operation. For standard stock items and nonessential components, specification review and acceptance by the supplier may not be extensive. For custom or essential components, finished devices, and services, a formal, written, supplier agreement is more common, and often expected by regulatory agencies. Such agreements refer to the pertinent specifications, the conditions related to the Quality System, environmental requirements (if applicable), financial terms, confidentiality terms, warranties, length of the contract term, and contract responsibilities.

Supplier agreements for key products and services, such as sterilization and contract manufacturing, should address creation and retention of production records, such as the DMR and device history record (DHR). These records need to be controlled by the supplier, but must be accessible to the manufacturer when needed in the normal course of business. Agreements should address access to supplier maintained DMRs and DHRs, when needed for corrective actions, regulatory inspections, and supplier monitoring. In addition, supplier agreements should describe change control practices (including necessary approvals) for documents included in the DMR.

For purchased services, it is common for a manufacturer, after discussions with the supplier, to initiate a request for service or proposal, which defines the service requirements. The service organization responds to the request for service or proposal with a contract or letter of understanding. After they reach agreement, both parties sign the contract.

Supplier agreements and contracts are typically controlled by a manufacturer's representative who is responsible for ensuring that contract activities are clearly defined and documented. The manufacturer's representative may review such contracts annually with the component or service provider to ensure that the requirements are still appropriate. Contracts are also reviewed when changes occur to product, processes, services, or other terms.

After the device manufacturer's specifications are generated, the manufacturer's document control system is used to document the generation, modification, approval, distribution, and retrieval of obsolete documents. The manufacturer's system may need to work in concert with the suppliers' document control system, to ensure changes are adequately reflected in all affected documents. Some manufacturers have co-sign off procedures for both firms' change control forms.

Purchase Orders

A manufacturer's purchase order typically contains part number (including revision level), a description of the product or service, the quantity being ordered, the delivery dates, and the cost. When placing orders with suppliers of products or services, manufacturers typically refer to specifications, reports, data requirements, or contracts on the purchase order documents. Some manufacturers include a copy of the related specifications with each purchase order. In the case of manufacturers that transmit purchasing documents to their suppliers electronically, the personnel placing the orders need access to the current documentation to ensure that the correct revisions of each document are provided to the supplier.

Purchasing representatives verify that the information presented on purchase orders conforms to approved purchasing documents (e.g., specifications, drawings, and contracts) and that the product or service orders are placed only with approved suppliers. These practices are usually documented in standard operating procedures.

Notification of Changes

In many cases, purchase orders contain boilerplate statements that require suppliers to notify the purchaser when changes are made to the product or service being provided. Because some changes can have a major effect on the performance or safety of the finished device, it is advisable to make this requirement explicit by incorporating into the supplier agreement document a requirement that no change be made without prior written approval of the purchaser.

If a supplier does not agree to these terms and the manufacturer is unable to replace the supplier, additional control of the supplier is necessary. This may include some combination of:
- increased inspection and testing of incoming product;
- on-site supervision when product is being produced, processed, or tested (i.e., source inspection); and
- frequent audits of the supplier.

CHAPTER 9. IDENTIFICATION AND TRACEABILITY (SUBPART F)

820.60 Identification

The Requirement

***820.60 Identification.** Each manufacturer shall establish and maintain procedures for identifying product during all stages of receipt, production, distribution, and installation to prevent mixups.*

Discussion of the Requirement

Manufacturers are required to establish systems for identification and control of all product, including components, manufacturing materials, subassemblies, finished devices, packaging, and labeling. These systems must encompass all phases of production, from receipt through distribution and, where applicable, installation.

The purpose of the required controls is to prevent mixups by providing:
- written procedures that describe the systems used for identifying materials;
- physical, spatial, or other means of separating incoming, quarantined, accepted, and rejected parts; and
- methods of, and controls for, identifying the status of materials.

Industry Practice

Identification relates to acceptance status; however, these two terms differ in meaning. "Identification" is the description of the product that distinguishes it from other product. Typically, a part number provides unique, distinguishable identification. In some cases, a revision level or lot number may also be needed to uniquely identify the product. "Acceptance status" is the result of evaluating whether the product conforms to its specification (i.e., whether it passed or failed the inspection or test). Acceptance status is discussed further in Chapter 11.

Manufacturers use various physical and electronic methods for identifying and controlling materials, including tags, placards, and separation. It is typical for a manufacturer to have a separate physical location (quarantine area) for holding uninspected incoming materials.

When the manufacturer uses tagging methods for identification, the information on the tag varies greatly. Some manufacturers identify only a part number and status. Others include such additional information as lot, batch, or work order identification; quantity; and supplier. The amount of identification information included may be based upon the complexity and risk of the product.

Regardless of the method, written procedures are commonly used to define the means for identifying product and to designate the individuals responsible for carrying out the procedures. These procedures typically define the following elements:
- methods of identification to be used,
- assignment of designated responsibility for identification activities, and
- segregation of unapproved and approved product.

820.65 Traceability

The Requirement

820.65 Traceability. Each manufacturer of a device that is intended for surgical implant into the body or to support or sustain life and whose failure to perform when properly used in accordance with instructions for use provided in the labeling can be reasonably expected to result in a significant injury to the user shall establish and maintain procedures for identifying with a control number each unit, lot, or batch of finished devices and where appropriate components. The procedures shall facilitate corrective action. Such identification shall be documented in the DHR.

Discussion of the Requirement

Manufacturers of devices whose failure could result in serious injury or harm to the user are required to establish a documented traceability system. This system must enable each unit, batch, or lot of finished devices to be traced by control number. This requirement also applies to appropriate components of the finished device.

It is the responsibility of manufacturers to determine whether this GMP requirement applies to their devices. FDA has indicated that critical devices—as listed in the *Federal Register* notice of March 17, 1988 (53 FR 8854)—and *in vitro* diagnostics (as per 809.10) are subject to the traceability requirement. In addition, FDA has made it clear that traceability for implantable devices should encompass the components and the materials used.

The Preamble to the Quality System regulation (comment 120) makes it clear that it is the manufacturer's responsibility to determine the appropriate level of traceability.

> *… Therefore, it is imperative that manufacturers use the definition within the requirement of § 820.65 to determine if a particular device needs to be traced; it may not be sufficient to rely solely on the 1988 list. Manufacturers may find it advantageous to provide unit, lot, or batch traceability for devices for which traceability is not a requirement to facilitate control and limit the number of devices that may need to be recalled due to defects or violations of the act.*

Industry Practice

When determining which components and raw materials may be required to be traceable, many manufacturers perform risk analysis or use the essential outputs list developed during the design control activities to help determine this. Others use as guidance the definition of critical components[7] given in the July 21, 1978, version of 21 CFR 820.

Manufacturers use various methods for and levels of traceability, ranging from no traceability to complete traceability of each component to its supplier or raw material lot

---

[7] Section 820.3(e), "Current Good Manufacturing Practice for the Manufacture, Packaging, Storage and Installation of Medical Devices and In Vitro Diagnostic Products," 21 CFR 820, July 21, 1978 (obsolete), stated: "'Critical component' means any component of a critical device whose failure to perform can be reasonably expected to cause the failure of a critical device or to affect its safety or effectiveness." The current GMP does not define or use this term, but instead states requirements for "essential outputs" in 820.30, "Design controls."

number. The Preamble to the Quality System regulation, also comment 120, provides contrast between tracking and traceability requirements.

> *... It is important that the traceability requirements in part 820 are not confused with the Medical Device Tracking regulation in part 821 (21 CFR part 821). The <u>tracking regulation</u> is intended to ensure that tracked devices can be traced from the device manufacturing facility to the person for whom the device is indicated, that is, the patient. Effective tracking of devices from the manufacturing facility, through the distribution network (including distributors, retailers, rental firms and other commercial enterprises, device user facilities, and licensed practitioners) and, ultimately, to any person for whom the device is intended is necessary for the effectiveness of remedies prescribed by the act, such as patient notification ... or device recall In contrast, the <u>traceability provision</u> requires that a device that meets the definition of a "critical device" can be traced from the manufacturing facility only to the "initial consignee" as discussed in § 820.160 <u>Distribution</u>.*

In addition to regulatory reasons, manufacturers may also establish device traceability for liability or economic reasons.

Many manufacturers' traceability systems include the following elements:

a. Written procedures describe the control numbering system used, the assignment of control numbers, and how and where control numbers are to be recorded (e.g., in the DHR).

b. Lot numbers, control numbers, or other suitable numbers (e.g., serial numbers for finished devices) are assigned to each lot of designated components, manufacturing materials, subassemblies, finished devices, packaging, and labeling in order to aid in their identification in the manufacturing process from the time of receipt onward.

c. In-process parts or their containers are physically identified with the part number and assigned lot or control number throughout production.

d. Finished devices are physically identified with the assigned lot, control, or serial number.

e. The assigned lot, control, or serial number is recorded in finished device distribution records.

When traceability is performed to the component level, it is common practice to assign a control number to each lot of incoming materials. Control numbers, in the form of lot or work order numbers, are also assigned for lower-level operations performed by the manufacturer (e.g., molding or subassembly work). A final control number is assigned to the finished device and is commonly recorded in the distribution record for the device. See Chapter 17 for more information on Distribution requirements.

CHAPTER 10. RECEIVING, IN-PROCESS, AND FINISHED DEVICE ACCEPTANCE (SUBPART H)

820.80 Receiving, In-Process, and Finished Device Acceptance

The Requirement

820.80 Receiving, In-Process, and Finished Device Acceptance.
(a) General. *Each manufacturer shall establish and maintain procedures for acceptance activities. Acceptance activities include inspections, tests, or other verification activities.*

Discussion of the Requirement

This section of the Quality System regulation requires manufacturers to establish and maintain systems and procedures for acceptance activities to verify that all products, including finished devices, work-in-process, components, packaging, labeling, and manufacturing materials, conform to specified requirements. In other words, manufacturers are expected to define the nature and type of acceptance activities that are required throughout the entire production process to ensure that a given product meets its predetermined quality requirements.

Recognized acceptance activities include, but are not limited to, inspections, tests, review of certificates of analysis, and verifications, including supplier audits. The acceptance activities actually used at different points in the production process may vary, but manufacturers are expected to determine what activities are necessary and appropriate to ensure that specified quality requirements are met.

Industry Practice

Manufacturers recognize that acceptance activities are an integral part of a good Quality System but that proper performance of these activities does not, by itself, satisfy the GMP requirements for producing a safe and effective device. Acceptance activities are control methods designed to ensure that product is made according to the manufacturer's specifications. They are intended to prevent further processing or release of a product that does not conform to those specifications. The output of acceptance activities is often used to generate information that may be used in a quality improvement project.

Historically, most manufacturers implemented "tollgate" systems to test and inspect products at receiving, in-process, and finished stages to determine the suitability for use of those products. The responsibility for making the determinations was typically assigned to the quality control personnel. These activities rely on sampling, inspection, and testing plans to verify that materials meet established criteria for physical characteristics and performance after processing operations.

There are serious shortcomings to tollgate inspection operations. The most significant shortcoming is that it is performed too late to prevent costly and time-consuming problems with material or product quality. With the increasing use of just-in-time, Lean, and similar manufacturing systems, and the continually evolving competition in the global marketplace, larger demands have been placed on traditional quality control activities.

Understanding the critical control points throughout the "value stream" of the product allows for better control of waste and better management of product through the manufacturing cycle. [8]

In this changing environment, manufacturers recognize that traditional methods of manufacturing, inspecting, and testing may not meet the increasing need to be more timely and cost-effective. Many progressive manufacturers have developed their inspection, test, and verification activities with the intention of preventing material or product quality problems. In addition, newly developed acceptance techniques provide improved methods of demonstrating that processes and products meet specifications. The advantage of such systems is that manufacturers are able to act on quality issues early in the manufacturing process, before operations are completed and severe difficulties are encountered. Many of these tools continuously monitor identified programs for compliance so that manufacturers can identify, address, and correct noncompliances and other concerns before manufacturing activities begin.

These progressive techniques not only meet the requirements set forth in the regulation but also accomplish product acceptance effectively and with efficiency and cost containment. Manufacturers who rely on prevention techniques are able to recognize and solve product quality problems much earlier in the product design or manufacturing cycle, thus lowering the quality costs related to device complaints, reworking, scrap, and downtime.

Effective acceptance procedures and systems directly affect the ability of a manufacturer to demonstrate that processes and product meet specifications. These procedures and systems are developed during the design stage and undergo the same design reviews as the product and process designs do.

820.80(b) Receiving Acceptance Activities

The Requirement

> ***820.80(b) Receiving acceptance activities.*** *Each manufacturer shall establish and maintain procedures for acceptance of incoming product. Incoming product shall be inspected, tested, or otherwise verified as conforming to specified requirements. Acceptance or rejection shall be documented.*

Discussion of the Requirement

Each manufacturer is expected to establish an effective receiving acceptance program for all product entering into its warehouse or manufacturing facility. The program must ensure that product arriving at the receiving dock is or has been properly inspected, tested, evaluated, or verified to determine whether it meets defined specifications. This evaluation results in a documented decision to accept or reject the product. The program also must describe and require documentation of the methods used to release product for further processing. All parts, components, and materials that will become part of the finished device or part of the manufacturing materials used in the processing of the device must go

---

[8] See Appendix A (Bibliography) for *Lean Thinking*, 2003, Womack and Jones.

through a receiving acceptance process. This requirement does not necessarily mean that the device manufacturer must inspect and test each lot, batch, or item, but there must be a defined method of evaluating whether a lot, batch, or item meets the predetermined quality requirements.

FDA has noted that manufacturers are permitted to release for "urgent use" incoming items that have not yet been proven acceptable for use, provided that control of the unapproved item is maintained and that the manufacturer can retrieve products containing the item before distribution of finished devices. FDA does not permit distribution of unapproved finished devices based on the "urgent use" provision.

Industry Practice

Most manufacturers have established receiving inspection or incoming inspection organizations that are responsible for acceptance activities related to receiving products. Typically, a procedure is created to describe the overall process, which may involve source inspection programs, supplier audit or certification programs, test and inspection activities, or a combination of these and other methods.

Additional procedures are sometimes created to describe aspects of the process in greater detail (e.g., dock-to-stock programs). Supplemental documents are usually generated to describe the inspection and test requirements for specific products. These DMR documents may describe measurements to be made or tests to be run, any required instruments or gauges, sampling plans for each characteristic to be evaluated, and records necessary to document designated activities and results. Additional special requirements, such as outside laboratory tests, certificates of analysis, or certificates of compliance, may be described in these or other documents.

During design transfer, test procedures are released, test stations and equipment are qualified, and test methods are validated. All measuring equipment is under calibration control in accordance with section 820.72 (see Chapter 14).

Inspection and test results are typically recorded in a manner that facilitates review and analysis of the quality performance and quality variances of the product supplied. Many manufacturers recognize that analysis of quantitative test data produces results that are more useful than analysis of "pass/fail" data. They therefore require that quantitative measurements be recorded for future review. The data generated are used to monitor product and supplier performance trends. Quality System data review and analysis identify opportunities for improvement and permit timely changes to be made in the acceptance criteria, methods, or procedures for the product. For example, in-process surveillance may be increased if performance is slipping below the norm or reduced if performance is exceeding expectation. Quality System data review and analysis also provide feedback to suppliers so that supplier-related deficiencies can be detected and corrected before the next shipment. Conversely, good performance may result in a certification process or the implementation of some form of "skip-lot" or dock-to-stock program for particular suppliers.

Manufacturers typically document the results of acceptance activities on prepared forms or test records that are included in the DHR. Results also may be recorded in engineering notebooks or production forms that are more universal in their application. The DHR package either contains copies of these records or references the location of the documents. The documented receiving data generally include:

- date of the acceptance activity;
- part number or other unique product configuration identifier;
- lot, batch, or serial number identification provided by the supplier;
- supplemental control number, if the supplier identification is insufficient or incompatible with the manufacturer's method of recording this information (or if, according to section 820.65, a control number is required for the protection of public health);
- quantity received;
- quantity inspected or tested;
- numerical test data and resulting conformance determination;
- quantity of pass/fail items in the sample;
- quantity of lot or batch rejected;
- other pertinent information concerning disposition or special events surrounding the acceptance process; and
- specific acceptance data as required in 820.80(e).

Controls are usually implemented to ensure that product that has not yet been inspected or tested is quarantined. On inspection, many manufacturers physically identify materials by status. A common status labeling system is color-coded tagging. Segregation may be further enhanced by secure physical separation of parts based on their status (e.g., accepted or rejected). Chapter 11, "Acceptance Status", provides further details on identification of product acceptance status.

Not all manufacturers allow release of incoming items for "urgent use," although this practice is becoming more common. Where this practice is permitted, documented systems are developed to ensure that proper controls are in place. In addition to material identification, these systems include mechanisms to prevent finished devices from being released for distribution before successful completion of the receiving acceptance activity. Urgent use controls are often tied to the record review and release process of the finished device lot or batch.

820.80(c) In-Process Acceptance Activities

The Requirement

820.80(c) In-process acceptance activities. Each manufacturer shall establish and maintain acceptance procedures, where appropriate, to ensure that specified requirements for in-process product are met. Such procedures shall ensure that in-process product is controlled until the required inspection and tests or other verification activities have been completed, or necessary approvals are received, and are documented.

Discussion of the Requirement

When appropriate and feasible, in-process acceptance activities are performed at designated points in the process to ensure that any in-process quality requirements have been met. These acceptance activities must be performed according to written procedures that include but are not limited to descriptions of the necessary equipment, required methods, and acceptance criteria. As under the requirements for incoming items, manufacturers can use product under defined, documented conditions before all in-process acceptance activities have been completed. However, these activities must be completed *before* the finished device is released for distribution. When in-process acceptance activities are performed, they must be documented.

Industry Practice

In general, the purpose of in-process acceptance activities is to verify that defined quality requirements for in-process products are met. In-process acceptance activities typically also allow early detection of nonconformances, thereby preventing further processing of nonconforming items. Effective in-process acceptance increases the probability of producing a finished device that meets specifications, and improves the efficiency of the entire operation.

In-process acceptance activities usually include quality control tests that yield quantitative measurements (e.g., weights, flows, pressures, pH, viscosity, porosity, voltage, and resistance). Visual inspections and tests that supply only "go/no go" results are also performed. For example, visual inspection of circuit boards for solder integrity is an in-process visual inspection. Automated circuit board testing is often performed, and "passed" or "failed" results are documented.

The "appropriateness" of the points at which in-process acceptance activities are performed depends on a number of factors. These include the extent of process validation, the complexity of the manufacturing process, the in-process material characteristics that can change with time, and material characteristics affected by previous and subsequent processes. Some manufacturers use techniques such as Hazard Analysis and Critical Control Points (HACCP) and process FMEA to establish in-process inspection requirements. Similarly, the extent to which in-process acceptance activities are performed depends on the type, complexity, and number of processes involved in the manufacturing of the device. In-process acceptance activities may involve:
- sampling according to a statistically valid plan;
- testing the beginning, middle, and end of a batch; or
- performing a setup inspection of an automated system.

In-process acceptance documentation includes the date and the results. In addition, the person who performed the activity typically stamps, signs, or initials the record to document the inspector's identity. In-process data also may be recorded on some type of statistical process control chart (e.g., pre-control or rainbow chart, X Bar chart, and R chart). These charts are used to monitor the variability of the process. If trends are seen, appropriate investigations are generally performed and corrective action taken.

An independent review of documented acceptance results is commonly performed to ensure that the acceptance activity was performed correctly and that the in-process product meets the specified criteria. For this purpose, an independent function may review or audit the records, or a routine audit of acceptance activities may be performed and documented.

Many manufacturers place in-process materials in an area designated as "quarantined" until the results of in-process acceptance activities are obtained and reviewed. Other common methods include the use of tags, colored stickers, computer labels, or other systems, as per section 820.86 (see Chapter 11).

Any in-process failures must be documented and the in-process material dispositioned accordingly (e.g., reworked, scrapped, or "used as is"), as defined by the nonconformance system (see Chapter 18). The nonconformance report is then filed or referenced in the DHR. This mechanism is particularly significant in cases where the disposition is "use as is," because it is a means of documenting a valid reason for such a disposition. When reworking is possible (i.e., when reworking will not adversely affect the product), this mechanism ensures that reworked material is reevaluated to determine whether it meets specifications.

The number and types of in-process test failures are typically included in the evaluation of the adequacy of the firm's Quality System (e.g., section 820.20(c), "Management review"). Documenting actual quantitative test results, when possible, provides more information for quality review and corrective action.

820.80(d) Final Acceptance Activities

The Requirement

> *820.80(d) Final acceptance activities. Each manufacturer shall establish and maintain procedures for finished device acceptance to ensure that each production run, lot, or batch of finished devices meets acceptance criteria. Finished devices shall be held in quarantine or otherwise adequately controlled until released. Finished devices shall not be released for distribution until:*
> *(1) The activities required in the DMR are completed;*
> *(2) the associated data and documentation is reviewed;*
> *(3) the release is authorized by the signature of a designated individual(s); and*
> *(4) the authorization is dated.*

Discussion of the Requirement

Manufacturers are expected to establish procedures that define the acceptance activities required for each production run, lot, or batch of finished devices. These procedures should include, but are not limited to, descriptions of any equipment required, the methods used to perform the activity, and the acceptance criteria. Some information, such as the acceptance criteria, may be in other DMR documents.

Finished device acceptance activities also must include a review of the DHR to ensure that all processing steps were performed and completed in accordance with the DMR. All finished devices awaiting final acceptance test or undergoing review must be prevented from being distributed until formally released. The DHR review must be performed by a designated individual. The results of the review must be documented and include the authorizing individual's signature and the date.

Industry Practice

Finished device acceptance activities augment the acceptance activities performed during processing and ensure that all manufacturing and packaging processes have been performed correctly. Finished device acceptance activities may include the use of a statistically valid sampling plan to test and inspect units from each lot or batch. In accordance with section 820.170, "Installation", finished devices that are installed or assembled on-site are required to be verified after installation (see Chapter 17). Finished device acceptance activities increase the probability of producing a finished device that meets specifications.

The extent and type of finished device acceptance activities performed generally depend on the complexity of the device and on the type, complexity, and number of processes involved in the manufacturing of the device. Other factors may include the type of in-process acceptance activities performed and the extent and adequacy of any process validations. In other words, how much "up-front" control has been implemented? Where possible, finished device acceptance activities commonly simulate actual conditions of use. Most manufacturers require some type of quantitative test results as part of the performance testing program for finished devices (e.g., weights, flows, pressures, pH, viscosity, porosity, voltage, and resistance).

Many manufacturers stipulate that testing and inspection responsibilities, including finished device testing, will be performed by personnel who are independent of the production department. In other firms, production personnel are sometimes responsible for performing finished device testing or inspection, and the results are reviewed by independent personnel to ensure that the testing was performed correctly and that finished devices meet the specified criteria. In addition, independent personnel may retest a few finished units as an audit of the finished device and the final test process.

Manufacturers commonly document the results of finished device acceptance activities on controlled forms. The DHR package either contains copies of these records or references the location of the records. The documentation includes the test results and the date. Also, the person who performed the acceptance activity typically stamps, signs, or initials the record, thereby documenting that the activity was performed.

Because finished devices need to be appropriately identified and quarantined to prevent their use until they have been accepted, many manufacturers place finished devices in an area designated as "quarantined" until the results of final acceptance activities are obtained and the DHR record has been reviewed. Other common methods include the use of tags, colored stickers, computer labels, or identification systems, as per section 820.86.

As part of the overall Quality System, any nonconformance identified during final acceptance requires prompt investigation. Nonconformance includes finished devices, packaging, and labeling that do not meet acceptance criteria. When a rework decision is possible (i.e., when reworking does not adversely affect the finished device), nonconforming material controls should ensure that the reworked device is reevaluated to confirm that it meets specifications.

The number and types of finished device failures are typically reviewed during the evaluation of the adequacy of the manufacturer's Quality System (e.g., management review). Documenting actual quantitative test results, when possible, will provide more information for quality review and corrective action activities.

820.80(e) Acceptance Records

The Requirement

> *820.80(e) Acceptance records.* Each manufacturer shall document acceptance activities required by this part. These records shall include:
> *(1)* The acceptance activities performed;
> *(2)* the dates acceptance activities are performed;
> *(3)* the results;
> *(4)* the signature of the individual(s) conducting the acceptance activities; and
> *(5)* where appropriate the equipment used. These records shall be part of the DHR.

Discussion of the Requirement

All receiving, in-process, and final acceptance activities must be recorded. Requirements for the associated records are spelled out in the regulation. Manufacturers are expected to have records that show that a stated acceptance activity was performed and that indicate whether the product passed or failed that activity. Each manufacturer also must determine when to identify the equipment used for the acceptance activity. It is strongly recommended that manufacturers record any quantitative data generated. Equipment identification should be recorded when deemed necessary for proper investigations into nonconforming product.

Industry Practice

Common record-keeping practices used by manufacturers are detailed in the "Industry Practice" portions of sections 820.80(b), 820.80(c), and 820.80(d). All acceptance records must include the information cited in section 820.80(e). Chapters 24 and 25 provide further information on requirements concerning electronic acceptance records.

CHAPTER 11. ACCEPTANCE STATUS (SUBPART H)

820.86 Acceptance Status

The Requirement

820.86 Acceptance status. *Each manufacturer shall identify by suitable means the acceptance status of product, to indicate the conformance or nonconformance of product with acceptance criteria. The identification of acceptance status shall be maintained throughout manufacturing, packaging, labeling, installation, and servicing of the product to ensure that only product which has passed the required acceptance activities is distributed, used, or installed.*

Discussion of the Requirement

The intent of this requirement is to minimize opportunities for mixups of acceptable and unacceptable product by requiring that the acceptance status be clearly identified. Systems developed to meet the requirements of section 820.60, "Identification," also may be used to help show the acceptance status required by section 820.86.

It must be possible to quickly and clearly establish the inspection status of product at any phase of the activities carried out during receiving, production, storage, distribution, installation, and servicing of the product. This requirement is especially important for those items that have been determined not to conform to acceptance requirements. The requirement also applies to servicing; therefore, the acceptance status of devices awaiting service and those that have already been serviced must be identified.

Industry Practice

Industry currently uses both physical and electronic methods for identifying the acceptance status of product. Acceptance status may be indicated by labels, tags, stickers, signatures, bar codes, or other means. For example, acceptance status is commonly identified with "accept" or "reject" labels, stamps, or stickers. "Accept" labels may be green, and "reject" labels are typically red, thus providing a color-coded indication of the product status. Some manufacturers indicate the acceptance status of incoming, in-process, and finished device by means of a traveler or history card that accompanies the product as it is moved from station to station. When these identifiers are used, they are displayed so that the status is readily visible to prevent inadvertent moving or use of product that is in quarantine.

A number of medical device manufacturers use computer systems to control released product in warehouses and product awaiting incoming acceptance. Product status is identified in a database, and product is selected automatically by an automated system for release or other disposition. In accordance with the GMP requirement, these systems are subject to validation under section 820.70(i).

Basically, any means may be used to indicate acceptance status, provided that it is proven to be effective. The method used must prevent mixups of acceptable and unacceptable product. The identification method indicates the status of the product with respect to whether it has been inspected or tested and whether it has been accepted, rejected, or placed on hold awaiting disposition. Identification of parts by status throughout the production process is an important method of ensuring the quality of finished devices. Methods may involve the tagging of parts with a status label, the use of identifying containers, the segregation of activities by location, or other means of ensuring that only approved parts are used in production.

Medical device firms with service functions must maintain acceptance status during servicing. This is often accomplished by physical segregation, with devices being returned for service stored in a separate area from those which have been serviced, or those awaiting inspection. Those devices ready to be returned to customers after successful inspections or testing should also be segregated. A copy of the service record normally accompanies the device throughout this process, further aiding in identifying the unit's current acceptance status. See Chapter 21, "Servicing", for more information on servicing requirements.

V

CHAPTER 12. STATISTICAL TECHNIQUES (SUBPART O)

820.250 Statistical Techniques

The Requirement

820.250 Statistical techniques.
(a) Where appropriate, each manufacturer shall establish and maintain procedures for identifying valid statistical techniques required for establishing, controlling, and verifying the acceptability of process capability and product characteristics.
(b) Sampling plans, when used, shall be written and based on a valid statistical rationale. Each manufacturer shall establish and maintain procedures to ensure that sampling methods are adequate for their intended use and to ensure that when changes occur the sampling plans are reviewed. These activities shall be documented.

Discussion of the Requirement

The requirements of this section apply throughout the design process, production, and the evaluation of post-distribution data. Elsewhere in the Quality System regulation, only three references are made to statistical techniques (sampling plans, service reports, and quality problems). However, manufacturers are expected to use valid statistical methods whenever appropriate. The techniques and methods used are left to the discretion of the manufacturer; however, they must be capable of withstanding statistical scrutiny.

In addition, device manufacturers must establish and maintain procedures to ensure that any sampling methods are appropriate for their intended use and are regularly reviewed. The sampling plans selected must be adequate to ensure that unacceptable product quality is detected. If the quality goals of the manufacturer, suppliers, or users change, it will be necessary to select a different sampling plan. When more units of unacceptable quality are detected than are allowed by the selected sampling plan, the associated manufacturing processes should be adjusted.

Industry Practice

It is common for manufacturers to use statistical methods throughout the life cycle of a device. These techniques are incorporated into the design phase, carried though production, and used in the analysis of post-distribution quality data. They are beneficial in a wide variety of circumstances, including the collection and analysis of data. Appropriate statistical techniques can assist the manufacturer not only in deciding which data to obtain, but also in making the best use of the data.

Statistical methods are commonly used for:
- product and process limit determination;
- defect rate estimation;
- process capability and control;
- sampling plan and quality-level determination;
- sampling for acceptance activities and investigations;
- nonconformity analysis;
- reliability, maintainability, and product shelf life testing;

- risk determination;
- root causes determination;
- evaluation of clinical data;
- data assessment; and
- verification and measurement.

This section implies that when statistical tools are used to analyze quality data, baseline, alert, and action threshold levels should be established, reviewed, and revised on a regular basis. Common statistical methods include Pareto charts, histograms, control charts, design of experiments, regression analysis, and analysis of variance. Trending is the most common statistical method used, because it supports the proactive analysis of quality data, as required under section 820.100(a), "Corrective and preventive action."

For purposes of sampling product for inspection and testing, many manufacturers rely on published sampling plans recognized by FDA (e.g., ANSI/ASQ Z1.4, *Sampling Procedures and Tables for Inspection by Attributes*). However, an increasing number of companies are developing their own sampling plans in order to evaluate processes and product efficiently and effectively. Whatever the basis for the sampling plan is, it must be statistically valid. Manufacturers often use the established change control process to ensure that changes to sampling plans are thoroughly evaluated before they are implemented and to consider the effects of production or material changes on sampling plan validity.

V

NOTES:

V

"The traditional solution of 100% inspection in not satisfactory because it is always imperfect ... The real solution is to stop making the nonconforming product."
D. Wheeler and D. Chambers, *Understanding Statistical Process Control*, 1986

SECTION VI. PRODUCTION AND PROCESS CONTROLS

CHAPTER 13. PRODUCTION AND PROCESS CONTROLS (SUBPART G)

820.70 Production and Process Controls

The Requirement

820.70 Production and process controls.
(a) General. *Each manufacturer shall develop, conduct, control, and monitor production processes to ensure that a device conforms to its specifications. Where deviations from device specifications could occur as a result of the manufacturing process, the manufacturer shall establish and maintain process control procedures that describe any process controls necessary to ensure conformance to specifications. Where process controls are needed they shall include:*
(1) Documented instructions, standard operating procedures (SOP's), and methods that define and control the manner of production;
(2) Monitoring and control of process parameters and component and device characteristics during production;
(3) Compliance with specified reference standards or codes;
(4) The approval of processes and process equipment; and
(5) Criteria for workmanship which shall be expressed in documented standards or by means of identified and approved representative samples.

Discussion of the Requirement

The objective of this GMP requirement is to ensure that each manufacturer produces medical devices that conform to specifications defined and approved during the design phase. Each manufacturer is responsible for evaluating manufacturing processes to determine whether the lack of process controls could affect the reliability and repeatability of the manufacturing process. If it is determined that process controls are required, these controls must be established, implemented, monitored, and verified to the degree necessary to prevent product nonconformance. The generation of procedures is necessary to ensure consistency in manufacture. Process controls include standards, production methods and instructions, procedures, workmanship criteria, drawings, process validation, inspection, testing, and evaluation.

The controlled process must be monitored to ensure that it remains in control. Documented evidence of the monitoring of process parameters and device and component characteristics is expected. The documentation should identify the equipment used, the operating conditions, and the personnel who perform activities. When the process is observed to be out of control, appropriate action is expected to be taken to evaluate the product and the continuation of the process.

If it is determined that a process does not have an effect on product quality and thus does not require process controls, there must be a documented rationale with an approval date and the signature of the responsible authority.

The Quality System Inspection Technique (QSIT) includes Production and Process Controls as one of the four major subsystems addressed during a baseline facility inspection. QSIT Production and Process Control objectives include consideration of processes and production activities, process validation, equipment controls, and qualification of personnel. In addition, as part of a Production and Process Control subsystem inspection the QSIT includes additional objectives for adequate control of sterilization processes (if applicable to the manufacturer's products). Chapter 1, "FDA's Organization and Regulatory Strategies," provides more details on the QSIT.

Industry Practice

Typically, manufacturers begin in the design phase to develop the manufacturing process on the basis of the product design, materials and components, and quality characteristics required. The development of the manufacturing process often involves assessment of the environment, the required utilities, the skill requirements for production personnel, and the compatibility of materials with equipment. Device complexity is a determining factor in process controls. Some processes are simple assembly operations; others may require soldering, grinding, or plating. Still other processes are even more complex, such as aseptic filling or sterilization. The characteristics of the device define the process and the required process controls.

Device manufacturers document procedures and process specifications, describing the manner of the device production. From the process specifications, process controls are implemented. Processes that require process controls include, but are not limited to, sterilizing, aseptic filling, cleaning, soldering, electroplating, mixing, injection molding, package sealing, water systems, heat treating, and heating, ventilation, and air conditioning (HVAC) systems.

Manufacturers may validate production processes, often through a series of qualifications, which can include equipment installation qualification, operational qualification, and performance qualification (see Chapters 15 and 27). On the basis of these activities, documented instructions (e.g., procedures, process specifications, routers, drawings) are developed for routine production controls. These documents commonly identify:
- process conditions, including accepted variances;
- types of equipment and instruments required;
- responsibilities for approving, operating, and monitoring the process;
- frequency of monitoring;
- instructions (e.g., steps, sequence, start-up requirements, and required checks);
- requirements for requalification;
- materials required;
- criteria for workmanship (e.g., drawings, master samples, test methods, and limits);
- process control indicators (e.g., dosimeter, biological indicators, metal detector standards, gauges, and dials);
- environmental conditions, when required; and
- documentation requirements.

To support the operation, programs for equipment preventive maintenance, for calibration, and for employee training and certification are also established.

820.70(b) Production and Process Changes

The Requirement

820.70(b) Production and process changes. Each manufacturer shall establish and maintain procedures for changes to a specification, method, process, or procedure. Such changes shall be verified or where appropriate validated according to § 820.75, before implementation and these activities shall be documented. Changes shall be approved in accordance with § 820.40.

Discussion of the Requirement

Each manufacturer is required to establish and maintain procedures for changes to any requirement with which a product, process, service, or other activity must comply. Changes must be subject to controls as stringent as those applied to the original specification, method, process, or procedure. Prior to approval and implementation, the change must be verified or, if determined necessary, validated in accordance with section 820.75, "Process validation."

Approved changes must be communicated to the appropriate personnel (e.g., line operators, supervisors, suppliers, sterilizer operators, purchasing personnel, or suppliers) in a timely manner to allow for implementation and, if necessary, training.

Industry Practice

It is common for manufacturers to develop one change control program that is used for all documents, design changes, and production changes (see Chapter 22). When a single program is used, changes are typically classified by type (e.g., specification, procedure, or process), because design, production, and process changes may require more detailed evaluation and approval—including verification or validation—than other routine document changes.

As part of the change control program, manufacturers typically include an assessment of the regulatory impact for each change. For some changes, a new 510(k) or Premarket Approval (PMA) supplement may be necessary.

820.70(c) Environmental Control

The Requirement

820.70(c) Environmental control. Where environmental conditions could reasonably be expected to have an adverse effect on product quality, the manufacturer shall establish and maintain procedures to adequately control these environmental conditions. Environmental control system(s) shall be periodically inspected to verify that the system, including necessary equipment, is adequate and functioning properly. These activities shall be documented and reviewed.

Discussion of the Requirement

The objective of this GMP requirement is to ensure that environmental conditions that could have an adverse effect on product quality are controlled. Each manufacturer is expected to evaluate the environment in which components, manufacturing materials, packaging, labeling, and in-process, finished, and returned devices are manufactured and held to determine what, if any, environmental controls are necessary. The degree of environmental control must be consistent with the intended use of the finished device.

Requirements for environmental controls must be defined and documented. In addition, written procedures are required to ensure control of conditions and periodic inspection of the control systems. This inspection must include any applicable equipment (e.g., pumps, filters, and measurement equipment).

Industry Practice

Manufacturers maintain environmental controls commensurate with the product being manufactured and the function of a given manufacturing or storage area. Conditions that are routinely considered for control include lighting, ventilation, temperature, humidity, air pressure, air flow, filtration, airborne contamination, microbial contamination, and electrostatic discharge (ESD).

Industry practices related to the control of the environment vary. Some manufacturers use comprehensive clean-room controls for the production of sterile and aseptic products. Others control ESD for the manufacture of products that contain electronics or that may be damaged by ESD. Many institute general control of particulates, humidity, and temperature.

The degree of control for particular environmental element may also vary within a given facility. For example, ESD controls can range from a combination of protective packaging, grounded wrist straps, and conductive work surfaces to the combined use of protective packaging, conductive holding fixtures, grounded wrist straps, floor mats, antistatic clothing, conductive work surfaces, ionized air blowers, and conductive chairs, floors, shoes, carriers, and storage shelves. The necessary controls and the effectiveness of ESD controls installed are determined as part of the validation of the process or activity. Consideration of ESD controls includes evaluation of manufacturing processes such as packaging, molding, and other activities that may generate damaging electrical charges.

Written procedures are typically developed to define the environmental conditions being controlled. These procedures may encompass the following items:
- elements to be controlled,
- areas affected,
- environmental specifications and action limits,
- types and locations of controls,
- methods and frequency of monitoring,
- frequency of inspection intervals,
- frequency of calibration intervals (if applicable),
- procedures for corrective action,

- documentation requirements, and
- training requirements (if applicable).

Examples of control system inspection activities include particle count tests, calibration of control instrumentation, and the review of strip charts for temperature and relative humidity measurements. The inspection and review of environmental control systems are usually part of the production quality assurance (QA) program.

820.70(d) Personnel

The Requirement

820.70(d) Personnel. Each manufacturer shall establish and maintain requirements for the health, cleanliness, personal practices, and clothing of personnel if contact between such personnel and product or environment could reasonably be expected to have an adverse effect on product quality. The manufacturer shall ensure that maintenance and other personnel who are required to work temporarily under special environmental conditions are appropriately trained or supervised by a trained individual.

Discussion of the Requirement

Manufacturers must define requirements and establish written procedures when unclean employees, inappropriately dressed employees, or employees with medical conditions could adversely affect the quality of the product. Manufacturers must determine and document the requirements for acceptable attire, hygiene, and personal practices applicable to the device being manufactured. Typical requirements for attire range from clean street clothes to use of smocks, coveralls, masks, gowns, head coverings, beard coverings, gloves, or safety apparel. Hygiene requirements are generally focused on hand washing practices and use of toilet facilities. Personal practices often relate to restrictions concerning storage of food and drink in work areas, eating, drinking, disposal of food-related refuse, and smoking.

Sterile devices and cleanroom or environmentally-controlled operations may necessitate a higher level of control in order to minimize the bioburden and particulate contamination. The goal is to minimize contamination of the device and the operations environment. Each manufacturer must evaluate the extent of cleanliness required on the basis of device cleaning procedures, aseptic operations, or terminal sterilization.

It is expected that all personnel working under special environmental conditions will be trained in the requirements for working in those areas, including requirements for hygiene, health, dress, cleanliness, and personal practices. Manufacturers are also required to define and document requirements for temporary personnel, such as maintenance, cleaning, and temporary employees. The requirements may include appropriate training of such personnel and direct supervision by a trained individual.

Industry Practice

Manufacturers typically establish and document in their Quality Systems some basic requirements for personnel with regard to dress codes and cleanliness, and they provide designated areas, separate from production and laboratory operations, for eating, drinking, and smoking. Applicable procedures commonly include:

- required attire,
- manufacturing areas affected,
- entry and exit gowning practices,
- handling of adverse medical conditions, and
- training requirements.

For the manufacture of *non-sterile* devices, clean everyday attire is usually adequate. In operations such as machine shops, clean everyday attire also may be adequate if the device will be cleaned and controlled in later stages of manufacture. Many manufacturers provide uniforms or lab coats to personnel for use on the premises, if such garments are deemed necessary. For electronic products ESD-controlling smocks or shoes may be necessary.

For *sterile* devices, aseptic operations, and some electronic devices, the requirements become more specific. The requirements are based on the effect to product quality, whether it is bioburden levels, particulate contamination, or sterility assurance. However, the requirements may vary depending on downstream processing.

Dress codes are commonly mandated for operations requiring a cleanroom or environmentally controlled room. Required attire typically includes head coverings, beard and mustache covers, gowns or coveralls, masks, and shoe coverings. In some areas, finger cots or gloves may also be necessary.

Procedures for the reporting of employee medical conditions (e.g., coughing, sneezing, lesions or sores, conjunctivitis) are important in these areas and for these products, because those conditions can affect product quality and the environment. Personnel report such conditions to a supervisor, who evaluates the potential effect on activities. Often, personnel are assigned different tasks until the condition improves.

Manufacturers provide specialized training to all personnel working under special environmental conditions. The level of training may differ for non-production personnel and for temporary employees. In the absence of training, direct supervision should be provided.

820.70(e) Contamination Control

The Requirement

> ***820.70(e) Contamination control.*** *Each manufacturer shall establish and maintain procedures to prevent contamination of equipment or product by substances that could reasonably be expected to have an adverse effect on product quality.*

Discussion of the Requirement

Each manufacturer must establish and maintain procedures to prevent contamination of equipment, components, manufacturing materials, in-process devices, finished devices, and returned devices by substances that could adversely affect device safety or effectiveness. There must be periodic, documented checks or inspections to verify that the contamination control system is properly functioning.

The system must include adequate cleaning procedures and schedules if such controls are necessary to meet manufacturing specifications. Sewage, trash, byproducts, chemical effluvium, and other refuse that could adversely affect a device's quality also must be adequately controlled.

Industry Practice

Manufacturers typically establish and document basic contamination control requirements within the Quality System. The following are common elements of a contamination control program:

a. Cleaning and sanitation procedures and schedules are typically necessary to meet manufacturing specifications, including periodic facility cleaning of work surfaces, floors, and shelving.

b. Personnel practice procedures should address personnel cleanliness, personnel dress codes, and designated areas for eating, drinking, and smoking (as per section 820.70(d)).

c. Procedures should be designed to prevent contamination of equipment, components, or finished devices by rodenticides, insecticides, fungicides, fumigants, other cleaning and sanitation substances, and hazardous substances.

d. Procedures may be necessary for handling sewage, byproducts, chemical effluents, and other refuse of the manufacturing process in a timely, safe, and sanitary manner.

VI

Manufacturers typically establish general cleaning and sanitation procedures and schedules for all areas (e.g., manufacturing and personnel support areas) to ensure a clean working environment for all employees. There are usually separate procedures and schedules for areas that require special environmental conditions. In these areas, dress codes and other special requirements are posted so that all personnel are notified of the restrictions.

Contamination control procedures for rodenticides, insecticides, fungicides, fumigants, hazardous substances, and the like are typically established for the entire facility. Outside service suppliers or contractors may be consulted as needed. When cleaning functions are performed by a service supplier, purchasing control activities include clear communication of those procedures.

Procedures for cleaning, sanitation, and other contamination control measures typically address:
- affected areas and locations;
- materials and chemicals to be used;
- special instructions or precautions;
- applicable contracts, when necessary;
- documentation requirements; and
- applicable schedules, when required.

820.70(f) Buildings

The Requirement

820.70(f) Buildings. Buildings shall be of suitable design and contain sufficient space to perform necessary operations, prevent mixups, and assure orderly handling.

Discussion of the Requirement

The manufacturer is responsible for evaluating the manufacturing facility to ensure that the building, utilities, and space allow for proper product and area identification and for the performance of necessary manufacturing and associated functions. The manufacturer is responsible for providing adequate space to prevent mixups and to ensure orderly handling of:

- incoming components;
- rejected or obsolete products;
- in-process products;
- finished devices;
- labeling;
- products that have been reprocessed, repaired, or reworked;
- equipment, drawings, blueprints, tools, molds, patterns, and records;
- testing and laboratory operations; and
- quarantined products.

Industry Practice

Manufacturers ordinarily document a floor plan that establishes the flow of product and designates:

- receiving areas;
- areas for acceptable and rejected products;
- manufacturing areas;
- storage areas for components and finished goods;
- rework, reprocessing, and repair areas;
- office space; and
- non-manufacturing areas (e.g., cafeterias and restrooms).

This approach enables them to plan growth, locate personnel support functions close to appropriate areas, and eliminate excessive handling of product (including finished goods) during the manufacturing process. It also helps in designing the product flow such that mixups are less likely to occur.

820.70(g) Equipment

The Requirement

820.70(g) Equipment. Each manufacturer shall ensure that all equipment used in the manufacturing process meets specified requirements and is appropriately designed, constructed, placed, and installed to facilitate maintenance, adjustment, cleaning, and use.

(1) Maintenance schedule. Each manufacturer shall establish and maintain schedules for the adjustment, cleaning, and other maintenance of equipment to ensure that manufacturing specifications are met. Maintenance activities, including the date and individual(s) performing the maintenance activities, shall be documented.

(2) Inspection. Each manufacturer shall conduct periodic inspections in accordance with established procedures to ensure adherence to applicable equipment maintenance schedules. The inspections, including the date and individual(s) conducting the inspections, shall be documented.

(3) Adjustment. Each manufacturer shall ensure that any inherent limitations or allowable tolerances are visibly posted on or near equipment requiring periodic adjustments or are readily available to personnel performing these adjustments.

Discussion of the Requirement

Section 820.70(g) requires manufacturers to ensure that all equipment (e.g., fabrication, molding, extrusion, assembly, packaging, and sterilization equipment) is appropriately designed and installed to facilitate maintenance, adjustment, cleaning, and use. Equipment must also meet requirements that ensure its proper functioning in the manufacture of the device.

A maintenance schedule must be developed if a manufacturer determines that maintenance is required on a particular piece of equipment. The schedule must be available to designated individuals who operate and maintain the equipment.

When maintenance activity is required, the manufacturer must document and follow procedures for maintenance activities. The objective of the inspection is to ensure that such activities are conducted according to schedule, that all activities have been completed, and that equipment specification requirements continue to be met. Records must be maintained for each piece of equipment, documenting maintenance activities performed and including the signature of the person who performed the activities. This requirement applies to maintenance performed by both internal and external resources (i.e., service suppliers).

Records must be maintained of maintenance activity inspections, including the date of the inspection and the name of the person who conducted the inspection. Inspection findings must be reviewed by management and corrective or preventive action must be taken, as appropriate.

If adjustments are required to maintain equipment operation, the limits and tolerances must be documented and made available to those individuals responsible for making the adjustments (that is, operators and maintenance personnel). This information can be provided as an approved document posted on the equipment or located nearby in the work area.

Industry Practice

Manufacturers typically prepare equipment specifications on the basis of needs identified during the design phase. When required, installation qualification protocols are developed and documented for each piece of equipment to ensure that it meets specification and functions in the intended manner. The qualification activities include verification of all parts, functions, codes, and utilities; establishment of cleaning, maintenance, and (when required) calibration methods; confirmation of adequate placement and installation; and operational performance testing.

Manufacturers develop maintenance procedures and schedules to maintain equipment operation and reduce the risk of major repair and service. The initial maintenance activities are often based on information provided in equipment operating or maintenance manuals. Typically, a schedule identifies each piece of equipment, the maintenance activity required, the maintenance methods to be used, and the frequency of maintenance. This information is often documented in a master schedule or card file system, with supporting maintenance forms that provide instructions and also serve as records of activities. Many manufacturers use off-the-shelf software programs to document and manage the equipment maintenance program. These software programs often provide formats for master schedules, work orders, records, and reports.

Records of maintenance activities commonly include the dates of service, the service performed, and the signature of the individual who performed the activity. In most cases, maintenance records are reviewed for completeness and conformance by a supervisor and are signed and dated by that person. When maintenance activity is performed by service suppliers, the manufacturer most often maintains the schedule and identifies the activities to be performed. The service supplier then provides a record of service, which is reviewed and approved by the manufacturer's designated employee.

Operators may be allowed to make some adjustments as part of normal production operations. The allowable adjustments are defined in process specifications or procedures, which are maintained in the work area in the form of an approved chart posted on equipment, as part of the device master record (DMR), or as a procedure available to the operator.

820.70(h) Manufacturing Material

The Requirement

> *820.70(h) Manufacturing material. Where a manufacturing material could reasonably be expected to have an adverse effect on product quality, the manufacturer shall establish and maintain procedures for the use and removal of such manufacturing material to ensure that it is removed or limited to an amount that does not adversely affect the device's quality. The removal or reduction of such manufacturing material shall be documented.*

Discussion of the Requirement

Section 820.3(p) defines "manufacturing material" as "any material or substance used in or used to facilitate the manufacturing process, a concomitant constituent, or a byproduct constituent produced during the manufacturing process, which is present in or on the finished device as a residue or impurity not by design or intent of the manufacturer." Examples of such substances are cleaning agents, mold-release agents, lubricating oils, latex proteins, sterilant residues, and other materials or substances that naturally occur as part of the manufacturing process.

The manufacturer is responsible for evaluating manufacturing materials used during the manufacturing process and for determining the effect of such materials on a device's fitness for use. This requirement applies only when the manufacturing material could potentially have an adverse effect on product.

Under the requirements of section 820.70(h), manufacturers are expected to establish procedures for the use and removal of any manufacturing material and to document the removal or reduction of the material. In documenting the removal process, manufacturers are not required to state how much (i.e., what percentage) of the removal occurred by natural means (e.g., evaporation of isopropyl alcohol) or how much was removed by a subsequent removal operation. Depending on the manufacturing material and the device, the degree of control required may vary.

The requirement also applies to processing, reprocessing, repair, and rework. All product supplied by third parties must also be evaluated for any manufacturing materials used and must meet the appropriate specification requirements.

Industry Practice

During the development phase of a project, manufacturers customarily identify the manufacturing materials to be used and evaluate the potential adverse effects of the manufacturing materials on product quality. When required, manufacturers document how such a material will be used and how the removal or reduction will be performed. The removal or reduction process is commonly documented as part of the DHR.

For product supplied by third parties, allowable manufacturing materials should be documented in the specification requirements, and the supplier is responsible for documenting the use and removal or reduction of such materials as part of the DHR.

For some manufacturing materials, industry standards can provide the procedure for ensuring adequate reduction. For example, ISO 11135 provides guidelines for reducing ethylene oxide (EtO) residuals to acceptable, safe levels after sterilization.

820.70(i) Automated Processes

The Requirement

> ***820.70(i) Automated processes.*** *When computers or automated data processing systems are used as part of production or the quality system, the manufacturer shall validate computer software for its intended use according to an established protocol. All software changes shall be validated before approval and issuance. These validation activities and results shall be documented.*

Discussion of the Requirement

The intent of the Quality System regulation is to ensure that all software used in production or in the Quality System, whether for design, manufacture, distribution, or traceability, is validated for its intended use. Procedures must be established to ensure that validation is properly performed. These procedures must define how the manufacturer will validate software to ensure that the software will consistently perform as intended in its chosen application and that its use will not result in undetected errors. Such validation activity must also address computer hardware.

The manufacturer has primary responsibility for ensuring that the software is adequate. Validation requirements apply to software developed in-house by the manufacturer, specific software developed by a third party for the manufacturer, and off-the-shelf software. When a manufacturer purchases off-the-shelf software, the manufacturer must ensure that it will perform as intended in its chosen application. When source code and design specifications cannot be obtained, "black box" testing should be performed to confirm that the software meets the user's needs and is suitable for its intended uses.

Manufacturers must evaluate all automated processes, to determine the effect of those processes on product safety, performance, and reliability. From this evaluation, they determine the extent of validation required. Software programs that control critical areas will require more extensive validation activity and documentation than those that are of lesser risk. Furthermore, software whose output is subject to subsequent inspection or review will also require less rigor.

The Food and Drug Administration's (FDA's) QSIT advises investigators who are evaluating the Production and Process Control subsystem "If the process chosen is automated with software, review the software requirements document, the software validation protocol, software validation activities, software change controls and software validation results to confirm that the software will meet user needs and its intended use .... For software developed elsewhere, confirm that appropriate software and quality requirements were established and provided to the vendor and that purchasing data (and validation results) support that the requirements were met."

Although FDA does not specifically define how software validation is to be performed, several documents issued by FDA can be used for guidance in establishing a validation program, including *General Principles of Software Validation — Final Guidance for Industry and FDA Staff,* published in January 2002. This and related FDA software guidance documents are discussed in further detail in Chapter 29, "New Directions in Software Validation."

Software and software changes must be formally reviewed and approved before implementation. Changes must be assessed to determine their effect on product quality, including their effect on other software modules in the system. A documented system is expected to be followed to control the use of software (application, versions, changes, manuals) and to ensure its validation. Records must be maintained to demonstrate adequate software validation, including validation of software changes.

Industry Practice

The use of computers and automated data processing systems for production and Quality Systems is commonplace in the medical device industry. Examples of process software include the following:

a. Test software is used in the testing of subassemblies, such as circuit boards and electronic components, or in final acceptance testing of finished devices.

b. Software is used to implement and support Quality System procedures, such as evaluation of materials or product by test and inspection equipment, calibration, control of DMRs, complaint handling, design, and trend analysis.

c. Software is used to manage data, where information on a manufacturing process or Quality System activity is collected and analyzed without operator intervention to control the activity or verify the results, and where action is taken on such results.

d. Manufacturing software is used to control various manufacturing processes and equipment, such as wave solder machines, robotics, computerized numerical control (CNC) machines, environmental chambers, sterilization equipment, and sequential assembly processes.

Manufacturers typically establish a policy for the development and validation of process software. The policy will identify the development process, including the determination of specification requirements; an outline of the validation process, including test protocols and approval; definition of change control requirements; and identification of required documentation. Software validation procedures also commonly address the manufacturer's validation approach for in-house, third-party, and off-the-shelf software, if applicable.

Additional guidance on software validation principles and current industry practice can be found in Chapter 29.

Software Validation Approaches

Manufacturers validate process software in several different ways:

a. The software is validated independently of the process that it controls. This approach is typically used for software that resides in a personal computer and controls a piece of equipment through an electronic interface. This approach is also used for Quality System software that resides on a personal computer, a computer accessed via a network, or a mainframe computer.

b. The software is validated as part of the process that it controls. This method of validation applies when a piece of computer-controlled manufacturing or test equipment is purchased. The computer is built into the equipment and allows the user to select various options from a menu, enter a variety of parameters, print reports, and control the process by means of limited data entry. Examples are automated test equipment (ATE), ionization detection equipment, and circuit board test fixtures.

c. In some cases, a piece of computer-controlled manufacturing or test equipment contains software that is not obvious or accessible to the user (e.g., computer-controlled environmental chambers for which the user can only set time and temperature within preset limits). In this case, the software itself cannot be validated by the user. When the process is validated through operational qualification and performance qualification, the internal software is also validated by default. As a result, this software is validated during process validation.

Required Documentation

Validation is documented in a protocol that includes at least the software and hardware requirements definition, formal test plans, and acceptance criteria. Validating process software is based on first establishing the requirements for the software, which could include a processing sequence, a description of an existing manual operation, or a database structure with accompanying data manipulations.

Manufacturers document software validation test plans and procedures to ensure that all requirements have been correctly implemented. Specific test cases typically include normal as well as abnormal operation and show that known "bad" parts are identified as failures and that known "good" parts pass. Parameter limits are validated to show that values within and at the limits are found to be acceptable and that values outside the limits are found to be unacceptable. It is routine for each test case to include the expected results. In the case of Quality System software, many programs use off-the-shelf spreadsheet or database systems. Manufacturers do not commonly validate these off-the-shelf systems as a whole, but they do validate the specific application programs that use these systems.

The results of validation testing must be documented. It is common to express the test results as actual results versus expected results, which are the basis for assessing the pass/fail criteria.

Computerized Numerical Control Programs

Computerized numerical control (CNC) programs fall in the category of software that may be validated as part of the process that it controls. However, such programs require special consideration because of the types of processes that they control. The requirements for a CNC program are typically described in the form of a mechanical drawing; the output is usually a machined part. The CNC program can be validated by machining a number of parts and measuring all dimensions according to the drawing used to develop the program. Each dimension (e.g., hole size or cut angle) should be within the limits of tolerance specified on the drawing.

In many cases, the CNC program is downloaded across a network to the specified CNC machine; alternatively, it can be loaded directly into the machine from a disk. Such programs should be validated when first developed and whenever they are changed. However, CNC machine tools tend to wear out and may require periodic adjustment. These adjustments do not normally require revalidation, but samples from each newly machined lot are commonly measured as a normal QA activity.

In all cases, the validation is documented, including identification of the program and program version, the date of validation, the number of parts measured, and the actual measurements for each dimension.

Purchased Software

Process software is often purchased in one of the following forms: off-the-shelf; modified off-the-shelf (configured by the manufacturer); or custom software developed by a third party for the manufacturer.

For off-the-shelf software, the requirements are established on the basis of the intended use of the software as it relates to the specific application. The requirements established by the manufacturer (user) are not necessarily based on the user's manual that comes with the software. If purchased software is modified by the manufacturer, the validation specifically addresses the modifications as well as the effects of the modifications on the rest of the system.

For custom-developed software, it is typical for a manufacturer to request that the software be developed according to GMP and other FDA requirements. It is best if the manufacturer's personnel who use the system develop the requirements for the software and determine the criteria for acceptance. Ultimately, the manufacturer is responsible for ensuring that custom software meets the user's requirements.

Revalidation

When a manufacturer modifies a process software program for any reason (e.g., to enhance its capabilities or to fix problems), the software change is revalidated before implementation. The nature of the change is documented, and the validation specifically addresses the change as well as the effect of the change on the system. Documentation of the change and the revalidation is maintained and controlled as part of the DMR.

CHAPTER 14. INSPECTION, MEASURING AND TEST EQUIPMENT (SUBPART G)

820.72 Inspection, Measuring, and Test Equipment

The Requirement

820.72 Inspection, measuring, and test equipment.
(a) Control of inspection, measuring, and test equipment. Each manufacturer shall ensure that all inspection, measuring, and test equipment, including mechanical, automated, or electronic inspection and test equipment, is suitable for its intended purposes and is capable of producing valid results. Each manufacturer shall establish and maintain procedures to ensure that equipment is routinely calibrated, inspected, checked, and maintained. The procedures shall include provisions for handling, preservation, and storage of equipment, so that its accuracy and fitness for use are maintained. These activities shall be documented.
(b) Calibration. Calibration procedures shall include specific directions and limits for accuracy and precision. When accuracy and precision limits are not met, there shall be provisions for remedial action to reestablish the limits and to evaluate whether there was any adverse effect on the device's quality. These activities shall be documented.
    (1) Calibration standards. Calibration standards used for inspection, measuring, and test equipment shall be traceable to national or international standards. If national or international standards are not practical or available, the manufacturer shall use an independent reproducible standard. If no applicable standard exists, the manufacturer shall establish and maintain an in-house standard.
    (2) Calibration records. The equipment identification, calibration dates, the individual performing each calibration, and the next calibration date shall be documented. These records shall be displayed on or near each piece of equipment or shall be readily available to the personnel using such equipment and to the individuals responsible for calibrating the equipment.

Discussion of the Requirement

To provide confidence in decisions or actions based on measurement data, manufacturers must maintain proper calibration, storage, and handling controls for all measuring and test systems used in the development, production, installation, and servicing of product. Calibration should be performed at least over the range of use of the particular instrument so that the accuracy of the "usable" portion of the instrument is known. All measuring and test equipment must be calibrated and maintained according to written procedures.

Calibration procedures must include accuracy and precision limits and must specify the ranges over which the calibrations should be performed. Calibration procedures must specify the remedial action process to be followed if a piece of measurement equipment is found to be out of calibration. Remedial action involves not only an evaluation of the measures required to recalibrate (or, if necessary, replace) the equipment, but also an evaluation of the effects of the out-of-calibration equipment on the quality of any materials, parts, components, packaging, or finished devices produced since the last successful calibration.

Standards used for calibration should be traceable to National Institute of Standards and Technology (NIST) standards or similar recognized international standards. The standards used must be generally accepted as the prevailing standards. If such standards do not exist, the manufacturer should use an independent, reproducible standard or create and maintain an appropriate, reproducible, in-house standard.

Calibration records must include the actual calibration results, the date of calibration, the signature or other identification of the person who performed the calibration, and the next calibration date. The equipment must also be clearly identified in the calibration records. If the records are not displayed on or near the equipment, they must be readily available to personnel who use the equipment so that the calibration status is readily known and out-of-calibration equipment is not used.

The necessary accuracy, precision, and resolution required of the measuring and test equipment must be considered and will depend on the degree of accuracy required of the measurements for which the equipment is being used. Calibration procedures also must account for any environmental controls that may be necessary to properly perform the calibrations. The procedures also should indicate how the equipment should be handled and stored after use, to ensure that the equipment is properly maintained and protected from adjustments that could invalidate the calibration. Provisions must be in place to ensure that improperly calibrated equipment is not used.

Industry Practice

Manufacturers commonly develop an overall calibration procedure to describe a general calibration policy for measurement equipment. Examples of measurement equipment include: gauges, sensors, meters (e.g., voltmeters and pH meters), timers, thermocouples, and software/firmware erasure instruments. Typically, separate procedures are used to perform the actual calibration of each piece of equipment.

Most manufacturers consider the necessary accuracy, precision, and resolution required for the measuring and test equipment during the establishment of their manufacturing and test procedures. Otherwise, the manufacturer may discover at a later date that the equipment is not suitable (i.e., not accurate or precise enough to provide reliable measurement or test results).

The initial frequency with which measurement and test equipment is calibrated usually is based on the equipment supplier's recommendations. As a manufacturer gains experience with a particular piece of equipment, the manufacturer may find it necessary to change this frequency.

"Accuracy" is basically defined as conformance to a traceable standard, and "precision" is the repeatability of or closeness between measurement results obtained during calibration. Generally, measuring equipment is at least 4 times and preferably 10 times more accurate than specified tolerances. Traceable standards are typically at least 4 times and preferably 10 times more accurate than the particular measuring or test equipment being calibrated. Various national and international standards discuss the quantification of calibration errors, determination of the degree of uncertainty of a calibration system to ensure the accuracy of traceable standards, and qualifications of calibration service suppliers.

VI

Performing Calibration

Companies generally assign calibration responsibilities to one individual or department. Maintenance of the calibration program, including procedures, documentation, and physical care of the equipment, is coordinated or directly handled by that individual or department. Calibration functions include indicating the calibration status of each piece of measurement equipment, so that if a processing operation requires the use of a calibrated piece of measurement equipment, its status can readily be determined before use. For this purpose, a calibration sticker can be applied to the equipment, indicating the calibration date, the calibrator, and the due date for the next calibration. Alternatively, the calibration records can be maintained near the point of use or in an easily accessible location.

Many manufacturers use outside calibration laboratories. Unfortunately, outside calibration laboratories do not always document all calibration results, nor do many of them understand or have knowledge of the GMP calibration requirements for medical devices. To remedy this situation, many manufacturers are performing audits of calibration laboratories when on-site calibrations cannot be performed or requiring calibration suppliers to maintain certifications of their laboratories. Because proper evaluation of calibration laboratories is required under section 820.50, it is in the manufacturer's interest to ensure that the procedures of outside calibration laboratories comply with GMP requirements and any other established quality criteria. Note that the calibration records requirements apply whether calibration is performed by the manufacturer's personnel or by a qualified supplier.

Some manufacturers have calibration laboratories perform calibration on-site, to the extent possible, so that the calibration laboratory's procedures can be audited during the calibration process. Some calibration laboratories provide copies of their calibration procedures so that the manufacturer can review them and can ensure compliance with GMP requirements.

Calibration Records

Typically, calibration records include the actual calibration results (i.e., the readings before and after calibration) so that appropriate remedial action can be taken if required. If calibration results indicate only "in calibration" or "out of calibration and adjustments were made," there will be insufficient information to perform an adequate investigation and determine the appropriate remedial action. In addition, calibration records commonly include or reference other information, such as the date of calibration, the identification of the person who performed the calibration, and the standards used, so that appropriate remedial action can be taken if required.

Remedial Action

Manufacturers commonly define within the general calibration procedure the action to be taken when a calibration operation results in an out-of-tolerance determination. Manufacturers that evaluate the effects of out-of-calibration results frequently document this evaluation on the calibration records themselves. Manufacturers typically perform root cause investigations to determine why out-of-calibration results are occurring and to prevent them from recurring; this analysis is an important and necessary part of the quality assurance program.

If corrective action is necessary, it is important to determine the cause of the out-of-calibration problem so that it can be prevented in the future. For example, should the frequency of calibration be increased? Should daily or weekly instrument checks be instituted? Is adequate equipment storage available? The results of this analysis may make it necessary to rework, scrap, or retest finished devices or to perform corrective action on them in the field.

Some manufacturers actually plot quantitative calibration results, using percentage error over time, to determine any trends in calibration results. This information is used to adjust calibration frequencies accordingly.

Many manufacturers use "checks" or verifications between normal calibrations to detect any equipment drift before an out-of-calibration condition occurs. For example, standards of known accuracy are used to perform daily checks of certain types of equipment (e.g., scales). These daily checks are recorded on a log sheet. This is good preventive action, because the amount of necessary remedial action in the event of a problem is proportional to the amount of time between calibrations. In other words, the sooner a problem is detected, the easier it is to isolate the materials or products affected and take corrective action.

Regardless of whether calibrations are performed in-house or by calibration laboratories, manufacturers may go to great lengths to prevent equipment from going out-of-tolerance. In addition to the possibility of an out-of-tolerance piece of measurement equipment resulting from improper handling and storage, manufacturers should consider the cost of recalibrating that piece of equipment. For example, a manufacturer may determine that it is necessary to use an appropriate soft cloth to remove hand oils from pin gauges or to use a storage box with a soft cloth lining to protect gauges from scratches. These practices may be described in the calibration procedures themselves or in a separate procedure describing the care of the equipment during handling and storage.

VI

CHAPTER 15. PROCESS VALIDATION (SUBPART G)

820.75 Process Validation

The Requirement

820.75 Process validation.

(a) *Where the results of a process cannot be fully verified by subsequent inspection and test, the process shall be validated with a high degree of assurance and approved according to established procedures. The validation activities and results, including the date and signature of the individual(s) approving the validation and where appropriate the major equipment validated, shall be documented.*

(b) *Each manufacturer shall establish and maintain procedures for monitoring and control of process parameters for validated processes to ensure that the specified requirements continue to be met.*

> **(1)** *Each manufacturer shall ensure that validated processes are performed by qualified individual(s).*
>
> **(2)** *For validated processes, the monitoring and control methods and data, the date performed, and, where appropriate, the individual(s) performing the process or the major equipment used shall be documented.*

(c) *When changes or process deviations occur, the manufacturer shall review and evaluate the process and perform revalidation where appropriate. These activities shall be documented.*

Discussion of the Requirement

It is the intent of the Quality System regulation to define the essential elements necessary to ensure that a medical device will consistently meet its predetermined specifications. Section 820.3(z) defines "validation" as a "confirmation by examination and provision of objective evidence that the particular requirements for a specific intended use can be consistently fulfilled." *"Process validation"* is defined in section 820.3(z) (1) as "establishing by objective evidence that a process consistently produces a result or product meeting its predetermined specifications."

The Preamble to the Final Rule of the Quality System regulation (see comment 41) states that one of the principles on which the Quality System regulation is based is that all processes require some degree of qualification, verification, or validation. It further states that manufacturers should not rely solely on inspection and testing to ensure that processes are adequate for their intended uses.

Manufacturers are expected to evaluate the processes used to manufacture their devices and determine which "cannot be fully verified by subsequent inspection and test." These processes are subject to the requirements of section 820.75. When a determination not to validate has been made, the rationale supporting the manufacturer's decision should be documented.

Although section 820.75(a) applies to initial validation of a process, section 820.75(b) applies to the performance of a process after validation. Documentation methods for monitoring and control are required for validated processes. It is expected that manufacturers will assign the performance of validated processes to personnel qualified for those particular activities. The type and frequency of monitoring and control must be determined by the manufacturer on the basis of the process itself and should be evaluated periodically to ensure that specified requirements are still met, especially during revalidation of the process. In addition, production records for validated processes should identify, when appropriate, the process equipment and the individual performing the process.

FDA's QSIT states, "All processes that may cause a deviation to a device's specification and all validated processes must be monitored and controlled in accordance with established procedures. Just because a process is validated, does not mean verification activities utilized to monitor and control the process are unnecessary." Thus, by evaluating a process that should be validated during an inspection, FDA investigators can assess both the process validation program and the process monitoring and control activities.

Rework methods must also be reviewed to determine the need for validation. Rework may adversely affect the safety and effectiveness of the product, and this possibility must be eliminated before a particular method is used. A manufacturer must decide on the need for validation on the basis of knowledge of the product, the process, and the interaction between product and process.

FDA's QSIT includes Production and Process Controls as one of the four major subsystems addressed during a baseline facility inspection. As part of inspection of a Production and Process Control subsystem, the QSIT includes additional objectives for adequate control of sterilization processes (if applicable to the manufacturer's products). Chapter 1, "FDA's Organization and Regulatory Strategies," provides more details on the QSIT.

VI

Chapter 27, "Process Validation in a Global Marketplace," provides information on CDRH's participation in the development by the Global Harmonization Task Force (GHTF) of guidance on process validation and the content of recent guidance. This chapter discusses the regulatory requirements for validation and determining which processes to validate; Chapter 27 addresses an approach for implementing a validation program.

Industry Practice: Process Validation Programs

Device manufacturers commonly use two types of validation: retrospective and prospective. "Retrospective validation," as defined in FDA's *Guideline on General Principles of Process Validation*[9], is "validation of a process for a product already in distribution based upon accumulated production, testing and control data." "Prospective validation" is defined as "validation conducted prior to the distribution of either a new product, or product made under a revised manufacturing process, where the revisions may affect the product's characteristics."

Prospective validation is usually applied when a product or process is initially released to manufacturing or when there is a major change to the product or process. This type of validation requires use of a pre-approved protocol, with: clearly stated acceptance criteria; statistically valid production runs and sample sizes; and clear documentation. The documentation must show data that demonstrate adequate process control and

---

[9] CDRH has implemented the GHTF's 2004 process validation guidance in lieu of FDA's 1987 guidance. See Appendix A (Bibliography) for reference to these documents.

repeatability. Again, the emphasis is on evidence—with a high degree of assurance—of process reproducibility.

In retrospective validation, the expectation is that the adequacy of the process will be demonstrated by examining accumulated historical test data on the product and records of the manufacturing procedures used. Retrospective validation is not always acceptable, because the data collected do not lend themselves to analysis with statistical confidence. The accumulated data need to be more than pass/fail results demonstrating lot-to-lot conformance to specifications. This type of validation requires measurement data and the maintenance of records that describe the operating characteristics of the process, such as time, temperature, humidity, and equipment settings.

The Preamble gives only a few examples of processes that should be validated: sterilization, aseptic processing, injection molding, and welding. However, FDA has presented information on process validation at numerous industry conferences. The following list, which is not intended to be all inclusive, identifies processes that traditionally have been considered by FDA to require validation:

Test methods	Plastic bonding	Formulations
Welding	Calibration	Software-controlled processes
Air systems	Wave/hand soldering	Water systems
Injection molding	Utilities	Extrusion
Sanitization	Dipping	Cleaning
Mixing	Aseptic processing	Lyophilization
Sterilization	Sealing	Filling
Unique filtration		

Further discussion of processes that should be validated is included in the GHTF process validation guidance, which is discussed in Chapter 27.

Manufacturers use various types of systems to validate processes and to ensure the proper monitoring and control of those processes. An effective program adequately addresses the assignment of responsibilities. Regardless of the size of the manufacturer, it is common for validation activities to be supported by various groups with different specialties, such as engineering design, product operations, and quality assurance. This diversity helps increase the probability that all relevant information about a particular product and process will be made available.

The medical device industry encompasses a wide range of technologies and applications, ranging from simple hand tools to complex computer-controlled surgical machines, from implantable screws to artificial organs, from blood-glucose test strips to diagnostic imaging systems and laboratory test equipment. These devices are manufactured by companies of varying size, structure, volume of production, and number of manufacturing steps per unit (e.g., soldering or welding steps)—factors that significantly influence how process validation is actually implemented.

The GHTF guidance describes the validation process as a mechanism or system used by the manufacturer to plan validation activities, obtain data, record data, and interpret data. These activities may be considered to fall into three phases:

- an initial qualification of the equipment used and provision of necessary services—also known as "installation qualification" (IQ),
- a demonstration that the process will produce acceptable results and establishment of the limits (worst case) of the process parameters—also known as "operational qualification" (OQ), and
- establishment of long-term process stability—also known as performance qualification (PQ).

This approach is discussed more fully in Chapter 27.

Revalidation

In the third paragraph of section 820.75(c), the Quality System regulation requires that when changes or process deviations occur, the manufacturer shall review and evaluate the process and perform revalidation when appropriate. For example, product batch sizes increase or decrease, depending on facility capacity, resource availability, or market demands. Changes also occur in manufacturing equipment, equipment operating parameters, process location, component suppliers, methods of formulation, formulas, analytical techniques, packaging, or other processes that could affect product effectiveness or product characteristics.

It is common for revalidation concerns to be addressed in Quality System procedures or the original validation protocol. This system is often integrated with the change control system. When a change is proposed, it is evaluated according to the revalidation procedures. The extent of revalidation will depend on the nature of the change and how it affects the process or the product. In addition, some industry standards (e.g., sterilization process control standards, such as ISO 11135) stipulate a periodic revalidation interval to be followed, whether changes have been instituted or not.

Documentation

Protocols, procedures, reports, and the data collected commonly make up the documentation that supports a validation study. A process required to be validated typically is not released for use in routine manufacturing without an approved, documented validation study.

Test data are considered useful only if the methods and results are specific enough to substantiate conclusions. It is insufficient for a manufacturer to assess the process solely on the basis of lot-by-lot conformance to specifications if test results are merely expressed in terms of pass/fail or attribute data. Quantitative, measurable data can be statistically analyzed, and the variance in data can be determined. Operating parameters and equipment settings are typically recorded during the validation and made part of the process controls applied to routine manufacturing.

Qualification of Staff Who Operate Validated Processes

Manufacturers often provide a higher degree of training to operators of validated processes, in order to comply with section 820.70(b)(1). Rather than simply training operators on the established standard operating procedures and instructions, validated process training often includes an "operator observation" or a "skills test" element in the training program.

VI

After successfully completing the procedure training and having been observed to operate the process correctly, these operators are considered formally "qualified." Under this type of training scheme, a periodic requalification is typically performed for each operator to ensure that the process is monitored effectively and controlled in accordance with the criteria established during the validation effort.

When processes are revalidated, because of product changes, process changes, or periodic revalidation requirements, qualified operators are often re-qualified in conjunction with the revalidation effort.

Industry Practice: Typical Validation Approaches

The examples described in the following paragraphs highlight various processes and typical approaches used for validation throughout the medical device industry.

Test Methods. The purpose of test method validation is to provide evidence that the method is appropriate for the specification being assessed, that the method is specific and sensitive enough to discriminate a borderline acceptable product from an unacceptable product, and that the test method is accurate, precise, and reliable over repeated applications.

Facility Design. Among the considerations are the following:

    a. Space to operate the process properly. Adequate space is needed to prevent damage to materials, to clean and maintain equipment properly, and to move materials and product in a manner that will prevent damage and mixups. Parameters to be addressed include the dimensions of the facility and the layout of the equipment, furniture, personnel, materials, power sources, and support systems.

    b. Construction and other materials. Materials used in facility construction are chosen to prevent environmental and product contamination and to be easily cleaned. Requirements include ceiling material that is non-shedding and nontoxic; wall and floor materials or finishes that are easily cleaned, non-shedding, and nontoxic; personnel dress materials that are non-shedding, do not support microbial growth, and can easily be cleaned or sterilized or are disposable; and work surfaces that are easily cleaned or sanitized, nonporous, and non-shedding.

    c. Support systems. Support systems such as air conditioning; heating; air filtration (e.g., high-efficiency particulate air, or HEPA, filters); water (sterile, non-pyrogenic, distilled, treated by reverse osmosis); compressed air; compressed gases; and liquid gases may be needed to create the environment required to meet product and process specifications. Relevant parameters include the number of air changes per time period, amount and speed of air flow, temperature, relative humidity, efficiency of cooling, microbial levels in water, number of particulates in air and water, inorganic and organic contaminant levels, and characteristics of pre-filters.

    d. Type of manufacturing area. This specification is determined by the requirements of the product. The required environment might, for example, be a non-controlled white room or a classified clean room.

    e. Need for monitoring. Facility monitoring may be necessary to ensure that the specifications approved for the facility design are reliable over time and to provide feedback for preventive maintenance. Among the considerations are preventive maintenance procedures for each system, frequency of monitoring, type of monitoring, calibration of monitoring equipment, and trend analysis of data collected.

Air Systems. Validation of air systems usually includes a review of the system requirements, the installation, and the maintenance history. Some elements to be examined include the chiller equipment for the air conditioning systems. Typical parameters examined are power, capacity, capability, and controls included in the chillers for proper performance and maintenance of the cooling parameters. Other elements of air systems include volume of air, recirculation of air, air exhaust, air quality, compressor requirements, and controls for proper performance and maintenance.

Water Systems. If the water can contaminate or create an environment for contaminating the product, the installation of the water system is typically evaluated, as are any elements of its installation that could contribute to contamination.

A common water treatment system is reverse osmosis. Characteristics of reverse osmosis systems that are commonly evaluated include the source of the water, the capacity of the system to produce and maintain a stated volume, the parts of the system that treat the water, the delivery path controls, and the method of water distribution. The materials of which the water treatment and delivery system are composed also are evaluated to ensure that they meet specifications and that the water will be processed correctly.

Utilities. Validation of power utilities usually involves evaluation of the power fluctuations and power reductions at the source into the manufacturing facility and as it is distributed throughout the facility. Measurements are taken and evaluated with respect to the needs of the processes and support systems within each manufacturing facility and, if applicable, within multiple buildings. Consideration is given to the reliability of the utilities and how any variations will affect process reliability. The worst-case challenge for this type of validation is to evaluate the amount of fluctuation, reduction, or spiking that occurs when the maximum number of systems and equipment are using power at the same time. Power utilities are commonly evaluated and monitored over a period of time to determine normal patterns and to assess whether the utilities will support the needs of the process reliably over time.

Cleaning, Sanitizing, or Degreasing. When deciding whether to validate a cleaning, sanitizing, or degreasing operation, manufacturers take into account the purpose of the process, considering in the evaluation the product specifications and requirements as well as the needs and requirements of subsequent processes. Some cleaning processes are conducted in controlled environments. Any specific environmental conditions must be taken into account in the process validation.

Aseptic Processing. Validation of aseptic processing is similar to validation of cleaning and sanitizing processes. Issues to be addressed include the quality of the filling and closing environment in terms of minimizing microbial contamination. Among the process elements normally controlled are buildings and facilities, components, containers and closures, production time, laboratory variables, and sterility testing. Validation considerations include air quality and control; facility cleaning; microbiological quality of components, containers, closures, and the aseptic processing facility; and depyrogenation of containers and closures.

Unique Filtration Processes. The purpose of the filtration aids a manufacturer in determining the rigor of the validation required. Sterile filtration requires the most intense validation and involves use of a microbial challenge. The filter is challenged with the worst-case microbial population and organism, and the challenge is repeated for a sufficient number of trials to ensure reliable performance to meet specifications. The principle used is that if the filtering process can adequately filter the smallest organism at a population 1,000 to 100,000 times that of the normally expected microbial population, the filter can adequately remove organisms found in routine manufacturing. Environmental controls are maintained and monitored to control the microbial population at an acceptable level and to identify changes that could affect the validation.

Filling Operations. Validation of filling operations is primarily concerned with accuracy of fill volume and contamination of the product. If the product is to be filled sterile, then aseptic processing validation is performed. If the product will be terminally sterilized, then facility design, environmental monitoring, support systems, and control of materials are validated separately. Pumps used for filling are designed and qualified to prevent contamination. Controls commonly include preventive maintenance and a cleaning, sanitization, and sterilization program to ensure the cleanliness of the pump before each use.

Plastic Bonding. The manufacturer's main focus for this validation is the bond and how it is formed. Examples of parameters associated with various types of bonding include the amount of energy applied, dwell time, dimensions, curing temperature, type of solvent, and amount of solvent. Such parameters are routinely monitored during a bonding process.

Calibration. Because recognized national or international standards are typically used for calibration, calibration methods are not routinely validated. When no standard calibration method is available and the manufacturer has to develop one, the new method is qualified and validated. This validation process is similar to validation of a unique test method, because the validity of the calibration can have direct effect on product quality.

Wave and Hand Soldering. Typical parameters that can influence wave-soldering processes are the wave height; the distance of the printed circuit board (PCB) from the wave crest; the speed of the PCB through the equipment; the temperature of various equipment zones; the temperature of the PCB; and the temperature, cleanliness, and level of solder. Whether or not a hand-soldering process needs to be validated depends on the use of the soldering. Parameters reviewed include the temperature of the soldering gun, its ability to maintain a stable temperature, the condition of the flux and the solder, and the procedure used to define the process.

Plastic Injection Molding and Extrusion. Many variables can affect the quality of a molded part: barrel temperature; ram pressure; screw speed; type, temperature, and moisture content of the material; mold temperature; cooling rate; mold design and flow characteristics; cycle time; and configuration of the part. Extrusion processes operate on principles similar to molding processes, but parts are made by pushing the heated material through a die rather than into a mold.

Dipping Plastic and Rubber. Variables associated with dipping plastic and rubber include formulation of the material; batch-to-batch variability of the formulation; environmental temperature and humidity; time limitations of production; number of "dips"; and whether the dipping operation is manual, automated, or a combination of the two.

Mixing. The principal concern in a mixing process is the homogeneity of the mixture produced by the process. Among the factors that affect mixing are the types of materials being mixed; the characteristics of the materials (e.g., thickness or mixability); the equipment used; cleanliness of the equipment; the speed of mixing; any sampling of the mixture; and the length of time the material is mixed.

Lyophilization. Among the factors that affect lyophilization processes are the stability of the utilities, the temperature of the cooling water in refrigeration units, the condenser temperature, the vacuum levels, the rate of heat transfer, the sublimation rate, the shelf loading and freezing rate, the frozen product dwell time and temperature, the shelf temperature ramp and soak functions, and the product temperature. The parameters that define the quality of the product include phase transition temperature, moisture content, reconstitution rate, product assay, and pH.

Packaging Operations. Considerations involved in the validation of a packaging operation include the purpose of the product being packaged, the function performed by the packaging, and the type of packaging. Examples of packaging parameters include temperature; dwell time; pressure; ultraviolet energy level; and speed of the conveyor through the ultraviolet tunnel or form, fill, and seal machine. Packages sealed to provide sterile barriers are commonly assessed for seal strength and leakage to determine seal integrity.

VI

Sterilization. Various sterilization processes are used in the medical device industry, including dry heat, steam, EtO, plasma, radiation, and hydrogen peroxide. Factors that influence sterilization processes include the materials used in the product, the orientation of the product within the process, the density of the product and its packaging, the humidification of the product, and equipment performance. Some parameters are unique to a particular sterilization process, such as gas concentration in EtO sterilization and conveyor speed in gamma and electron beam radiation sterilization. Although different parameters may be monitored in different sterilization processes (e.g., vacuum, temperature, and dwell time for gas sterilization; dose, time, and distance from the energy source for radiation sterilization), the purpose of validation is the same. Process performance is monitored, and product samples or biological indicators are tested for sterility. For validation and control these processes, national and international standards are commonly followed.

Formulation Methods. Formulation methods usually address the number of ingredients and the order and manner in which they are added together. Factors influencing the final result include the condition of the ingredients at the time of addition, the order in which the ingredients are added, the condition of the ingredients already added, the time of addition, and any heating or cooling needed to achieve the proper formulation.

Software-Controlled Processes. Manufacturers validate software that contributes to the quality of the device, either directly by supporting manufacturing processes or indirectly by supporting Quality Systems. Such software includes that used in data-processing systems that support design, manufacturing, distributing, tracking, or other quality activities.

Whether custom or purchased off-the-shelf, software programs are validated for their intended use.

Typically, software purchased with equipment was developed by the equipment manufacturer, and the software code is unknown or inaccessible. This type of software is usually validated using a "black box" approach; that is, the software is exercised for functionality only and is not validated at the code level. Manufacturers evaluate software for proper installation and proper function by designing a set of test conditions and expected inputs to test the software's performance in its environment. Expected test inputs include probable process errors.

Validation also is required for software used to support data analysis. The extent or depth of validation of support software depends on the use of the software and on whether the software has been customized by the manufacturer. A common validation approach for off-the-shelf, "used as is" software is to demonstrate that it has been installed correctly and that the functions used produce valid results from the data input.

Software validation is discussed in more detail in Chapters 13, under "Automated processes" and in Chapter 29.

Industry Practice: Manual Processes

Processes performed manually (i.e., processes whose output is primarily controlled by a person's actions) are not validated in the classic sense. Because of the unpredictable sources of variation, these processes can only be qualified. However, to meet the intent of the validation requirements, these processes should be qualified. The intent is still to demonstrate, by objective evidence, that the process is repeatable and that this conclusion can be substantiated with a stated statistical confidence level. Some manufacturers refer to this as a *manual process qualification* rather than a validation.

An example of a manual process is hand welding. For these types of processes, whose output is not fully verifiable, manufacturers typically pursue a number of activities that lead to a conclusion about process capability. First, the process is evaluated for the potential addition of custom fixtures to help minimize variability. By establishing the use of fixtures, the manufacturer may improve overall process output quality.

Second, work environment factors often are subjected to significant scrutiny. Seating height, work surface height, lighting, heating and air conditioning, and work break frequency may play a significant role in the consistent performance of the process. Variability in process output may be reduced further by ensuring that these factors are optimized for the process and the operators. Training of personnel is also an important part of reducing variability.

Third, equipment is qualified, and any measurement tools or aids are subjected to gauge repeatability and reproducibility (R&R) studies. Gauge R&R studies determine tool accuracy, precision, and repeatable performance when used by different operators. Such studies provide objective evidence that the tools are capable of supporting the manual process and that the tools do not contribute to process outcome variability.

Fourth, the process instructions and forms are critically evaluated for clarity. This activity typically involves the use of operators who have not been qualified for the process. By observing an unfamiliar operator performing the process solely on the basis of written instructions, manufacturers may identify weaknesses in the instructions. Improving instruction clarity and flow; adding graphical instruction support; and implementing visual acceptance criteria, photographs, or "gold standards" can improve overall process output quality.

Finally, the manual process qualification typically consists of a detailed assessment of process output by various qualified operators to ensure overall consistency in operation of the process and in related process outcomes.

VI

**NOTES:**

VI

NOTES:

VI

"Consistency in quality means not allowing the ordinary rush of business and even extraordinary events to slow or suspend the process."
Juran Institute, *Quality Benchmarks for Executives: Executive Planning Guide,* 1991

NOTES:

VI

> "Why spend all this time finding, fixing and fighting when you could have prevented the problem in the first place?"
>
> P. Crosby, *Quality is Free: The Art of Making Quality Certain*, 1980

CHAPTER 16. LABELING AND PACKAGING CONTROL (SUBPART K)

820.120 Device Labeling

The Requirement

820.120 Device labeling. Each manufacturer shall establish and maintain procedures to control labeling activities.

> *(a) Label integrity. Labels shall be printed and applied so as to remain legible and affixed during the customary conditions of processing, storage, handling, distribution, and where appropriate use.*
>
> *(b) Labeling inspection. Labeling shall not be released for storage or use until a designated individual(s) has examined the labeling for accuracy including, where applicable, the correct expiration date, control number, storage instructions, handling instructions, and any additional processing instructions. The release, including the date and signature of the individual(s) performing the examination, shall be documented in the DHR.*
>
> *(c) Labeling storage. Each manufacturer shall store labeling in a manner that provides proper identification and is designed to prevent mixups.*
>
> *(d) Labeling operations. Each manufacturer shall control labeling and packaging operations to prevent labeling mixups. The label and labeling used for each production unit, lot, or batch shall be documented in the DHR.*
>
> *(e) Control number. Where a control number is required by § 820.65, that control number shall be on or shall accompany the device through distribution.*

Discussion of the Requirement

As part of the device master record (DMR), each manufacturer must develop written specifications for labeling that include requirements for the physical design (e.g., material of construction, dimensions, color, appearance) and content of the labeling. In addition, manufacturers are required to establish written procedures to maintain labeling integrity (legibility and application) and to prevent mixups from occurring during handling, storage, and distribution. The integrity of the label should be demonstrated through qualification under actual processing conditions.

In accordance with written procedures, manufacturers must examine labeling for conformance to specification requirements before it is used. Labeling includes printed packaging and label material, containers, lid stock, pouches, bags, and instructions. Records of such inspections must be maintained with, or referenced by, the device history record (DHR) and must include the date and the signatures of any individuals who performed the examination. When specific information (e.g., expiration date or control number) is printed on the label, that information must be verified before packaging and labeling activities are initiated.

Written control procedures are required when segregation of labels during storage, packaging and labeling operations is necessary to prevent a labeling mixup. In addition, the manufacturer is expected to establish written control procedures for performing inspections of the production line, line clearance activities, or label reconciliation activities in the area of the facility in which packaging and labeling will take place to ensure removal of devices and labeling from a previous operation, including any in-process rejects.

Industry Practice

Manufacturers perform design validation of finished device labeling under actual conditions of processing, including, for sterile devices, actual sterilization process conditions. A statistically-based number of runs are usually performed as part of the evaluation, which is detailed in a written protocol describing the labeling specifications and the packaging and labeling process parameters. Design validation of the packaging and labeling under actual conditions may be performed concurrently, under the same validation protocol. Packaging validation is discussed further under section 820.130.

Manufacturers may use the following control measures to ensure label integrity and prevent mixups during production:

a. Written procedures describe the method of label printing (e.g., verification of the revision level, removal and destruction of any excess labels from previous operations, and use of approved ink and adhesives) and label control (formal change control for label text, construction, and color).

b. Written procedures describe the method of label application (manual versus automated application, and validated equipment settings).

c. Written procedures describe the sampling plan and method of inspection for examining labeling before release for storage or use. The results of inspections, including the date and the signature of the person who performed the inspections, are documented in the DHR. Any nonconforming labeling is rejected. If automated readers are used, the process is typically monitored by a designated individual who examines a sample of labels to confirm the results from the automated reader.

d. Adequate facilities are provided—and written procedures describe the requirements—for label identification, spatial segregation, and limited accessibility to prevent label mixups. Generally, labels are stored in a locked or otherwise secure area that is accessible only to persons with authority for material control. Labeling is frequently identified by an item code number assigned to each label type. The item code number may include the revision level of the label. As part of the change control process, obsolete labeling is removed from approved labeling storage areas and is destroyed to prevent mixups.

e. Written procedures describe the control measures taken to prevent mixups during labeling and packaging operations. Typical operational controls include area inspections of the facility, line clearance activities, or label reconciliation activities to ensure removal of devices and labeling from previous lots, and verification of labeling materials against the DMR before use. During the packaging and labeling operation, manufacturers may choose to implement periodic inspections to confirm label integrity and application or to conduct such inspections of the finished lot. Also, when the sterilization process is completed, finished device specifications often require visual inspection of the labeled device to ensure label integrity (legibility and application).

    f. Written procedures describe the assignment and application of a control number on the device or its immediate packaging label.

When a third party, including a repacker or relabeler, performs packaging and labeling, the manufacturer is responsible for ensuring that appropriate and effective written procedures are established at the firm where packaging and labeling operations are performed.

The type and extent of controls that must be applied are determined by the manufacturer based on the design of the packaging process and the likelihood of a label mixup (given historical trends and corrective and preventive actions).

820.130 Device Packaging

The Requirement

> *820.130 Device Packaging. Each manufacturer shall ensure that device packaging and shipping containers are designed and constructed to protect the device from alteration or damage during the customary conditions of processing, storage, handling, and distribution.*

Discussion of the Requirement

Manufacturers are required to determine design characteristics and specifications of packaging and shipping containers to ensure protection of the device during routine processing, storage, handling, and distribution. The device packaging specifications must be included as part of the DMR and maintained under a formal change control system that requires review and approval of the packaging design and any design changes.

VII

Industry Practice

It is common for manufacturers to perform design validation of device packaging as part of the overall design validation program. Package performance is typically evaluated using real-time or accelerated test conditions, or both, to determine its acceptability under routine, as well as potentially adverse, conditions. The intent is to evaluate conditions that may be encountered during processing and storage, and throughout the device's expected shelf life or expiration dating period.

Studies are typically conducted under a formal validation protocol that defines the packaging material specifications, the processing conditions, and the storage conditions to be used during manufacturing and distribution. A statistically-based number of production runs are usually performed to determine conformance to the acceptance criteria for packaging design characteristics that are intended to provide protection against damage or contamination. A variety of characteristics should be evaluated for the device packaging:

    a. Package integrity evaluation determines parameters such as seal integrity; seal strength; and absence of tears, holes, or punctures. Package integrity is an essential output for sterile devices.

    b. It is critical to maintain device sterility after sterilization. Microbial barrier properties are typically demonstrated by microbial challenge testing.

c. Toxicological properties may be affected by packaging or sterilization processes. Testing should confirm the absence of leachables or extractables that may contaminate the device.

d. The evaluation must consider potential effects of exposure of the device and its packaging to adverse environmental conditions (e.g., temperature, humidity, pressure, or light), which may be encountered during storage and distribution.

As part of the design activities, manufacturers should also evaluate the compatibility of the device, the packaging materials, the labeling, and the packaging process at various stages, including:

a. Packaging and labeling stage, where processes directly affect package integrity. Manufacturers may use manual or automated methods for placement of the device in the packaging container and for sealing the container. Package sealing processes may include heat sealing, capping, forming, and so on. Placement methods and sealing processes can significantly affect package integrity and can also affect label integrity, depending on the order of operations. Thus, manufacturers should evaluate packaging operations to ensure that processes do not adversely affect the finished device.

b. Sterilization stage, where the process could adversely affect package integrity or label legibility. For terminally sterilized devices, exposures to sterilization process conditions are necessary to evaluate the compatibility of the device, packaging materials, and packaging seals with the selected sterilization conditions. Additionally, manufacturers should determine if reprocessing will be allowed when deviations from the sterilization process or packaging and labeling errors occur.

c. Transportation stage, where product is shipped between two or more facilities. When packaging, sterilization, and distribution may take place at different locations, packaging and shipping containers may need to withstand several shipping events. Normal shipping conditions may include extreme environmental (humidity, temperature, or pressure) variations, dropping or other impact events, and wear or abrasion on surfaces that touch. Any of these conditions might adversely affect the device or legibility of the labeling if the packaging is not designed with normal shipping in mind. Also, some manufacturers evaluate whether transport containers may be reused.

d. Storage stage, where packaged, labeled devices are placed in a warehouse or storeroom. Storage conditions may affect the device throughout the expected shelf life or expiration dating period and between significant manufacturing operations (e.g., storage of the device prior to packaging and labeling).

The Food and Drug Administration (FDA) has identified various consensus standards relating to the evaluation and design validation of finished device packaging. FDA maintains a consensus standards database, which provides information on the extent of FDA's recognition of each standard (see FDA's website at www.fda.gov/cdrh/stdsprog.html).

CHAPTER 17. HANDLING, STORAGE, DISTRIBUTION, AND INSTALLATION (SUBPART L)

820.140 Handling

The Requirement

820.140 Handling. Each manufacturer shall establish and maintain procedures to ensure that mixups, damage, deterioration, contamination, or other adverse effects to product do not occur during handling.

Discussion of the Requirement

Under this section of the Quality System regulation, each manufacturer is expected to have a documented system that defines product handling requirements at all stages of manufacture to prevent mixups, damage, deterioration, or other adverse effects. The system should be able to identify and segregate quarantined, accepted, and rejected product by using physical, spatial, labeling, or other means to prevent mixups. In addition, the system should take into consideration factors that may cause deterioration of parts, subassemblies, or finished devices and should provide for appropriate measures to address these factors to protect the product.

Industry Practice

Most manufacturers have documented handling systems that provide appropriate measures to identify and protect product at all stages of manufacture—from components through finished devices awaiting distribution.

Manufacturers typically separate stages of manufacturing or assembly by assigned workstation, workspace, or, when appropriate, separate rooms specifically designated for each significant processing step. Manufacturers often use rolling carts, rolling shelves, or hand trucks to move product between work areas. For some product, adequate protection may be achieved by using of totes or bins that move with the product as it is assembled. Other product may be adequately differentiated during production by careful in-process labeling of materials and use of discrete identification systems, such as work order numbers or lot numbers. Paperwork that typically accompanies production, such as production travelers or batch record sheets, may provide an additional measure of assurance.

When measures are deemed necessary because of product specifications or processing requirements, manufacturers use environmental controls to protect product from undesirable exposure to excessive temperature or humidity, particulate contamination, electrostatic discharge (ESD), and other environmental stresses. Also, some personnel controls provide protection from handling damage (e.g., use of gloves during assembly operations). In addition, damage or deterioration of parts or product is often addressed by means of packaging controls or controls provided by the physical design of the manufacturing facility.

820.150 Storage

The Requirement

820.150 Storage.
(a) Each manufacturer shall establish and maintain procedures for the control of storage areas and stock rooms for product to prevent mixups, damage, deterioration, contamination, or other adverse effects pending use or distribution and to ensure that no obsolete, rejected, or deteriorated product is used or distributed. When the quality of product deteriorates over time, it shall be stored in a manner to facilitate proper stock rotation, and its condition shall be assessed as appropriate.
(b) Each manufacturer shall establish and maintain procedures that describe the methods for authorizing receipt from and dispatch to storage areas and stock rooms.

Discussion of the Requirement

Manufacturers must establish systems for storing components, manufacturing materials, subassemblies, finished devices, packaging, and labeling that provide for physical barriers, procedural controls, or both. Such systems preclude mixups, deterioration, or damage to devices during their manufacture, distribution, and installation. Procedures must be established that describe stockroom receipt and issuance practices and ensure that only authorized product is released for use or distribution.

When appropriate, a stock rotation system, such as a "first-in, first-out" (FIFO) system, should be implemented to prevent the use or distribution of product nearing or exceeding a labeled shelf life limit or expiration date. In addition, such inventory should be periodically checked, inspected, or otherwise assessed to ensure that quality requirements are met over time.

Industry Practice

Manufacturers generally establish procedures that describe their product storage practices to prevent mixups and to assure that only product meeting its quality requirements is used or distributed.

Identification practices, such as assigning part or lot numbers or indicating "quarantine," "accept," or "reject" product status, are frequently used to differentiate discrete runs of production or batches of raw materials or components. Spatial segregation or use of designated storage bins or locations are also common methods of preventing mixups and damage.

Manufacturers frequently restrict access to storage areas to authorized personnel and define specific practices for moving stock into and out of assigned areas. These practices generally address requisition of parts, usage records, return of unused stock, and required authorizations to minimize the possibility of unauthorized product being used or distributed. Although consumables may not be assigned part numbers, they may be maintained at an established stock level for general use during production.

VII

For products that have a limited shelf life or that are labeled with a specific expiration date, FIFO stock rotation systems or periodic inventory checks are typically used. Also, when controlled storage environments are necessary to prevent deterioration of the product, manufacturers usually specify, control, and monitor any such requirements and include them in the DMR. These practices allow manufacturers to identify and use inventory before it is rendered unfit for use or to discard any inventory that is unfit for use before it can adversely affect production and the quality attributes of the finished device.

Many manufacturers take advantage of physical inventory audits that are performed primarily for financial reasons to also perform visual inspection of storage areas. This activity may reveal nonconforming or suspect product when storage or handling procedures are insufficient or have not been followed.

820.160 Distribution

The Requirement

820.160 Distribution.
(a) *Each manufacturer shall establish and maintain procedures for control and distribution of finished devices to ensure that only those devices approved for release are distributed and that purchase orders are reviewed to ensure that ambiguities and errors are resolved before devices are released for distribution. Where a device's fitness for use or quality deteriorates over time, the procedures shall ensure that expired devices or devices deteriorated beyond acceptable fitness for use are not distributed.*
(b) *Each manufacturer shall maintain distribution records which include or refer to the location of:*
    (1) The name and address of the initial consignee;
    (2) The identification and quantity of devices shipped;
    (3) The date shipped; and
    (4) Any control number(s) used.

VII

Discussion of the Requirement

Each manufacturer is expected to have written procedures for the distribution of finished devices, including the recording of the initial consignee, device identification, lot number, and quantity in each shipment. Procedures must exist to ensure that only approved finished devices are shipped. Also, in the case of devices that may deteriorate over time, established methods of inspection or other practices must ensure the continued fitness for use of items in approved inventory.

Industry Practice

Manufacturers generally distribute finished devices according to a written procedure that addresses the selection of finished devices for shipping; the recording of shipment details on a pick list, invoice, or other record; and the retention of hardcopy shipment records, electronic shipment records, or both.

At some point before a shipment is prepared for distribution, manufacturers review the corresponding DHR or production records to ensure that the finished device meets its quality attributes and that the records themselves are in order. Some manufacturers choose to conduct this review immediately after production so that the finished device can be moved to an "accept" finished goods storage area and pulled as needed to fill customer orders. Other manufacturers conduct this review as a "tollgate" or "final check" action, prerequisite to finished devices being pulled from inventory for distribution.

Regardless of which method is preferred, manufacturers generally use some method of verifying the acceptability of a finished device prior to distribution. An additional goal of this verification step is to ensure that when deterioration over time is known to occur, expired devices or otherwise deteriorated devices are withheld from distribution.

The initial consignee is the first entity outside the manufacturer's immediate control that receives a finished device. This consignee could be a contracted distributor, a customer (such as a hospital purchasing organization), a user facility (hospital or clinic), a user, or a patient.

Distribution records, whether paper or electronic, include the name of the consignee; the part number, lot number, or serial number; the quantity shipped; and the date shipped. These records are typically verified for accuracy by a second individual. Aside from business considerations, one goal of the distribution record system is to facilitate an efficient recall should one ever be necessary.

820.170 Installation

The Requirement

820.170 Installation.
(a) Each manufacturer of a device requiring installation shall establish and maintain adequate installation and inspection instructions, and where appropriate test procedures. Instructions and procedures shall include directions for ensuring proper installation so that the device will perform as intended after installation. The manufacturer shall distribute the instructions and procedures with the device or otherwise make them available to the person(s) installing the device.
(b) The person installing the device shall ensure that the installation, inspection, and any required testing are performed in accordance with the manufacturer's instructions and procedures and shall document the inspection and any test results to demonstrate proper installation.

Discussion of the Requirement

When installation of a device is necessary, the manufacturer must establish adequate instructions and procedures to ensure proper installation and to verify acceptable performance against established specifications. These instructions must be provided or made available to the personnel performing the installation, whether they are the manufacturer's personnel, the customer's personnel, or the personnel of a third party. The installer must ensure that the installation was done correctly and according to the manufacturer's instructions and must be able to demonstrate proper installation to FDA through an installation record.

Industry Practice

The manufacturer, the manufacturer's representative, or the customer frequently performs installation in accordance with an installation manual or other form of written instruction, such as a procedure. Installation manuals or procedures may include instructions for installation and operational qualification, testing, inspection, and verification of safety and performance. Controlled versions of these documents are a part of the DMR.

Both the manufacturer and the customer routinely use and retain installation checklists. Training of customer staff by the manufacturer or the manufacturer's representative is commonly part of the installation process. Many manufacturers treat installation records as an element of the DHR and update them during servicing to reflect and record replacement parts and their lot numbers. Other firms maintain the installation records as part of the service record, cross-referencing to the DHR.

NOTES:

VII

"We may be very busy, we may be very *efficient*, but we will also be truly *effective* only when we begin with the end in mind."
                    S. Covey, *The 7 Habits of Highly Effective People*, 1990

SECTION VIII. MONITORING AND FEEDBACK

CHAPTER 18. NONCONFORMING PRODUCT (SUBPART I)

820.90 Nonconforming Product

The Requirement

820.90 Nonconforming product.
(a) Control of nonconforming product. *Each manufacturer shall establish and maintain procedures to control product that does not conform to specified requirements. The procedures shall address the identification, documentation, evaluation, segregation, and disposition of nonconforming product. The evaluation of nonconformance shall include a determination of the need for an investigation and notification of the persons or organizations responsible for the nonconformance. The evaluation and any investigation shall be documented.*
(b) Nonconformity review and disposition.
    (1) Each manufacturer shall establish and maintain procedures that define the responsibility for review and the authority for the disposition of nonconforming product. The procedures shall set forth the review and disposition process. Disposition of nonconforming product shall be documented. Documentation shall include the justification for use of nonconforming product and the signature of the individual(s) authorizing the use.
    (2) Each manufacturer shall establish and maintain procedures for rework, to include retesting and reevaluation of the nonconforming product after rework, to ensure that the product meets its current approved specifications. Rework and reevaluation activities, including a determination of any adverse effect from the rework upon the product, shall be documented in the DHR.

Discussion of the Requirement

Under this part of the Quality System regulation, device manufacturers are expected to have adequate systems and established procedures in place for the identification, control, segregation, evaluation, and disposition of nonconforming product. Each manufacturer's Quality System must include controls to ensure that components, manufacturing materials, and finished devices that fail to conform to specifications are not inadvertently used or distributed.

The purpose of the required controls is to prevent the use or installation of nonconforming product by ensuring that:

    a. Authority and responsibility for handling nonconforming components and finished devices are established and communicated.

    b. Nonconformances are investigated, when appropriate.

    c. Nonconforming product is held or identified in a manner that will prevent its use.

    d. Organizational functions concerned with nonconforming product are properly notified.

When appropriate, nonconforming product must be investigated in accordance with written procedures, and the investigation must be documented. The investigation of nonconformances is an important part of the Quality System. The purpose of this activity is to determine the cause and effect of a nonconformance and to prevent its recurrence. The extent of the investigation depends on the particular component or product involved, the degree of complexity, and the suspected or confirmed effect of the nonconformance on product performance or use.

Nonconforming product must be identified and segregated from other similar materials to preclude its inadvertent use until final disposition can be made. When applicable, this control should extend to finished devices that have been released for distribution. Each manufacturer should develop suitable record-keeping procedures to adequately document the product's acceptance status before and after disposition, as required by section 820.86.

Reworked or otherwise reprocessed devices and components are to be processed and re-inspected in accordance with written procedures to ensure that the reworked device or component meets the original or subsequently modified and approved requirements and that it has no effect on device safety or performance. The manufacturer is required to make a determination as to the effect of reworking on a device, whether or not there is "repeated" reworking.

If a manufacturer decides to use the nonconforming material "as is," this disposition must be documented, and an evaluation must be performed to ensure that continued use of the nonconforming material does not compromise the safety and effectiveness of the finished device. The justification for concessions (i.e., "use as is" disposition) must be documented. The Food and Drug Administration (FDA) requires that the justification for concessions be based on scientific evidence and objective decision making. Such concessions should be closely monitored and not become accepted practice. Section 820.100, "Corrective and preventive action," requires analysis of concessions as a means of identifying actual or potential quality problems.

Industry Practice

Manufacturers use various methods to ensure proper control of nonconforming product. One of the most common is the creation of a material review board (MRB) or a material review committee (MRC) that is responsible for conferring on the investigation, the cause and effect of a nonconformance and, in some cases, the feasibility of use of nonconforming product. The members of the MRB or MRC are identified and authorized to:
- investigate product nonconformances,
- establish controls to prevent nonconforming material from being used inadvertently,
- evaluate the effect of the possible use of nonconforming product on the functionality of finished devices,
- agree on the disposition of nonconforming product, and
- concur on corrective action, as appropriate.

In smaller companies, MRB-type actions are usually agreed upon by one or more members of the management team or others who are aware of the effect of using the material on the finished device and who are empowered to make the technical decisions.

Regardless of company size, written procedures characterize the practice used and designate the responsible individuals with authority to make final decisions. The procedures typically include methods of identifying the product involved, identifying those responsible for making the disposition decision, providing for a written rationale or justification for the disposition decision, and requiring signatures of those approving the disposition.

These procedures typically include a form for identifying the material, the nature of the problem, those responsible for investigation and follow-up, the proposed disposition, and the corrective action to be taken. One or more approval signatures are typically required for the form or report, which then becomes part of the device history record (DHR) for the affected material.

Standard dispositions of nonconforming product include:
- use as is (i.e., concessions);
- accept, with rework or other reprocessing;
- reject or scrap;
- downgrade for use in other applications; and
- return to supplier.

"Use as is" disposition of nonconforming product is documented with written justification and with approvals by those authorized to release the material. Such concessions should not become standard practice, because they are often a symptom of inadequate supplier performance, unrealistic specifications, or other quality problems. The procedures also may include the requirement that before a disposition action is taken that directly involves a component supplier or the finished device purchaser, those parties should make additional concession approvals. These approval records are maintained as part of the DHR.

To preclude their unauthorized use until suitable disposition is made, nonconforming materials are usually identified and segregated from other products in a controlled area. Ideally, the material should be tagged and removed to a restricted or quarantined area pending disposition. When nonconformances can be corrected or reworked in a timely manner, the product is not necessarily moved, provided that it is properly identified.

VIII

In addition, manufacturers routinely have suitable rework procedures in place to address nonconforming product destined for rework or repair. Reworked product should be reevaluated or retested to ensure that it meets its original specifications. The results of reworking and reevaluation are then recorded in the DHR.

Information on nonconforming product, its disposition, and any necessary corrective action is typically communicated to the various affected organizational units responsible for the nonconformance. If a particular person or organization is responsible for a nonconformance, that individual or organization should be notified to ensure that future nonconformances are prevented. While the methods used for this communication will depend on the nature of the nonconformance, communication should be made in a timely manner to preclude the specific recurrence. It may be practical for personnel to officially acknowledge receipt of this information to provide evidence of compliance with the regulation.

CHAPTER 19. CORRECTIVE AND PREVENTIVE ACTION (SUBPART J)

820.100 Corrective and Preventive Action

The Requirement

820.100 Corrective and preventive action.
(a) Each manufacturer shall establish and maintain procedures for implementing corrective and preventive action. The procedures shall include requirements for:

    (1) Analyzing processes, work operations, concessions, quality audit reports, quality records, service records, complaints, returned product, and other sources of quality data to identify existing and potential causes of nonconforming product, or other quality problems. Appropriate statistical methodology shall be employed where necessary to detect recurring quality problems;

    (2) Investigating the cause of nonconformities relating to product, processes, and the quality system;

    (3) Identifying the action(s) needed to correct and prevent recurrence of nonconforming product and other quality problems;

    (4) Verifying or validating the corrective and preventive action to ensure that such action is effective and does not adversely affect the finished device;

    (5) Implementing and recording changes in methods and procedures needed to correct and prevent identified quality problems;

    (6) Ensuring that information related to quality problems or nonconforming product is disseminated to those directly responsible for assuring the quality of such product or the prevention of such problems; and

    (7) Submitting relevant information on identified quality problems, as well as corrective and preventive actions, for management review.

(b) All activities required under this section, and their results, shall be documented.

Discussion of the Requirement

This section requires that each manufacturer establish procedures and controls for implementing corrective and preventive action. Manufacturers are expected to analyze those processes related to the production, distribution, and servicing of a product, including customer complaints. Corrective and preventive action (CAPA) may also apply to a manufacturer's design control program, particularly with respect to problems encountered during design reviews, design validation or verification, and process validation. In addition, the Quality System must provide for control and action to be taken for finished devices both distributed and not yet distributed.

Procedures must include or refer to the statistical methodology that employees should use to identify recurring problems. Decisions based on analysis of data will play a key role in the quality improvement effort. Success requires application of the correct analytical tools.

The procedures must clearly define the criteria to be followed to determine what information is relevant to the action taken (or not taken) and why. FDA has emphasized that management is responsible for ensuring that all nonconformances are handled appropriately. An important part of CAPA is the investigation of a problem to identify the action needed to eliminate the cause or source of the problem. An effective investigation will help prevent a potential problem from occurring in the first place or an existing problem from recurring.

The manufacturer must ensure that actions taken to eliminate or minimize the causes of actual or potential nonconformances are appropriate for the magnitude of the problem and for the risks encountered. Although the regulation cannot dictate the degree of action to be taken, FDA does expect manufacturers to develop procedures for assessing risk, for defining the actions to be taken for different levels of risk, and for correcting problems and preventing them from recurring.

Verification or validation of the solution is a vital step in the CAPA process. After implementing a corrective action, data should be collected and analyzed to ensure that the action taken was effective and does not adversely affect the product or process in question. This follow-up activity closes the loop on the CAPA process.

Similar to the requirement of section 820.90(a), procedures for CAPA must ensure that proper organizational functions are notified of information related to nonconforming product or quality problems. In addition, relevant information on actions taken must be submitted to management for review in accordance with systems established to meet the requirements of section 820.20(c).

CAPA activities and results must be documented. It is important to note that FDA has the authority to review records pertaining to corrective and preventive action. These records are not protected under the regulation in the same manner as internal audit and management review records (see Chapter 23 for record exceptions during FDA inspections.)

The Quality System Inspection Technique (QSIT) includes Corrective and Preventive Actions as one of the four major subsystems addressed during a baseline facility inspection. QSIT CAPA objectives cover each subpart under 21 CFR 820.100, as well as sections 820.90(b) and 820.250. In addition, as part of a CAPA subsystem inspection, the QSIT includes additional objectives for "Medical Device Reporting" (21 CFR 803), "Corrections and Removals" (21 CFR 806), and "Medical Device Tracking" (21 CFR 821). Chapter 1, "FDA's Organization and Regulatory Strategies," provides more details on the QSIT.

VIII

Industry Practice

The Quality System regulation states that the procedures include provisions for analyzing quality data: processes, work operations, quality reports and records, service reports, concessions, customer complaints, returned devices, management reviews, and other sources of quality data.. This analysis of available quality data is a proactive activity designed to detect problems that might otherwise go undiscovered, whether existing or potential quality problems.

Quality problems might result from:
- improper design;
- inadequate or nonexistent component or product specifications;
- failures of or problems with purchased materials;
- inadequate manufacturing instructions, processes, tools, or equipment;
- improper facilities or equipment for storing or handling materials or products;
- poor scheduling;
- inadequate training or lack of training;

- inadequate or improper working conditions; or
- inadequate resources.

Regardless of regulatory requirements, managers of successful companies strive to meet their customers' expectations and work on methods for continuous improvement. Improvement is often accomplished by developing a comprehensive, closed-loop CAPA system that spans the entire organization.

These programs can vary from broad systems suitable for large, diversified organizations to simple systems for small organizations housed in a single location. Regardless of the degree of complexity of a manufacturer's CAPA program, the following elements are typically found in an effective system:

a. The organization of people puts the closed-loop process into practice, including the way that responsibility for managing the system is distributed within the organization.

b. The closed-loop process itself is composed of sequential activities that identify, correct, or eliminate existing or potential problems.

c. The tools for managing the closed-loop system include the written procedures and work instructions used to define the closed-loop process, as well as some form of information system for managing the information associated with corrective and preventive actions.

There are many ways of designing and implementing an effective CAPA program. In one approach, the closed-loop process consists of the following stages:

a. *Documenting the Problem.* This stage has two principle steps: (a) identifying and describing the problem, and (b) assigning a unique control number for tracking action items.

b. *Establishing a Priority Level and Correcting the Defect.* When a problem is discovered, someone first needs to determine its urgency and importance, which generally depend on the risk associated with the problem. If the problem affects components or finished devices, the next step is to segregate the defective items. A recall may be necessary if the finished devices have already been distributed.

c. *Determining Whether the Problem Requires Action.* Not all problems require action. Simple quality or assembly problems may, for example, be deferred for higher priority items.

d. *Analyzing the Data and Developing an Action Plan.* When action is in order, the root cause of the problem needs to be identified, before developing an action plan. An investigation must be undertaken to identify the root cause and any contributing factors. For complex problems, it may be necessary to develop a detailed action plan and assign responsibility for carrying out various pieces of the plan.

e. *Identifying, Implementing, and Validating the Appropriate Solution.* Analyzing the data may lead to more than one viable solution. The appropriate solution is then selected and implemented. Implementation may require a change order and may have a broad effect on the organization. The solution can be verified, but it may not be possible to fully validate it until the change is implemented in a production environment.

f. *Escalating the Action.* It may be necessary to escalate a corrective or preventive action. Not all action plans proceed as anticipated, and management intervention may be required.

g. *Documentation and Follow-Up Monitoring.* Documentation and follow-up monitoring are the final activities in the CAPA process. The activities and action are documented, along with any important decisions about the action taken. The action is also monitored to ensure that it was effective and did not adversely affect the finished device. If additional problems are discovered, the process starts over.

VIII

CHAPTER 20. COMPLAINT FILES (SUBPART M)

820.198 Complaint Files

The Requirement

820.198 Complaint files.
(a) Each manufacturer shall maintain complaint files. Each manufacturer shall establish and maintain procedures for receiving, reviewing, and evaluating complaints by a formally designated unit. Such procedures shall ensure that:
    (1) All complaints are processed in a uniform and timely manner;
    (2) Oral complaints are documented upon receipt; and
    (3) Complaints are evaluated to determine whether the complaint represents an event which is required to be reported to FDA under part 803 of this chapter, Medical Device Reporting.

Discussion of the Requirement

This section of the regulation requires a manufacturer to establish and maintain complaint files as well as a written procedure for processing complaints. The complaint-handling procedure must provide for processing of all complaints in a uniform and timely manner, for documentation of oral complaints, and for evaluation of complaints for Medical Device Report (MDR) reportable events under the requirements of 21 CFR 803.

Section 820.3(b) of the regulation defines a "complaint" as "any written, electronic, or oral communication that alleges deficiencies related to the identity, quality, durability, reliability, safety, effectiveness, or performance of a device after it is released for distribution." According to this definition and the requirements of section 820.198, a report need not be confirmed by a manufacturer to be considered a complaint. FDA expects manufacturers to classify all information that relates to possible inadequate performance of a medical device as a complaint. This position has been maintained to ensure that manufacturers consider all sources of alleged device defect information and take appropriate action when problems are found.

FDA has stated that one group, unit, or individual must be made responsible for coordinating all complaint-handling functions, regardless of the size of a manufacturer, the number of facilities or divisions, the extent of the manufacturer's product lines, or the number of different complaint-handling units within the organization. The intent is to ensure uniformity in applying the manufacturer's complaint procedures. Responsibility may, however, be delegated to appropriate functional units within a company for various aspects of complaint handling, including complaint investigations.

If a manufacturer provides maintenance, service, or repairs for its devices, an adequate system must be in place to screen requests for repair and service to ensure that any reports representing complaints are handled through the complaint-handling system. In addition, service and repair records must be reviewed for MDR reportable events. Any such reports must automatically be processed as complaints.

VIII

Industry Practice

Most manufacturers have a formal complaint-handling procedure, with a documentation system for recording complaints and following up on them. Manufacturers typically focus first on satisfying customer needs and concurrently on determining whether a quality problem actually exists, the source of the problem, and the appropriate corrective action.

The manner in which manufacturers handle complaints varies considerably. Small companies often direct all complaints to a single individual or department, whereas large companies with multiple facilities often designate one functional unit within each facility to coordinate all complaint-handling activities. Manufacturers that also service their devices frequently direct service calls or calls requesting technical information to a different functional unit from the group that handles complaints.

The challenge manufacturers face is to ensure that all information that may represent a "complaint," as defined in the regulation and company procedures, is properly directed and handled, regardless of whether the information comes from customers external or internal to the manufacturer. Good written procedures and extensive training of personnel help to ensure proper, consistent complaint handling.

Manufacturers may record complaints manually or enter the information in a computer database. The advantage of using a computer for complaint handling is that most databases can be configured to provide trending information readily. If complaints are not directly entered in a computer system, a mechanism is needed to ensure that all complaint information is properly registered and transcribed.

Most companies' written complaint-handling procedures cover all the elements identified in the regulations. An effective documented procedure covers:
- assignment of responsibility for complaint handling;
- the process for defining, recording, evaluating, investigating, and processing complaints;
- instructions for obtaining and documenting complaint information, including that pertaining to returned devices;
- corrective actions;
- segregation and disposition or reprocessing (including decontamination) of customer returns;
- the records to be maintained, the location where customer correspondence and other records are to be filed, and the record retention time;
- complaint closure requirements, including time periods; and
- statistical analysis or trending requirements.

The formally designated unit usually has responsibility for tracking complaints to ensure that they are handled in a timely fashion and that appropriate information is provided. The complaint-handling procedure may contain or refer to a separate procedure for screening repair and service requests as complaints, as well as for evaluating complaints and requests for repair and service as MDRs.

VIII

820.198(b) and 820.198(c): Complaint Evaluation and Investigation

The Requirement

820.198(b) Each manufacturer shall review and evaluate all complaints to determine whether an investigation is necessary. When no investigation is made, the manufacturer shall maintain a record that includes the reason no investigation was made and the name of the individual responsible for the decision not to investigate.

820.198(c) Any complaint involving the possible failure of a device, labeling, or packaging to meet any of its specifications shall be reviewed, evaluated, and investigated, unless such investigation has already been performed for a similar complaint and another investigation is not necessary.

Discussion of the Requirement

Manufacturers are required to ensure that all complaints are evaluated to determine whether an investigation is needed. Duplicative investigations are not necessary, provided that the manufacturer can demonstrate that the same type of failure or nonconformity has already been investigated. If no investigation is performed, the reason must be documented and signed by the individual who made the decision not to investigate. Unless a similar complaint has already been investigated, a manufacturer is required to conduct an investigation if the finished device, its labeling, or its packaging may have failed to meet specifications.

Industry Practice

As part of their complaint-handling procedures and records, many manufacturers have a step requiring a designated individual to determine whether an investigation is required and, if not, to document the reason. The responsibility for determining whether a complaint investigation is required is usually assigned to an individual with a thorough understanding of the device, its labeling and packaging, and clinical use. The individual also needs an appreciation of the importance of complaint information to a manufacturer's Quality System, quality improvement programs, and customer satisfaction.

FDA believes that some type of investigation is appropriate for most complaints to determine whether the complaint can be confirmed, the cause(s) of the complaint, and identification of corrective action. In addition, because manufacturers implement comprehensive Quality Systems to make continuous improvements in product quality, they find that thorough investigation of device problems yields valuable information.

Such investigations may involve a review of records (e.g., complaint files, DHRs, or other Quality System records) to determine if deviations occurred in the manufacturing process or if similar failures have occurred with the product line in question or with related product lines. Failure investigation may also involve testing of returned or retained devices, auditing of suppliers, review of design documentation (i.e., the design history file), or other actions appropriate to identify the root cause of a problem.

VIII

Most manufacturers typically do not conduct a complaint investigation when they have already identified the problem on the basis of an earlier complaint or when the complaint is a well-known phenomenon unrelated to product quality or performance.

820.198(d): Complaint Reportability

The Requirement

> ***820.198(d)*** *Any complaint that represents an event which must be reported to FDA under part 803 of this chapter shall be promptly reviewed, evaluated, and investigated by a designated individual(s) and shall be maintained in a separate portion of the complaint files or otherwise clearly identified. In addition to the information required by § 820.198(e), records of investigation under this paragraph shall include a determination of:*
>   *(1) Whether the device failed to meet specifications;*
>   *(2) Whether the device was being used for treatment or diagnosis; and*
>   *(3) The relationship, if any, of the device to the reported incident or adverse event.*

Discussion of the Requirement

The Quality System regulation clearly mandates that any complaint received by a manufacturer that must be reported to FDA under part 803 must be immediately processed through the complaint-handling system. The manufacturer is required to conduct an investigation of any such report. These complaints must either be maintained separately in the complaint file or be clearly identified as incidents relating to death, injury, or hazards to health.

FDA expects each manufacturer to make a serious effort to gather information on all complaints. However, any investigations under this part must contain a determination as to whether the device actually failed, whether the device in question was being used to treat or diagnose a patient, and whether any relationship existed between the device and the reported incident.

VIII

Industry Practice

Special provisions to ensure adequate documentation of complaints pertaining to reportable events are common in complaint-handling and MDR reporting procedures. Manufacturers take complaints of this nature very seriously, not only because FDA requires them to do so, but also because serious product issues and legal implications may arise.

It is not unusual, however, for a manufacturer to do an inadequate job of documenting the complaint investigation and the reporting decision-making process. Many manufacturers have found that standardizing the process for handling all complaints ensures that the necessary information is captured for reports pertaining to death, serious injury, or hazards to safety. Using checklists for gathering information and performing investigations, and decision trees for reportability supports standardized data collection and reporting.

For a number of manufacturers, because of the patient population for whom the device is intended, reports of deaths or serious injuries are not uncommon. For example, manufacturers of implantable defibrillators, anesthesia equipment, apnea monitors, and heart valves receive numerous reports of serious injuries and patient deaths. For companies that manufacture these types of devices, it is important for the manufacturer to determine whether the device may have caused or contributed to a problem or whether the device was not associated with the death or injury.

Few manufacturers physically segregate reports of this nature from other complaints. These events are typically identified with unique file numbers, recorded on paper of a different color, or flagged in the computer database.

820.198(e): Complaint Records

The Requirement

> *820.198(e) When an investigation is made under this section, a record of the investigation shall be maintained by the formally designated unit identified in paragraph (a) of this section. The record of investigation shall include:*
>   *(1) The name of the device;*
>   *(2) The date the complaint was received;*
>   *(3) Any device identification(s) and control number(s) used;*
>   *(4) The name, address, and phone number of the complainant;*
>   *(5) The nature and details of the complaint;*
>   *(6) The dates and results of the investigation;*
>   *(7) Any corrective action taken; and*
>   *(8) Any reply to the complainant.*

Discussion of the Requirement

The requirements under this section mandate that a written record be kept of any complaint investigation. The written record of the investigation must be maintained by the formally designated unit with responsibility for complaint files. The specific items required are clearly identified in section 820.198(e). These items include the information that must be collected regarding the complainant and the incident, as well as the details of the investigation and the corrective action taken.

Industry Practice

Many manufacturers try to obtain detailed information about customer complaints on first contact with the complainant, so that an investigation can be performed and the problem, if any, can be identified and corrected. However, the extent to which a manufacturer tries to obtain information about a complaint may be related to the seriousness of the complaint with respect to potential health hazards. Likewise, if a reported problem is one that a manufacturer believes to be well recognized and understood, the amount of inquiry may be more limited than if the problem is a new one.

Incident-Specific Information. Manufacturers often have difficulty obtaining complete information from customers, even about details or specifics related to the alleged incident and device in question. Likewise, a manufacturer may simply accept the complaint information provided by the complainant and not ask sufficient additional questions to enable the manufacturer to understand the complaint, determine reportability, perform an adequate investigation, or take an appropriate corrective action. The GMP requirements make clear that manufacturers should either obtain the specified information or document their efforts and their inability to do so. Checklists or question-answer guidelines may be helpful for personnel who receive customer contacts, especially by phone. These tools help standardize the complaint receipt process.

Investigation Results. Even when detailed information is available, a manufacturer sometimes has difficulty duplicating a reported incident or identifying a single cause (or causes) of a particular problem during the investigation. Because it is important that the cause of any problem needs to be identified and appropriate corrective action implemented, manufacturers should expend additional efforts in these areas. The amount of effort is directly proportional to the significance of the reported event. The results of a manufacturer's investigation typically include the dates of the investigation, the details of the complaint, the details of the investigation, and a description of the corrective action taken. Many manufacturers establish investigation procedures to ensure that investigations are sufficient and complete, when possible.

Reply to the Complainant. Not all manufacturers reply to the complainant. When a reply is made, the method of response varies greatly from manufacturer to manufacturer. For some, a simple verbal communication by telephone or during a visit from a sales representative is typical. Others believe that the response customers find most appropriate is simply to replace problem devices and that customers may not have a real interest in the source or correction of the problem. The customer should be asked—and it should be documented in the complaint file—if they require a reply. Some manufacturers not only reply but also provide results of the investigation and an explanation of any corrective actions taken as a result of the report. A description or copy of the reply must be included in the complaint file.

820.198(f) and 820.198(g): Complaint Record Access

The Requirement

VIII

> *820.198(f) When the manufacturer's formally designated complaint unit is located at a site separate from the manufacturing establishment, the investigated complaint(s) and the record(s) of investigation shall be reasonably accessible to the manufacturing establishment.*

> *820.198(g) If a manufacturer's formally designated complaint unit is located outside of the United States, records required by this section shall be reasonably accessible in the United States at either:*
> > *(1) A location in the United States where the manufacturer's records are regularly kept; or*
> > *(2) The location of the initial distributor.*

Discussion of the Requirement

Complaint files, including records of investigations, must be maintained by the formally designated complaint unit and must be reasonably accessible to the actual manufacturing site when these locations are not the same. An example of making records reasonable accessible would be through use of duplicate paper files or a shared database. The objective of this requirement is to ensure that complaints are reviewed by the actual manufacturing facility so that quality problems can be identified in a timely fashion and appropriate corrective action can be taken. In addition, FDA must have access to these records in the United States.

Industry Practice

Manufacturers whose complaint-handling functions are at sites separate from the actual manufacturing facility typically have systems to ensure that copies of complaints associated with the manufacturing process are sent to the manufacturing facility. This requirement applies not only to the corporate headquarters of large companies with multiple facilities, but also to companies that subcontract the manufacture of their finished devices.

Although not an effective or efficient practice, companies with complaint-handling units at facilities remote from the manufacturing site often notify the manufacturing site only after a complaint has been processed and closed. This practice does not meet the intent of the Quality System regulation in that an inadequate investigation has been performed. In this scenario, the manufacturing site does not have the opportunity to provide input into decisions, and the complaint-handling unit may be making determinations about whether a particular complaint potentially represents a manufacturing error or deviation and whether an investigation is or is not required.

An effective system requires input from the actual manufacturer during the investigation process, when appropriate, allowing for quick response in the case of an actual manufacturing problem, as well as providing insight into the potential cause or causes of an alleged device incident report.

Many foreign manufacturers with U.S. importers and distributors permit their U.S. representatives to collect complaint information and forward it to the foreign manufacturer for investigation and resolution. Some foreign manufacturers ask that information be forwarded only for those complaints associated with the design or manufacture of the device. Often, although such practice is in violation of the GMP requirements, no information or incomplete information on the disposition of complaints is returned to the U.S. facility.

The Quality System regulation requires that a duplicate of any complaint and the results of the complaint investigation be kept or reasonable accessible in the U.S., at a location readily accessible to FDA. Manufacturers comply with this requirement by sending or faxing written copies of complaints to their U.S. importers, distributors, or representatives; by electronic transfer; or by sharing records.

CHAPTER 21. SERVICING (SUBPART N)

820.200 Servicing

The Requirement

820.200 Servicing.
(a) *Where servicing is a specified requirement, each manufacturer shall establish and maintain instructions and procedures for performing and verifying that the servicing meets the specified requirements.*
(b) *Each manufacturer shall analyze service reports with appropriate statistical methodology in accordance with § 820.100.*
(c) *Each manufacturer who receives a service report that represents an event which must be reported to FDA under part 803 of this chapter shall automatically consider the report a complaint and shall process it in accordance with the requirements of § 820.198.*
(d) *Service reports shall be documented and shall include:*
   (1) *The name of the device serviced;*
   (2) *Any device identification(s) and control number(s) used;*
   (3) *The date of service;*
   (4) *The individual(s) servicing the device;*
   (5) *The service performed; and*
   (6) *The test and inspection data.*

Discussion of the Requirement

This section applies only to original device manufacturers who service devices and to remanufacturers. Health care facilities that service their own devices and independent third-party servicers are not subject to section 820.200.

Section 820.200 requires manufacturers to establish and implement servicing programs that meet all applicable requirements of the regulation. The Quality System must ensure the following:

a. Components used for repair are acceptable for their intended use.

b. Written inspection and test procedures are established and included in the DMR.

c. Measurement equipment is properly calibrated and maintained.

d. Serviced devices will perform as intended after servicing.

e. Criteria are established for determining when a service event is an MDR reportable event.

f. All service events are screened against MDR reporting criteria.

g. Service reports are analyzed using "appropriate statistical methodology."

h. Trends are evaluated and are acted on under the requirements of section 820.100.

i. Individuals performing service have the appropriate documented training.

j. Records are maintained that contain the quantitative inspection and test results and the information required by section 820.200(d).

VIII

Industry Practice

Most U.S. medical device manufacturers that perform servicing have fully implemented the GMP requirements for servicing. These firms have detailed servicing procedures and routinely maintain records of service reports. The servicing procedures include a mechanism for assessing service reports to determine whether MDR requirements apply.

For the few manufacturers that operate field service activities totally independently of their Quality System, compliance issues are common. Device problems corrected in the field often are not accurately recorded or are not recorded at all in the manufacturer's Quality System. The result is that corrective and preventive action is not implemented and similar problems may recur.

Another problem faced by many manufacturers is the failure of field service personnel to accurately report product problems or to provide enough information for a comprehensive failure investigation. This problem can be corrected to some degree by properly training field service personnel in the recognition of product problems that should be reported and the type of information that should be gathered.

An effective servicing program includes provisions to ensure that service records are evaluated to determine if the request must be considered an MDR or a complaint and subject to an investigation. The regulation requires that all service reports classified as MDRs be processed through the manufacturer's complaint-handling system (see Chapter 20).

Appropriate statistical methods must be used, when necessary, to analyze repair and service quality data to identify potential problems with design, specific components, or premature failures. If trends occur, investigation and appropriate corrective action, are required. For those problems determined to be potential hazards to safety, immediate action through an appropriate system is required.

The servicing program also may address the following activities:
- clarification of servicing responsibilities,
- planning of service activities,
- validation of special tools or equipment used for repairing and servicing devices,
- control of measuring and test equipment,
- control of documentation,
- training of service personnel, and
- feedback and monitoring of service reports and information.

Manufacturers may include servicing activities within other systems and procedures in their Quality System or generate separate systems to handle service activities. Other Quality System requirements affected by servicing activities include: training; quality audits; purchasing controls; inspection and testing; control of inspection, measuring, and test equipment; nonconforming product; corrective and preventive action; documentation controls; and records.

NOTES:

VIII

"How many fixes backfire because the assumptions on which the fix was based turn out to be false?"
S. Murgatroyd and C. Morgan, *Total Quality Management and the School*, 1993

NOTES:

"If you don't measure, then you're left with only one reason to believe you are still in control: hysterical optimism."
> T. DeMarco, *Controlling Software Projects: Management, measurement and Estimation*, 1982

SECTION IX. DOCUMENTS AND RECORDS

CHAPTER 22. DOCUMENT CONTROLS (SUBPART D)

820.40 Document Controls

The Requirement

820.40 Document controls. Each manufacturer shall establish and maintain procedures to control all documents that are required by this part. The procedures shall provide for the following:

(a) Document approval and distribution. Each manufacturer shall designate an individual(s) to review for adequacy and approve prior to issuance all documents established to meet the requirements of this part. The approval, including the date and signature of the individual(s) approving the document, shall be documented. Documents established to meet the requirements of this part shall be available at all locations for which they are designated, used, or otherwise necessary, and all obsolete documents shall be promptly removed from all points of use or otherwise prevented from unintended use.

(b) Document changes. Changes to documents shall be reviewed and approved by an individual(s) in the same function or organization that performed the original review and approval, unless specifically designated otherwise. Approved changes shall be communicated to the appropriate personnel in a timely manner. Each manufacturer shall maintain records of changes to documents. Change records shall include a description of the change, identification of the affected documents, the signature of the approving individual(s), the approval date, and when the change becomes effective.

Discussion of the Requirement

Under the general requirements of this section, a manufacturer is expected to establish and maintain a documented system to develop, identify, distribute, change, and control all documentation required by the Quality System regulation and the manufacturer's operation. The system must apply to all product, process, and quality assurance documentation. It must be in place prior to transferring a design to production.

The system must encompass all new documents as well as any changes to existing controlled documents. It must ensure that the accuracy and use of documents are controlled, that obsolete documents are removed or prevented from being used, and that all documentation is adequate for its intended use or purpose.

A manufacturer's written procedures must provide methods for:
- document development, review, and approval to ensure that documents are accurate and meet the requirements of the regulation;
- distribution and maintenance to ensure that documents are made available at locations where they are used and to personnel who require them;
- preparation, review, approval, and qualification of revisions;
- timely implementation and notification of changes;
- archiving records of change;

- retrieval of obsolete or superseded documents to ensure that only the current and approved version is used; and
- verification of document distribution and retrieval.

In addition, those individuals or functions that originally approved a document must review any changes and the effects of such changes on the document, system, and product. Nevertheless, manufacturers are allowed to specifically designate individuals who did not perform the original review to review and approve changes. In those instances, the manufacturer must determine which individuals or functions are best suited to perform the review and approval.

Requirements for validating or verifying changes to specifications, methods, or procedures are addressed in section 820.30(i), "Design changes," and section 820.70(b), "Production and process changes."

Industry Practice

The numerous systems and methods of document control and configuration management used by the medical device industry illustrate that no one documentation control system works for all manufacturers. Systems range from completely manual systems with all paper copies to electronic paperless systems. Most manufacturers implement a system that is a combination of paper and electronic documentation control.

In one manner or another, document controls affect all aspects of a manufacturer's operation and activities, including design, purchasing, production, testing and inspection, quality assurance, installation, and service. Also encompassed are materials, product, and equipment—such as raw materials, components, software, labeling and packaging, manufacturing materials, finished devices, production equipment and tools, measuring equipment and tools, and workmanship standards.

Controlled documents may include, but are not limited to, blueprints, drawings, standard operating procedures (SOPs), specifications, inspection instructions, test methods, device master records (DMRs), forms, and labeling, including labels for in-process and final devices. Certain Quality System documents and records may also be controlled, such as inspection and test reports, qualification and validation protocols and reports, and audit reports. Both "masters" and "copies" are typically controlled through the document control system. Masters refer to original documents, which are created, approved, changed, and archived, while copies are the actual documents circulated and distributed for use.

It is common for manufacturers to centralize and assign document control functions to a single individual or department. When the function is centralized, the system typically allows some degree of flexibility by providing for various levels of review and approval of different types of documents and document changes (e.g., administrative changes versus release of a new document; release of a manufacturing procedure versus release of a product specification). Multiple, non-centralized systems have built-in flexibility, but many manufacturers have found such systems to be more difficult to maintain and control.

Manufacturers commonly describe the document control function in a written procedure in conjunction with one or more forms or checklists, which are often identified as:

- engineering/document change requests (ECRs/DCRs),
- engineering/document change orders (ECOs/DCOs), or
- engineering/document change notices (ECNs/DCNs).

Such forms capture the reasons for each document or change and identify the specific change. These forms often serve as the basis for a manufacturer's change control system. They typically address evaluation of the change; validation, training, and regulatory considerations; distribution and implementation issues; revision level; effectivity; and disposition of any affected materials.

The mechanics of the document control process typically encompass the following elements:

a. The need for the document, especially revisions to existing documents, is justified. The justification may include reference to applicable process improvements or corrective actions.

b. The scope of the change is described. The new document or change to be implemented is identified, as well as the devices, components, subassemblies, labeling, software, processes, and procedures that are affected. Any primary or secondary document sources, including instruction manuals and labels, that may require review and updating are also identified.

c. The new document or document change is evaluated. Factors commonly taken into consideration include: regulatory status (e.g., submission requirements or product licensing information); effect on risk; design change requirements; and process change requirements, including validation. The effect of the new or revised document on other products, documents, or systems is also commonly reviewed. Equally important, though often overlooked, is a financial evaluation of the new document or change.

d. The current and proposed revision levels are identified. A common practice among manufacturers is to use a numeric revision-level system for engineering (preproduction) documents and an alphabetical revision-level system for production documents.

e. The effectivity of the change is assigned by means of a date, lot number, serial number, work order number, or other method—such as the designation "upon depletion of stock."

f. If applicable, the disposition of all raw materials, components, work in progress, finished goods, and distributed devices is assigned. Product disposition is typically a concern when specifications are modified, which could invalidate existing product.

g. The responsibility for implementing the change is designated.

h. Any requirements for formal employee training or retraining are determined.

i. The document or document change is routed for review and approval. A signature matrix is often used to designate the individuals who are required to approve specific types of documents or changes to documents.

j. The document or document change is communicated to all affected parties.

k. The document is distributed to all persons responsible for operations affected by the document. Obsolete documents are retrieved or removed from the system.

IX

l.   It is verified that the change has been implemented and that obsolete or superseded
     documents have been removed or steps have been taken to prevent unintended use.

The Quality System regulation requires manufacturers to ensure that those individuals or
functions that originally approved a document review any changes made to that document.
The use of a signature matrix, designating appropriate individuals and approvals, is one
method of complying with this requirement.

IX

CHAPTER 23. RECORDS (SUBPART M)

820.180 General Requirements

The Requirement

820.180 General requirements. *All records required by this part shall be maintained at the manufacturing establishment or other location that is reasonably accessible to responsible officials of the manufacturer and to employees of FDA designated to perform inspections. Such records, including those not stored at the inspected establishment, shall be made readily available for review and copying by FDA employee(s). Such records shall be legible and shall be stored to minimize deterioration and to prevent loss. Those records stored in automated data processing systems shall be backed up.*

Discussion of the Requirement

Manufacturers are required to keep all records mandated by, or kept in order to comply with, the Quality System regulation, whether or not the record is product-specific. Whether maintained at the manufacturing site or at an off-site location, these records must be accessible to employees of the manufacturer and be readily available for review and copying by Food and Drug Administration (FDA) investigators. FDA interprets "readily available" as available during the course of an inspection. Given that FDA's goal for conducting a baseline Quality System Inspection Technique (QSIT) inspection is 4 days at the manufacturer's facility, "readily available" is a relatively short time.

A foreign manufacturer who maintains records at a remote site is expected to produce any requested records within 2 working days. In addition, records must be legible and must be stored so as to minimize deterioration and prevent loss. When record archives are extensive, storage practices must include an identification or index scheme that facilitates locating particular records easily.

When records are electronic, backups are required to ensure retention, ease of retrieval, security, and accuracy. As with all automated processes, validation of electronic record-keeping systems is required. General requirements for electronic system validation are contained in 21 CFR 820.70(i), "Automated processes." Validation applies to any system used to create or maintain records required by the Quality System regulation. Specific requirements for the functionality of the electronic record-keeping system and related validation are defined in 21 CFR Part 11, "Electronic Records; Electronic Signatures." Chapters 24 through 26 describe these requirements in detail.

When a signature or initial on a record is a Quality System regulation requirement, the signature or initial may be handwritten or electronic. Use of stamps to indicate approval, which is a common practice in certain countries outside the United States, is also permitted when appropriate controls are established to ensure unique identification of each person authorized to use a stamp in lieu of a signature. Use of electronic signatures and stamps must take into account the requirements contained in 21 CFR Part 11, "Final Rule for Electronic Records; Electronic Signatures." Use of electronic signatures and the associated regulations for such use are discussed in detail in Chapter 26, "Electronic Signatures."

Industry Practice

While written copies of records are commonly used in the workplace, many manufacturers have converted to paperless systems in which records are generated, stored, and controlled electronically. These documents are made available to employees through personal computers at workstations or offices.

Most typical is for a manufacturer to centralize the document control function and to maintain a combined system of both paper and electronic records. In this scenario, computers are used for generating and storing records, but paper copies are considered "official." It is still a common industry practice to circulate written procedures for review and signature by designated individuals.

It is the manufacturer's responsiblity to decide what information to make available to FDA during an inspection. Most manufacturers recognize FDA's right to review and copy records required under the Quality System regulation and provide investigators with broad access to procedures and records. Some manufacturers have inspection policies that address the policies, procedures, and records required under the Good Manufacturing Practice (GMP) requirements and that specify which documents are and are not available during an inspection.

A typical issue involving records being readily available to FDA is how quickly a record can be retrieved, especially with respect to foreign manufacturing sites and records stored off-site. With the increasing use of computer networks and the Internet, retrieval of electronic records is becoming less of an issue. However, ongoing access can become an issue if the electronic systems or hardware needed to operate the system become obsolete. Manufacturers without networks may need more time to retrieve records, but even they can readily fax records from one location to another within 1 to 2 days. Off-site storage continues to be a problem because many manufacturers have older records stored on paper and, as volume increases, move them to remote locations. The issue of ease of retrieval is typically addressed in a manufacturer's records retention policy.

Both FDA and manufacturers have encountered problems with illegible records. The Quality System regulation requirement is to maintain legible records and to store records in a manner that minimizes deterioration and prevents loss. Examples of illegible records include records filled out in pencil or non-waterproof pen, and records filled out by hand by employees with poor handwriting. Loss of records may result from earthquakes, floods, and fires. Manufacturers are expected to have reasonable controls in place to prevent such losses, particularly when problems may be anticipated. For example, controls to ensure integrity of records and protection from earthquakes would be expected of manufacturers in earthquake-prone areas.

820.180(a) Confidentiality

The Requirement

> **820.180(a) Confidentiality.** *Records deemed confidential by the manufacturer may be marked to aid FDA in determining whether information may be disclosed under the public information regulation in part 20 of this chapter.*

Discussion of the Requirement

The requirements of 21 CFR 20.20 provide for the fullest possible disclosure of FDA records, except for trade secrets and confidential commercial or financial information. Sections 20.60, 20.61, and 20.63 define the types of information that the federal government may hold confidential. Under section 20.27, the marking of records submitted to FDA as confidential raises no obligation by FDA to regard the records as confidential or to withhold those records from public disclosure. In situations in which confidentiality is uncertain and there is a request for public disclosure, FDA, under section 20.45, must consult with the person who submitted or divulged the information, or who would be affected by disclosure. Such consultation is required before determining whether such data or information will be publicly disclosed. Judicial review is available under 21 CFR 20.46 to any person whose request to hold information confidential is denied.

FDA makes every effort to protect information that it recognizes as confidential, and it considers manufacturers' claims of confidentiality quite carefully. FDA is required by law to release any information that does not meet the definition of information exempt from disclosure.

Industry Practice

Some manufacturers have inspection policies addressing how to determine whether certain types of company information are confidential with respect to disclosure by FDA. Manufacturers commonly mark as confidential any records subject to FDA inspection that contain trade secrets or proprietary information. Many manufacturers tend to be overly broad in claiming confidentiality, routinely stamping all procedures, drawings, and blueprints as confidential. A few manufacturers review documentation on a regular basis and carefully mark the information they believe to be confidential. However, the majority of companies address this matter only at the time a regulatory submission is made or documents are provided to FDA.

Among the types of information that manufacturers typically want to protect are device specifications and proprietary manufacturing processes that would enable a competitor to produce a similar device. Information that FDA does not regard as confidential includes customer complaints, except the name of any patient or user; written procedures for compliance with GMP requirements; and device history records (DHRs), except to the extent that they contain proprietary process information or specifications.

IX

820.180(b) Record Retention Period

The Requirement

> *820.180(b) Record retention period. All records required by this part shall be retained for a period of time equivalent to the design and expected life of the device, but in no case less than 2 years from the date of release for commercial distribution by the manufacturer.*

Discussion of the Requirement

All records, including quality records, are subject to the requirement of this section. Records must be retained for a period equivalent to the design and expected life of the device, but in no case less than 2 years, whether or not the record specifically pertains to a particular device. Manufacturers are permitted to request a variance from the 2-year requirement for devices with very short shelf lives, such as radioimmunoassay devices. For a device with a long expected life, the manufacturer is responsible for determining, on the basis of the expected life of the device, the appropriate time period for record retention.

Industry Practice

The regulation implies that a manufacturer will determine the expected life of a device to determine the required record retention period. Many manufacturers view assigning an expected life to a device as a potential liability. Consequently, in actuality, required retention times are often chosen arbitrarily, allowing a grace period long enough to ensure that the specified time period will not be questioned when evaluated against the device produced. Regardless of how record retention time is determined, the likelihood of field actions or other remedial activities is often considered, as is information on the device's fitness for use (e.g., complaints and service records). Some manufacturers proactively assess expected life of a device during design activities as part of a reliability test program.

Most manufacturers have a documented procedure for record retention, which includes a mechanism for disposing of records after the stated retention period has elapsed. Few manufacturers actually review records periodically and discard those records that fall outside the specified retention period. Consequently, many manufacturers keep records too long, and the majority of the records kept do not add value to the manufacturers' Quality Systems.

An important consideration for electronic record-keeping systems is maintenance of copies of obsolete or revised procedures. Many companies have a paper archive of procedures, which is, of course, an acceptable substitute for an electronic archive.

820.180(c) Exceptions

The Requirement

820.180(c) Exceptions. This section does not apply to the reports required by § 820.20(c) Management review, § 820.22 Quality audits, and supplier audit reports used to meet the requirements of § 820.50(a) Evaluation of suppliers, contractors, and consultants, but does apply to procedures established under these provisions. Upon request of a designated employee of FDA, an employee in management with executive responsibility shall certify in writing that the management reviews and quality audits required under this part, and supplier audits where applicable, have been performed and documented, the dates on which they were performed, and that any required corrective action has been undertaken.

Discussion of the Requirement

To ensure that manufacturers critically examine their systems and implement needed corrective actions and improvements, section 820.180 does not apply to reports of management reviews, internal audits, or supplier audits, which need not be provided to FDA during a routine inspection. However, these records may be available to FDA in litigation under applicable procedural rules or by inspection warrant when access is authorized by statute. Manufacturers are required to have written procedures for these activities, which must be available for routine review and copying by FDA.

The agency has the right to require a representative of executive management to certify in writing that the procedures required under sections 820.20, 820.22, and 820.50 have been followed; that the audits and management reviews have been performed; and that any necessary corrective actions have been undertaken.

Industry Practice

Most device manufacturers have written quality audit procedures that meet the requirements of section 820.22. These procedures are typically provided to FDA investigators on request and without question. Although most manufacturers do not provide copies of audit reports to FDA, some routinely do.

Manufacturers registered to ISO 9001/13485 already have written procedures in place for management review and supplier evaluation. Like audit procedures, these procedures are provided to FDA investigators upon request. The majority of companies will not provide the results of management reviews or supplier audits during routine FDA inspections.

FDA has other means of assessing the adequacy of auditing and management review practices, such as reviewing the complaint files, the incoming material and in-process acceptance records, the testing records of finished devices, and the corrective and preventive action system.

820.181 Device Master Record

The Requirement

> ***820.181 Device master record.*** *Each manufacturer shall maintain device master records (DMR's). Each manufacturer shall ensure that each DMR is prepared and approved in accordance with § 820.40. The DMR for each type of device shall include, or refer to the location of, the following information:*
> *(a) Device specifications including appropriate drawings, composition, formulation, component specifications, and software specifications;*
> *(b) Production process specifications including the appropriate equipment specifications, production methods, production procedures, and production environment specifications;*
> *(c) Quality assurance procedures and specifications including acceptance criteria and the quality assurance equipment to be used;*
> *(d) Packaging and labeling specifications, including methods and processes used; and*
> *(e) Installation, maintenance, and servicing procedures and methods.*

IX

Discussion of the Requirement

Section 820.3(j) of the regulation defines "device master record," or DMR, as "a compilation of records containing the procedures and specifications for a finished device." The DMR, which is specific for a particular design, must contain the necessary information for employees to perform both general and specific tasks related to the manufacture, testing, release, installation, and servicing of a device, device type, or family of related devices.

The purpose of the DMR is to document the performance and configuration characteristics established for the device, components, packaging, labeling, quality assurance program, production, installation, maintenance, and service so that these activities can be controlled. The DMR must contain all the documentation necessary to meet this objective. The manufacturer of the finished device must have ready access to the DMR for each device manufactured.

The Quality System regulation does not specify how the information in a DMR must be organized or stored, although, as required under section 820.180, the information must be accessible to employees who use the records in their day-to-day job functions. Manufacturers are required to maintain a DMR for each device, device type, or family of devices. Any method may be used, provided that it facilitates reasonable access to the required documentation, control and identification of the documentation, and control of documentation changes.

It is a GMP requirement that the DMR be prepared, dated, and approved by a qualified individual to ensure consistency and continuity within the DMR. All documents contained in the DMR must be under document control, and any changes must meet the applicable requirements of section 820.40.

Device specifications required for the DMR include specifications for the finished device and for all raw materials, components (including labeling and packaging), and in-process materials. These specifications may take the form of drawings or written specifications. Software specifications also must be included in the DMR.

Production process specifications include environmental specifications for air and water quality, when appropriate; specifications for all equipment; procedures for equipment qualification, operation, calibration, and maintenance; and record forms.

Production methods and procedures encompass all SOPs, assembly drawings, batch record forms, sterilization methods and procedures, and other documents and procedures used in every stage of manufacturing, from procurement of materials through packaging and final release.

Quality assurance documentation consists of the procedures for inspection; for evaluation or testing; and for release of raw materials, in-process devices, and finished devices. It also includes the specifications at each stage of evaluation, as well as the procedures for evaluating product to ensure adequacy, and the forms on which inspection and test results will be recorded. For any equipment used in inspection and testing, there must be written specifications; operation, calibration, and maintenance procedures; and forms for recording results.

Packaging and labeling specifications for finished device packaging, if different from incoming specifications, must be part of the DMR, along with procedures for receiving, inspection, production, packaging and labeling operations, in-process inspection, and release. Forms for the approval, production, and use of labels are required.

When applicable, the DMR must contain the procedures and methods for installing, maintaining, and servicing devices after they are released for distribution. This documentation must include the instructions provided both to the manufacturer's representatives and to users who install, maintain, or service the device themselves.

Industry Practice

Theoretically, if the DMR is constructed correctly, the contents could be taken from one manufacturing facility to another and could be used to produce a device that would be identical to the one produced at the original facility. A manufacturer may develop the DMR as:

- files or volumes containing the actual required documents and records,
- a list or index of the documents and records that identifies their location, or
- any combination of these two approaches.

The GMP requirement that all documentation contained or referenced in the DMR be evaluated and approved by designated, responsible individuals before changes are implemented is typically met through use of the document control system. The actual approval forms or documentation used to obtain approval is then included or referenced in the DMR.

To simplify DMR maintenance, many manufacturers maintain a change-controlled list or index that references all required DMR documents. Although it is not necessary to list every record in the DMR index, there should be traceability to each related document. Depending on the manufacturer, the DMR index may be in the form of an outline or a flowchart of the manufacturing process. Indented bills of materials are also commonly used as an index to the documents making up the DMR.

Before the requirements of section 820.186, "Quality system record," were promulgated, manufacturers typically created a "common" DMR index that included general Quality System documents applicable to all devices or device families (e.g., audit procedures, change control procedures, calibration programs, warehouse control methods, environmental specifications, and cleaning procedures). The number of this index was then referenced in each specific DMR index, making repetition of all the "general" document numbers unnecessary.

The DMR index may or may not designate document revision levels. Many manufacturers that use indices assign a document number and revision level to the index. The DMR index changes only when a new record is added or one is removed; the records listed in the index can change separately (new revisions) without changing the index. However, if revision levels are not specified in the DMR index, the manufacturer should have a system to demonstrate control over current revision levels. When a manufacturer uses a DMR index that specifies revision levels, such a system is not required, because the entire index is updated each time a single document is changed.

Examples of documents found in a DMR include:
- product and component specifications or formulations, including engineering drawings;
- packaging and labeling specifications;
- software specifications;
- production process procedures, methods, and specifications, including routine reprocessing;
- sterilization parameters and procedures;
- installation, maintenance, and service procedures;
- test and inspection procedures;
- environmental specifications and controls;
- equipment specifications;
- validation protocols and results;
- bills of materials;
- data sheets;
- process flow diagrams;
- operator's manuals; and
- service manuals.

For many manufacturers, the requirement that installation, maintenance, and servicing procedures be included in the DMR necessitates the generation of documents to guide their field service personnel. These activities—particularly maintenance and service—previously were handled on a case-by-case basis by qualified service technicians.

Most companies that manufacture software devices or software-controlled devices already have procedures for software development, testing, and validation, because this information is requested by FDA's Office of Device Evaluation or Office of In Vitro Diagnostics staff in the 510(k) or PMA process. Accordingly, it should be a simple matter for these manufacturers to add the required information to the DMR.

820.184 Device History Record

The Requirement

820.184 Device history record. Each manufacturer shall maintain device history records (DHR's). Each manufacturer shall establish and maintain procedures to ensure that DHR's for each batch, lot, or unit are maintained to demonstrate that the device is manufactured in accordance with the DMR and the requirements of this part. The DHR shall include, or refer to the location of, the following information:

(a) The dates of manufacture;
(b) The quantity manufactured;
(c) The quantity released for distribution;
(d) The acceptance records which demonstrate the device is manufactured in accordance with the DMR;
(e) The primary identification label and labeling used for each production unit; and
(f) Any device identification(s) and control number(s) used.

Discussion of the Requirement

Section 820.3(i) defines the "device history record" or DHR as "a compilation of records containing the production history of a finished device." "Lot or batch," according to section 820.3(m), "means one or more components or finished devices that consist of a single type, model, class, size, composition, and software version that are manufactured under essentially the same conditions and that are intended to have uniform characteristics and quality within specified limits." When these definitions are taken together, a DHR is a collection of records for a particular unit, batch, or lot of devices that includes information on the successful—or unsuccessful—completion of manufacturing steps and the results of receiving, in-process, and final acceptance activities, through distribution and, where appropriate, installation.

The DHR is intended to provide objective evidence that the requirements of the DMR were met and to provide information to facilitate failure investigations and corrective or preventive actions. The DHR provides traceability when the manufacturer is required to ensure traceability or when, for other purposes, the manufacturer requires identification of specific units or batches.

Each manufacturer is required to establish and implement written procedures to ensure that DHRs are maintained. All companies are required to produce a complete DHR containing certain minimum information, including dates of manufacture, quantities manufactured and released for distribution, and any identification or control number used.

The requirement that all labeling be included in the DHR reflects FDA's interest in increased control over labeling because of the many recalls that have occurred as a result of labeling errors. Requiring the DHR to include the primary identification label and labeling used for each production unit should help to ensure that proper labeling is used and will facilitate investigations. Furthermore, recording the control number or other identification used will support those activities.

Industry Practice

DHR contents vary according to the segment of the industry, the size of the company, and the complexity of the device. The manufacturer should determine the format of each specific DHR. DHR format should take into account the complexity of the device, its manufacturing process, raw materials, components, and the operations that are most important to the proper functioning of the finished device. In the orthopedic device industry, for example, the major portion of the DHR often consists of a traveler card that specifies the major steps in the manufacturing process (e.g., cutting, grinding, polishing, and cleaning), with each step being signed off or initialed by the operator. In the *in vitro* diagnostics industry, reagent DHRs often contain step-by-step instructions for measuring and mixing reagents, along with documentation of adjustments and test results, all of which are signed off by the operator. For sterile devices, the DHR contains information on the parameters of the sterilization process.

Manufacturers conduct a review of the DHR as part of final acceptance activities, as required by section 820.80(d). This review helps verify that the DHR contains or references the data and information necessary to show that the required activities specified by the DMR were completed. The review, often coupled with finished device release activities, is

IX

intended to ensure that the product meets its quality attributes and that the records are in order. Chapter 10 provides more information on acceptance activities.

In addition to ensuring that the DMR was followed during the manufacturing process, the DHR serves several other useful purposes for manufacturers. It contains information on incoming material acceptance, on the manufacturing process, and on testing results that can be used to perform trend analyses. Tracking or trending of quality data on materials and processes may identify production or supplier problems that require corrective action as well as areas of improvement for cost savings. The DHR also serves as the basis for investigating complaints and taking corrective action, because it provides a record of any shifts, changes, or variances in the manufacturing process that may result in problems with finished devices. Consequently, most companies maintain more than the minimum information specified for inclusion in the DHR.

When device identification, such as the serial, lot, or control number, is required (e.g., devices subject to tracking or *in vitro* diagnostics), this information is commonly recorded in the DHR. However, for many segments of the medical device industry (e.g., manufacturers of crutches, hospital beds, and orthopedic hand instruments), serial, lot, or control numbers are not used. Manufacturers often make decisions regarding device identification depending on the need for traceability to identify problems or recall devices.

Typically, a DHR procedure specifies the content and format of the record, and the review and approval process. Record maintenance, storage, and retention also may be addressed.

820.186 Quality System Record

The Requirement

> ***820.186 Quality system record.*** *Each manufacturer shall maintain a quality system record (QSR). The QSR shall include, or refer to the location of, procedures and the documentation of activities required by this part that are not specific to a particular type of device(s), including, but not limited to, the records required by § 820.20. Each manufacturer shall ensure that the QSR is prepared and approved in accordance with § 820.40.*

Discussion of the Requirement

The requirements of this section reflect FDA's efforts to harmonize the GMP requirements more closely with the international quality standards and to outline a hierarchy of the documents required for meeting the Quality System regulation. The intent is to allow the separation of general Quality System records from device-specific records that make up the DMR and DHR. This approach allows the development of a quality manual, or similar file, that contains or references the more general documentation used for the overall planning and administration of activities used to define and implement the Quality System.

Principles and requirements incorporated in this section of the Quality System regulation include:
- quality planning;
- a Quality System documentation outline or manual, as appropriate for a given manufacturer;

- documented responsibilities and authorities; and
- Quality System procedures and instructions that are not part of a specific DMR (e.g., Management Review SOP).

Industry Practice

Those manufacturers whose Quality Systems meet the requirements of the ISO 9001/13485 Quality System standard typically have a Quality System that includes most of the records specified in section 820.186. Furthermore, although procedures and documentation for device-specific quality have been required by the GMPs since first promulgated, manufacturers typically apply a single document control system and record retention policy to all Quality System documents and records. Therefore, the Quality System Record (QSR) almost always exists in "logical" form, if not in physical form. The most important aspect of maintaining the QSR is being able to locate documents when needed.

The requirements of section 820.20(b) indicate the appropriateness of a comprehensive set of documentation that establishes quality responsibilities and relationships. A manufacturer can meet those requirements by providing organizational charts and job descriptions if those documents relate the functions of each individual or group within a company to required activities.

IX

NOTES:

IX

"How empty is theory in the presence of fact!"
S. Clemens (Mark Twain), *A Connecticut Yankee in King Arthur's Court*, 1889

SECTION X. ELECTRONIC RECORDS AND ELECTRONIC SIGNATURES

CHAPTER 24. GENERAL PROVISIONS (SUBPART A) OF 21 CFR PART 11

11.1 Scope

The Requirement

> ***Sec. 11.1 Scope.***
> ***(a)*** *The regulations in this part set forth the criteria under which the agency considers electronic records, electronic signatures, and handwritten signatures executed to electronic records to be trustworthy, reliable, and generally equivalent to paper records and handwritten signatures executed on paper.*
> ***(b)*** *This part applies to records in electronic form that are created, modified, maintained, archived, retrieved, or transmitted, under any records requirements set forth in agency regulations. This part also applies to electronic records submitted to the agency under requirements of the Federal Food, Drug, and Cosmetic Act and the Public Health Service Act, even if such records are not specifically identified in agency regulations. However, this part does not apply to paper records that are, or have been, transmitted by electronic means.*
> ***(c)*** *Where electronic signatures and their associated electronic records meet the requirements of this part, the agency will consider the electronic signatures to be equivalent to full handwritten signatures, initials, and other general signings as required by agency regulations, unless specifically excepted by regulation(s) effective on or after August 20, 1997.*
> ***(d)*** *Electronic records that meet the requirements of this part may be used in lieu of paper records, in accordance with Sec. 11.2, unless paper records are specifically required.*
> ***(e)*** *Computer systems (including hardware and software), controls, and attendant documentation maintained under this part shall be readily available for, and subject to, FDA inspection.*

Discussion of the Requirement

Paper records and handwritten signatures have been used for centuries. They are familiar and well understood. Forensic methods for analyzing paper records and handwritten signatures and establishing their authenticity are also well established. Erasures, correction fluid, and cross-outs on paper records can be readily detected. Handwriting experts can analyze handwritten signatures to detect forgeries.

Electronic records and electronic signatures, in contrast, have been in use a relatively short time. Forensic methods for detecting unauthorized changes to electronic records and electronic signatures are not nearly as well established, nor are they as familiar to or understood by most people. Changes, deletions, or additions made to electronic records and forged electronic signatures are difficult and sometimes impossible to detect unless the records are maintained on a record-keeping system that provides specific tools for tracking and identifying such modifications.

The Food and Drug Administration (FDA) issued 21 CFR Part 11, "Electronic Records; Electronic Signatures," on March 20, 1997, in response to industry requests for guidance on the use of electronic records and signatures. Part 11 went into effect on August 20, 1997, having been developed in concert with industry over a period of 6 years.

Part 11 requirements are intended to ensure that electronic records maintained to comply with FDA record-keeping requirements or submitted to FDA are trustworthy, reliable, and authentic. Part 11 requirements for electronic signatures are intended to ensure that signers cannot repudiate records they have signed as not bearing their authentic signatures.

Part 11 applies to medical device, drug, and biologics manufacturers when any of the following conditions are met:

   a. A manufacturer maintains records to meet FDA record-keeping requirements (as defined by a predicate rule), and these records are maintained in electronic form.

   b. Electronic signatures or handwritten signatures are applied to electronic records.

   c. Electronic records are submitted to FDA.

Part 11 has two types of requirements: administrative and technical. Administrative requirements generally apply to people and their activities, whereas technical requirements concern design and operation of systems to maintain and protect electronic records and signatures.

FDA Guidance

FDA regularly provides guidance to its own staff and to industry in the form of non-binding "guidance" documents, which are issued in accordance with good guidance practices. Such guidance typically provides background information and details on implementing various regulations, or on applying general regulations to specific device types. FDA's guidance on Part 11 contains information on how to implement Part 11 controls for various types of records. More information about Part 11 is available on the FDA web site www.fda.gov/ora/compliance_ref/part11.

During the first 5 years of implementation, the Part 11 regulation had become the focus of numerous debates following a gradual increase in FDA enforcement activities of the regulation. A divergence of opinion seemed to exist within the industry on the impact of this regulation. For example, in June 2002, the "Industry Coalition on 21 CFR Part 11", a group composed of numerous regulated industry trade organizations, submitted a proposal on the scope of the regulation to the Dockets Branch of FDA. The proposal related specifically to audit trails and the scope of documentation requiring audit trails.

After Part 11 went into effect, industry consistently expressed concerns that some of FDA's interpretations of Part 11 would unnecessarily restrict the use of electronic technology, discourage innovation and technological advances, and increase the costs of compliance significantly.

In February 2003, FDA withdrew several previous guidance documents that it had issued relating to 21 CFR Part 11. Following the withdrawal of those documents, FDA issued a new draft guidance document: *Part 11, Electronic Records; Electronic Signatures—Scope and Application—Guidance for Industry*. This guidance indicated the following:

    a. FDA would narrowly interpret Part 11, and fewer records would be subject to Part 11 requirements.

    b. For those records that were subject to Part 11, FDA would:
- exercise enforcement discretion regarding validation, audit trails, record retention, and record copying;
- exercise enforcement discretion regarding legacy systems (i.e., systems in place prior to August 20, 1997); and
- enforce predicate rule requirements for records subject to Part 11.

In August 2003, FDA issued a new and more comprehensive guidance on Part 11, *Part 11, Electronic Records; Electronic Signatures—Scope and Application—Guidance for Industry.* In this guidance, FDA indicated the intention to reexamine Part 11 and initiate rulemaking to revise certain provisions. The August 2003 guidance describes how FDA intends to exercise enforcement discretion in regard to certain Part 11 requirements while reexamining Part 11 and carrying out rulemaking. FDA will continue to enforce other Part 11 requirements, including all administrative requirements. Exercising enforcement discretion means that FDA will not take action to enforce compliance with certain Part 11 requirements, usually under specified conditions.

The August 2003 guidance identifies which Part 11 requirements will be subject to enforcement discretion. The guidance provides manufacturers with more flexibility in complying with Part 11 requirements, but it also places more responsibility on manufacturers to make decisions about which types of electronic records and which electronic record-keeping systems will comply with Part 11. Establishing documentation of these decisions is extremely important and will be helpful during FDA inspections. This Part 11 guidance significantly alters the scope of electronic records that are subject to Part 11 requirements and controls.

Manufacturers are advised to remain aware of evolving regulatory issues for Part 11 by checking updates to FDA's Part 11 web site: www.fda.gov/ora/compliance_ref/part11.

Electronic Records and Signatures Used at Regulated Facilities

Manufacturers should determine which electronic records they maintain to meet predicate rule requirements and which electronic records they maintain for other reasons (not required by predicate rules). These determinations should be documented. For records that are not required by a predicate rule, Part 11 does not apply. Examples of records that are not covered by Part 11 are financial records and personnel records, with the exception of training records.

Additionally, Part 11 will not apply to those records that are required by predicate rules when:
- computers are used to generate paper printouts of electronic records,
- these paper records meet all predicate rule requirements, and
- persons rely on the paper records to perform regulated activities.

Part 11 will continue to apply when electronic records are used in place of paper records to meet predicate rule requirements, even if paper printouts are generated. For example, if a manufacturer uses electronic records to trend complaints and other quality problems, these electronic records would be subject to Part 11 requirements, even if paper printouts are used to maintain a permanent record of the complaints, the quality problems, and the results of trending.

Manufacturers should determine in advance whether they will use electronic records or only paper record printouts to perform regulated activities. Decisions concerning paper versus electronic record format should be documented in a standard operating procedure (SOP) or specification. This decision is especially important where only paper records will be used to perform regulated activities. Procedures should be used to help ensure that employees use only paper records and not the electronic records. Paper and electronic records can coexist if predicate rule requirements are met and the content and meaning of the records are preserved.

Part 11 will continue to apply to electronic signatures in either of these circumstances:

    a. Electronic signatures are intended to be the equivalent of handwritten signatures, initials, or other signings required by a predicate rule.

    b. Electronic signatures are used to document the fact that certain events or actions occurred in accordance with the predicate rule (examples include review, approval, or verification of an activity required by the predicate rule).

Electronic Records Submitted to FDA

Part 11 applies to electronic records submitted to FDA under a predicate rule even if the records are not specifically identified in the predicate rule. Part 11 does not apply to records that are not submitted to FDA but are used in generating an electronic submission, unless a predicate rule requires such records to be maintained.

Legacy Systems

Meeting Part 11 requirements clearly is challenging for manufacturers with legacy systems (i.e., systems that have been in use for an extended time), because these systems may not have been designed with Part 11-type requirements in mind. The August 2003 guidance specifically addresses the application of Part 11 to legacy systems. For the purposes of Part 11 enforcement, a legacy system is a computerized record-keeping system that was in operation before Part 11 went into effect on August 20, 1997.

FDA intends to exercise enforcement discretion with respect to all Part 11 requirements for legacy systems if all the following criteria are met for a specific legacy system:

    a. The system was operational and met all applicable predicate rule requirements before August 20, 1997.

    b. The system currently meets all applicable predicate rule requirements.

    c. Documented evidence shows the system is fit for its intended use and has an acceptable level of record security and integrity.

11.2 Implementation

The Requirement

Sec. 11.2 Implementation.
(a) *For records required to be maintained but not submitted to the agency, persons may use electronic records in lieu of paper records or electronic signatures in lieu of traditional signatures, in whole or in part, provided that the requirements of this part are met.*

(b) *For records submitted to the agency, persons may use electronic records in lieu of paper records or electronic signatures in lieu of traditional signatures, in whole or in part, provided that:*

(1) *The requirements of this part are met; and*

(2) *The document or parts of a document to be submitted have been identified in public docket No. 92S-0251 as being the type of submission the agency accepts in electronic form. This docket will identify specifically what types of documents or parts of documents are acceptable for submission in electronic form without paper records and the agency receiving unit(s) (e.g., specific center, office, division, branch) to which such submissions may be made. Documents to agency receiving unit(s) not specified in the public docket will not be considered as official if they are submitted in electronic form; paper forms of such documents will be considered as official and must accompany any electronic records. Persons are expected to consult with the intended agency receiving unit for details on how (e.g., method of transmission, media, file formats, and technical protocols) and whether to proceed with the electronic submission.*

Discussion of the Requirement

FDA record-keeping requirements are contained in predicate rules. A "predicate rule" is any FDA law or regulation that requires manufacturers to maintain records. Part 11 works in tandem with predicate rules. A predicate rule typically specifies the following:

- what records must be maintained;
- what information must be in the records;
- where signatures are required; and
- how long records must be maintained (i.e., the record retention period).

In contrast, Part 11 specifies *how* electronic records must be maintained to be reliable, authentic, and trustworthy and to ensure that signers cannot readily repudiate signed records as not genuine. A manufacturer is not required to maintain electronic records. However, if the manufacturer chooses to maintain required records electronically, the elements of Part 11 apply.

The Quality System regulation, 21 CFR Part 820, is a predicate rule because it includes record-keeping requirements for medical device manufacturers. A portion of the records required by the Quality System regulation include the following:

- Design History File (section 820.30(j)),
- Device Master Record (section 820.181),
- Device History Record (section 820.184),
- Quality System Record (section 820.186),
- complaint and complaint investigation files (section 820.198),
- service records (section 820.200(d)),
- training records (section 820.25(b)), and
- records of corrective and preventive action activities (section 820.100(b)).

Whether records are maintained on paper or electronically, they must be maintained in a way that meets the requirements of the predicate rule. If they are maintained electronically, they must be maintained in accordance with applicable sections of 21 CFR Part 11.

11.3 Definitions

Sec. 11.3 Definitions.
(a) *The definitions and interpretations of terms contained in section 201 of the act apply to those terms when used in this part.*
(b) *The following definitions of terms also apply to this part:*
(b)(1) **Act** *means the Federal Food, Drug, and Cosmetic Act (secs. 201-903 (21 U.S.C. 321-393)).*

Discussion: Section 201 of the Federal Food, Drug, and Cosmetic Act, as amended by the FDA Modernization Act (FDAMA) of 1997, contains a number of definitions that generally apply to medical device manufacturing.

11.3(b)(2) **Agency** *means the Food and Drug Administration.*

Discussion: FDAMA of 1997 affirmed FDA's public health protection role and defined the Agency's mission, which includes attaining reasonable assurance of the safety and effectiveness of devices intended for human use. Compliance with regulations such as 21 CFR 11 supports this mission.

11.3(b)(3) **Biometrics** *means a method of verifying an individual's identity based on measurement of the individual's physical feature(s) or repeatable action(s) where those features and/or actions are both unique to that individual and measurable.*

Discussion: Biometrics typically involves matching a digitally stored human characteristic with an actual rendition of that characteristic. Biometrics relies on uniqueness of various human features and actions. The most commonly used biometric technique is fingerprint matching. However, matching other unique physical or biological characteristics, such as voiceprint, retina pattern, iris pattern, or facial characteristics, and matching unique personal traits, such as handwriting, are also possible.

11.3(b)(4) **Closed system** *means an environment in which system access is controlled by persons who are responsible for the content of electronic records that are on the system.*

11.3(b)(9) **Open system** *means an environment in which system access is not controlled by persons who are responsible for the content of electronic records that are on the system.*

Discussion: Distinguishing between open and closed systems is important in terms of establishing expectations for the level of control that can be reasonably expected on the part of the manufacturer. An example of a closed system is a manufacturer's in-house complaint-handling system. Because the system is controlled directly by the manufacturer, it is closed.

X

An example of an open system (from the manufacturer's perspective) is a contract distributor's database for shipment data, which may be accessible by the manufacturer through an Internet connection. The distributor's database is controlled by the distributor; the manufacturer has less immediate control of the system, and thus it is an open system.

11.3(b)(5) Digital signature means an electronic signature based upon cryptographic methods of originator authentication, computed by using a set of rules and a set of parameters such that the identity of the signer and the integrity of the data can be verified.

11.3(b)(7) Electronic signature means a computer data compilation of any symbol or series of symbols executed, adopted, or authorized by an individual to be the legally binding equivalent of the individual's handwritten signature.

11.3(b)(8) Handwritten signature means the scripted name or legal mark of an individual handwritten by that individual and executed or adopted with the present intention to authenticate a writing in a permanent form. The act of signing with a writing or marking instrument such as a pen or stylus is preserved. The scripted name or legal mark, while conventionally applied to paper, may also be applied to other devices that capture the name or mark.

Discussion: Whether written by hand or electronically applied, every valid signature is unique to a specific individual and is applied with that individual's knowledge and intent to sign. The digital signature is an electronically rendered individual signature applied to a specific record or set of records.

11.3(b)(6) Electronic record means any combination of text, graphics, data, audio, pictorial, or other information representation in digital form that is created, modified, maintained, archived, retrieved, or distributed by a computer system.

Discussion: A record is merely evidence of the conduct of an activity. A record can include confirmatory evidence, such as data, or summary information, such as names and dates of individuals who performed the activity. The record is the "proof" that the activity was performed. Electronic records can be created and maintained in many formats, including databases, Internet web pages, and other electronically stored files.

X

CHAPTER 25. ELECTRONIC RECORDS (SUBPART B)

11.10 Controls for Closed Systems

11.30 Controls for Open Systems

The Requirement

Sec. 11.10 Controls for closed systems.

Persons who use closed systems to create, modify, maintain, or transmit electronic records shall employ procedures and controls designed to ensure the authenticity, integrity, and, when appropriate, the confidentiality of electronic records, and to ensure that the signer cannot readily repudiate the signed record as not genuine. Such procedures and controls shall include the following:

(a) Validation of systems to ensure accuracy, reliability, consistent intended performance, and the ability to discern invalid or altered records.

(b) The ability to generate accurate and complete copies of records in both human readable and electronic form suitable for inspection, review, and copying by the agency. Persons should contact the agency if there are any questions regarding the ability of the agency to perform such review and copying of the electronic records.

(c) Protection of records to enable their accurate and ready retrieval throughout the records retention period.

(d) Limiting system access to authorized individuals.

(e) Use of secure, computer-generated, time-stamped audit trails to independently record the date and time of operator entries and actions that create, modify, or delete electronic records. Record changes shall not obscure previously recorded information. Such audit trail documentation shall be retained for a period at least as long as that required for the subject electronic records and shall be available for agency review and copying.

(f) Use of operational system checks to enforce permitted sequencing of steps and events, as appropriate.

(g) Use of authority checks to ensure that only authorized individuals can use the system, electronically sign a record, access the operation or computer system input or output device, alter a record, or perform the operation at hand.

(h) Use of device (e.g., terminal) checks to determine, as appropriate, the validity of the source of data input or operational instruction.

(i) Determination that persons who develop, maintain, or use electronic record/electronic signature systems have the education, training, and experience to perform their assigned tasks.

(j) The establishment of, and adherence to, written policies that hold individuals accountable and responsible for actions initiated under their electronic signatures, in order to deter record and signature falsification.

(k) Use of appropriate controls over systems documentation including:

(1) Adequate controls over the distribution of, access to, and use of documentation for system operation and maintenance.

(2) Revision and change control procedures to maintain an audit trail that documents time-sequenced development and modification of systems documentation.

Sec. 11.30 Controls for open systems.

Persons who use open systems to create, modify, maintain, or transmit electronic records shall employ procedures and controls designed to ensure the authenticity, integrity, and, as appropriate, the confidentiality of electronic records from the point of their creation to the point of their receipt. Such procedures and controls shall include those identified in Sec.

11.10, as appropriate, and additional measures such as document encryption and use of appropriate digital signature standards to ensure, as necessary under the circumstances, record authenticity, integrity, and confidentiality.

Discussion of the Requirement

As discussed in Chapter 24, Part 11 has two types of requirements: administrative and technical. Administrative requirements concern procedures and practices that must be established to maintain the security of electronic record-keeping and electronic signature systems. Administrative requirements generally apply to people and their activities.

Technical requirements concern how electronic record-keeping systems and electronic signature systems must be designed and operated to maintain and protect electronic records and signatures. For the electronic record-keeping and signature systems, the technical requirements prescribe controls to ensure that records cannot be inappropriately modified.

The key electronic record administrative requirement is establishment of a policy for electronic records. Administrative requirements for electronic records also include the following, which should be addressed in the electronic records policy:
- combined identification codes and passwords that are unique for each individual's electronic signature;
- controls for identification codes and passwords;
- initial and periodic testing of tokens, cards or other devices that bear or generate identification code or password information;
- loss management procedures for tokens, cards and other devices;
- written policies to deter record falsification;
- control of system documentation;
- limitations on system access; and
- adequate training, qualifications and experience for individuals who develop, maintain and use the electronic record-keeping system.

The key technical requirements for electronic records are validation of electronic record-keeping systems and implementation of audit trails. Technical requirements for electronic record-keeping systems also include the following:

a. Implement the ability to generate accurate and complete copies of records in human readable and electronic form for inspection, review and copying by FDA.

b. Protect records to enable future retrieval.

c. Employ operational system checks that enforce the sequence in which steps or events are performed.

d. Institute authority checks, which ensure that only authorized individuals use the system.

e. Adopt device checks that identify valid and invalid sources of data input and operational instructions.

f. Develop additional controls for open systems to ensure the authenticity, integrity, and, as appropriate, confidentiality of electronic records from their point of creation to receipt.

X

The audit trail requirement is a key control in making electronic records reliable, authentic, and trustworthy. The audit trail records and documents:
- the identity of anyone who creates, modifies, or deletes an electronic record;
- the time and date when the action occurred; and
- anything that was done to the record (i.e., specific changes made).

Audit trails must be secure, computer generated, automatic, and independent of any operator actions, as well as associated with a specific record. A person reviewing the audit trail of an electronic record must be able to see what changes were made to the document, by whom, and when. Changes shall not obscure previously recorded information.

According to the August 2003 Part 11 guidance, *Part 11, Electronic Records; Electronic Signatures—Scope and Application—Guidance for Industry,* FDA will exercise enforcement discretion in regard to audit trail requirements. However, manufacturers must comply with all predicate rule requirements that (a) relate to date, time, and sequencing of events and (b) ensure that changes to records do not obscure previous entries.

Even in the absence of predicate rule requirements to document date, time, or sequence of events, an audit trail will help ensure the trustworthiness and reliability of records. Audit trails are especially appropriate when users are expected to create, modify, or delete regulated records during normal operations. When deciding whether electronic records should have audit trails, manufacturers should base their decisions on the following:
- the need to comply with predicate rule requirements,
- a justified and documented risk assessment, and
- a determination of the potential effect of lack of record integrity on product quality and safety.

Policies on Electronic Records and Electronic Signatures

Establishing policies concerning electronic records and electronic signatures and educating employees on those policies are crucial to maintaining the reliability, trustworthiness, and authenticity of electronic records and signatures. Policies must discourage falsification of electronic records and signatures, sharing of passwords, or sharing of access cards. Policies should also make clear that employees will be held responsible for the information and actions covered by their signatures on electronic records.

Validation of Electronic Record-Keeping Systems

Part 11 includes a requirement to validate electronic record-keeping systems. The purpose of validation is to ensure the accuracy, reliability, and consistent intended performance of the system, as well as its ability to discern invalid or altered records. The Quality System regulation also requires the validation of computer systems and automated data processing systems that are part of the production or Quality System under section 820.70(i). Refer to additional information on validation of automated processes in Chapters 13 and 29.

FDA's August 2003 guidance states that FDA intends to exercise enforcement discretion for Part 11 validation requirements. Although manufacturers of other commodities regulated by FDA do not have validation requirements in predicate rules, the Quality System regulation (21 CFR 820.70(i)) requires medical device manufacturers to validate certain computer systems. The relaxation of validation requirements for Part 11 *does not* apply to the validation requirements in the Quality System regulation. Device manufacturers must continue to validate computer systems, including electronic record-keeping systems that are used in manufacturing, and used in the Quality System. Validation must be in accordance with the requirements of 21 CFR 820.70(i), as described in Chapter 13.

Computer systems can affect the manufacturer's ability to meet predicate rule requirements and the accuracy, reliability, integrity, availability, and authenticity of required records and signatures. Therefore, the proper functioning of such systems must be formally assessed and documented in accordance with common software validation practices. In deciding how to approach validation, the manufacturer should use a justified and documented risk assessment in determining the potential effect the system has on product quality, product safety, and record integrity.

The basis for validation is establishing user requirements for the computer system, the software, or both. The user requirements define what the user expects from the system (i.e., a system's function based on the user's intent), often referred to as "intended use." The requirements established for the computer systems and software should include maintaining the reliability, authenticity, and trustworthiness of electronic records, as well as confidentiality where appropriate.

After a software developer knows what the users want a computer system or software to do for them, the developer can design the system and conduct validation to determine whether the system fulfills the user's requirements. Even if the software is an off-the-shelf product, documentation of the requirements for the manufacturer's particular usage is still important and still serves as the basis for validation.

As with any other validation activity, documentation of the validation tasks and results is essential. The user (i.e., device manufacturer) is ultimately responsible for validation of the system. Validation conducted by a contract software developer can serve as the foundation for the manufacturer's validation, but the manufacturer must validate the system to ensure that, as installed and used at the manufacturer's facility, it meets the manufacturer's requirements.

Generating Copies of Records for FDA

According to the August 2003 guidance, FDA intends to exercise enforcement discretion with regard to copies of records that manufacturers generate for FDA investigators. According to predicate rules, required records held by a manufacturer are subject to inspection. Manufacturers should provide FDA investigators with reasonable and useful access to records during an inspection. FDA investigators should be allowed to inspect, review, and obtain copies of records in human readable form at the manufacturer's site, using the manufacturer's hardware and following the procedures and techniques for accessing the records that the manufacturer has established.

If an FDA investigator requests copies of electronic records, the manufacturer's options include the following:

    a. Produce copies of records in common portable formats when records are maintained in these formats.

    b. Use established automated conversion or export methods, where available, to make copies in a more common format (for example, portable document format, or PDF; extensible markup language, or XML; or standard generalized markup language, or SGML).

The copying process used should produce copies that preserve the content and meaning of the record. If the manufacturer has the ability to search, sort, or trend records, the copies provided to FDA should preserve the same capability, if reasonable and technically feasible.

Record Retention

How manufacturers maintain and control records should be based on:
- predicate rule requirements,
- a justified and documented risk assessment, and
- a determination of the value of records over time.

Electronic records may be archived to non-electronic media such as microfilm, microfiche, or paper. Electronic records also may be archived in standard electronic file formats such as PDF, XML, or SGML. Manufacturers may delete the original electronic records after archiving them if:
- the manufacturer has complied with all predicate rule requirements, and
- archived copies preserve the content and meaning of the original records.

Part 11 Requirements Not Affected by August 2003 Guidance

As stated in the August 2003 Guidance, FDA intends to continue enforcing provisions relating to the following controls and requirements:

    a. Limit system access to authorized individuals.

    b. Use operational system checks, authority checks, and device checks.

    c. Determine that persons who develop, maintain, or use the electronic record-keeping systems have the education, training, and experience necessary to perform their assigned tasks.

    d. Establish and adhere to written policies that hold individuals accountable for actions initiated under their electronic signatures.

    e. Implement appropriate controls over system documentation.

    f. Develop controls for open systems corresponding to controls for closed systems listed above.

    g. Enforce requirements related to electronic signatures (i.e., sections 11.50, 11.70, 11.100, 11.200, and 11.300).

11.50 Signature Manifestations

11.70 Signature/Record Linking

The Requirement

> ### *Sec. 11.50 Signature manifestations.*
> *(a) Signed electronic records shall contain information associated with the signing that clearly indicates all of the following:*
>   *(1) The printed name of the signer;*
>   *(2) The date and time when the signature was executed; and*
>   *(3) The meaning (such as review, approval, responsibility, or authorship) associated with the signature.*
> *(b) The items identified in paragraphs (a)(1), (a)(2), and (a)(3) of this section shall be subject to the same controls as for electronic records and shall be included as part of any human readable form of the electronic record (such as electronic display or printout).*
>
> ### *Sec. 11.70 Signature/record linking.*
> *Electronic signatures and handwritten signatures executed to electronic records shall be linked to their respective electronic records to ensure that the signatures cannot be excised, copied, or otherwise transferred to falsify an electronic record by ordinary means.*

Discussion of the Requirement

Expectations concerning the meaning and display of electronic signatures are covered in 21 CFR 11 Subpart B and are discussed next. Other requirements concerning electronic signatures are covered in 21 CFR 11 Subpart C and discussed in Chapter 26. FDA's August 2003 Part 11 guidance does not affect requirements concerning electronic signatures. FDA will continue to enforce these requirements.

Information Displayed with an Electronic Signature

An electronic signature in a record shall display the following information:
- printed name of the signer;
- date and time when the signature was executed; and
- meaning associated with the signature (authorship, review, approval, etc.).

This information is required when the record is reviewed in an electronic form (e.g., on a computer monitor) and when viewed in a printed format.

Linking the Signature to the Electronic Record

A signature, whether electronic or handwritten, must be linked to its electronic records in such a way that the signature cannot be excised, copied, or transferred to falsify an electronic record by ordinary means. In all cases, it must be clear that the signature is applied to a specific record, and not just generally in the record-keeping system.

Industry Practice on Electronic Records: Small Company Perspective

Although within industry a wide range of application of electronic records and systems exists, small companies often focus on the following:

- Quality System documents (e.g., procedures, device master record (DMR) documents);
- quality records (e.g., device history record (DHR) contents used to demonstrate that activities were completed in accordance with the DMR); and
- use of quality data/records.

Those firms that maintain hand-signed paper copies of documents and records will find little effect on their business from Part 11 requirements. Quality data that are stored and processed electronically for regulated activities are subject to Part 11.

Quality System Documents

Most small companies maintain their Quality System documents (Quality Manual, standard operating procedures, instructions, etc.) in a paper format with handwritten signatures on either the document or on the release or approval form. These paper copies are used in the business practice of the firm. The documents are prepared and maintained in a word-processing system, but these word-processor files are not the form used for completing work on a day-to-day basis. FDA's August 2003 Part 11 guidance document indicates that the use of computers to generate paper documents would not trigger Part 11 requirements because the computer is "merely incidental in use." However, if electronic Quality System documents are used in lieu of paper records, Part 11 does apply.

Quality Records

It is fairly common practice for small companies to rely on paper records even if the records are created electronically. Many small firms maintain the original paper copy of records, such as the DHR, complaint files, and corrective and preventive action (CAPA) records.

Records that are maintained electronically in lieu of paper or that are submitted to FDA electronically are subject to Part 11. (Refer to the discussion of scope in Chapter 24 and in this chapter.) Record retention and archiving present some unique challenges for manufacturers for a number of reasons:

a. Access to electronic records depends on the application that created the records. Predicate rule record retention requirements (e.g., 21 CFR 820.180) may dictate that records should be available for many years past the record's archival date, depending on archival policies and the expected life of the medical device. Thus, archival processes must include a means of saving the application used to create the electronic records in addition to the particular records if the system is upgraded or retired.

b. Some types of electronic storage media degrade over time, particularly if they remain unused. For example, magnetic tape that is not periodically re-spooled may lose integrity of the data (i.e., data may not be retrievable years later if tapes are not "exercised" periodically). Thus, long-term electronic record storage may require ongoing maintenance of the storage media as well.

c. As hardware systems change over time, older electronic systems may not continue to operate correctly. Therefore, archival methods may need to address both the software applications and the hardware platforms needed to execute the software.

As a result of these challenges, manufacturers typically develop an electronic record retention and archival scheme that is broader than a paper record retention scheme.

Use of Quality Data and Records

Quality metrics, even in small firms, are often prepared using data and records stored in and processed by computers. Examples of such metrics include trends in customer complaints, tracking percentages of lots received and then returned to vendors as nonconforming, and process capability for key processes. When electronic data and systems are relied on to perform a regulated activity, such as trending analysis, Part 11 will apply. Even if the original paper documents are maintained, the data stored and processed electronically are subject to Part 11. In its August 2003 guidance document, FDA recommends identifying in a standard operating procedure (SOP) the quality records that are maintained and used electronically and those that are maintained on paper.

Although performing regulated activities such as trending can be done manually, most organizations benefit by using electronic systems. Judicious use of electronic systems, including appropriate validation of those systems, can enhance a manufacturer's Quality System effectiveness. The validation of these systems is governed by predicate rules, such as 21 CFR Part 820.70(i), "Automated processes." This section of the Quality System regulation includes the validation of software used to support or facilitate manufacturing and Quality System activity. Software within the scope of 820.70(i) needs to be validated for its intended use; refer to Chapter 29 for more details on automated process software validation.

Industry Practice on Electronic Records: Large Company Perspective

Many large medical device manufacturers (i.e., firms with 500 or more employees) have established separate corporate-level organizations to set corporate policies and procedures for electronic records. These organizations may be part of the regulatory affairs (RA), quality assurance (QA), or information technology (IT) departments, among others. In many cases, the electronic record and signature compliance staff were assigned in early 1998, in conjunction with the effective date of Part 11.

Early Large Company Practices (Pre-February 2003): Assessment and Planning

Large firms pursued early implementation of 21 CFR 11 policies by establishing guidelines in key areas, such as the following:
- corporate-wide planning for part 11 validation activities, including identification of systems subject to part 11 requirements;
- continued use of electronic record keeping systems before part 11 compliance was formally assured;
- responsibilities for developing and conducting validation for part 11 compliance of existing (legacy) systems;
- responsibilities for maintaining validation when systems are upgraded;
- responsibilities for staff training programs on part 11 issues;
- authorization methods for acquisition or development, validation, and implementation of new electronic record keeping systems; and
- record retention and archiving for electronic record keeping systems.

Corporate-wide planning activities often started with development of a comprehensive inventory of electronic record-keeping systems. Given the easy access to personal computers (PCs), coupled with the "standard" software tools typically provided on PCs (word processors, spreadsheets, and databases), employees often developed their own (uncontrolled) electronic tools for record-keeping. Some applications that started as an individual's ad hoc time-saving tool changed in purpose over time to become a key quality record repository. Many firms were surprised at the extent of such systems when the inventory was prepared. Thus, the inventory effort was often one of fact finding and investigation, which took many months to complete.

After the inventory was established, the firm determined where gaps in compliance existed. Gaps could indicate merely a need for formal validation or a need to modify the systems to address lack of functionality in those systems.

The culmination of the planning effort was to establish priorities for validation in a Master Validation Plan. Often, the priorities were based on the following:
- potential risks involved based on significance of the records in the overall Quality System,
- suspect integrity of records,
- potential impact of record loss, and
- pervasiveness of the system's use.

The Master Validation Plan provided a framework within which individual validation tasks were monitored. Coinciding with creation of the Master Validation Plan, corporate electronic record-keeping policies and procedures were established.

Early Large Company Practices (Pre-February 2003): Remediation and Validation

The Master Validation Plan was the "road map" for guiding remediation and validation activities. Some firms established a method for duplication of records while the validation effort was pending. Thus, systems previously used electronically were used in conjunction with paper-based archiving of the records. This "paper backup" process provided a level of assurance that the record content would continue to be available in the event of a system failure.

For some legacy electronic systems, whether developed in-house or purchased, validation to Part 11 requirements was simply not possible. This situation was not uncommon; many software packages were not designed with audit trail features. Such systems presented a particular challenge to manufacturers, because a migration and obsolescence strategy was necessary.

Manufacturers used a variety of methods to accomplish their Part 11 validation activities. Use of existing (or augmented) IT staff, R&D staff, or QA staff was not uncommon. Also, outsourcing provided a source of specialized, qualified contract staff to support Part 11 validation.

Large manufacturers typically established new processes for acquisition and implementation of new software systems. These processes also applied to implementation of upgrades when third-party software vendors offered upgraded features. By instituting proactive controls for software that created electronic records, firms began limiting compliance issues related to Part 11.

Current Large Company Practices (Post-February 2003)

FDA published the updated guidance on Part 11 in August 2003. The guidance provides clarification of a reduced Part 11 scope for ancillary systems (such as word processors); however, the overall intent of Part 11 remains intact. Thus, in many large firms, the Part 11 compliance offices have continued to function according to their established policies. The following aspects of large company practices for electronic records continue to represent the state of the industry:

a. Corporate policies, procedures, and milestones provide a framework for operating units within the firm.

b. Corporate-level governing boards or core teams maintain ongoing practices that are based on evolving industry practices and FDA guidance.

c. Reassessment and prioritization of validation activities are based on evolving FDA guidance and on internal risk assessments.

d. Libraries with guidelines, templates, tools, and "best practices" are generally available to support execution of the electronic records program.

e. Operating units (division, business unit, subsidiary, etc.) provide detailed plans and procedures for achieving and maintaining compliance within the corporate framework.

f. Training programs exist for general awareness and for execution of specific aspects of the electronic records program.

g. Corporate tracking of compliance status is based on inventories of systems covered by electronic record regulations.

In addition to establishing staff positions with focused responsibilities policies and procedures for compliance with Part 11 requirements, large companies commonly institute compliance practices in the areas of training and new software selection. Manufacturers may use in-house training related to the requirements for addressing Part 11 requirements as established by corporate policies. External training (seminars and workshops) is also commonly available.

The critical aspect of such training is to ensure that employees understand existing controls (unique, protected system access methods); policies concerning changes to existing systems; and acquisition of new electronic record-keeping systems. Manufacturers typically have training related to general awareness as well as detailed training for staff members who are responsible for software selection (related to electronic record-keeping and signatures) and software validation.

In ongoing operations, an assessment of Part 11 compliance is commonly included in the off-the-shelf or customized software selection process when the software is going to become an integral part of the Quality System. Manufacturers may choose to audit the software developer before completing a purchase. Furthermore, policies may require estimation of

X

the cost for in-house Part 11 validation as part of the total purchase price estimate and purchase order approval.

Manufacturers are advised to remain aware of evolving regulatory issues for Part 11 by checking updates to the FDA's Part 11 web site: www.fda.gov/ora/compliance_ref/part11.

X

CHAPTER 26. ELECTRONIC SIGNATURES (SUBPART C)

11.100 General Requirements

11.200 Electronic Signature Components and Controls

11.300 Controls for Identification Codes/Passwords

The Requirement

Sec. 11.100 General requirements.

(a) Each electronic signature shall be unique to one individual and shall not be reused by, or reassigned to, anyone else.

(b) Before an organization establishes, assigns, certifies, or otherwise sanctions an individual's electronic signature, or any element of such electronic signature, the organization shall verify the identity of the individual.

(c) Persons using electronic signatures shall, prior to or at the time of such use, certify to the agency that the electronic signatures in their system, used on or after August 20, 1997, are intended to be the legally binding equivalent of traditional handwritten signatures.

> *(1) The certification shall be submitted in paper form and signed with a traditional handwritten signature, to the Office of Regional Operations (HFC-100), 5600 Fishers Lane, Rockville, MD 20857.*

> *(2) Persons using electronic signatures shall, upon agency request, provide additional certification or testimony that a specific electronic signature is the legally binding equivalent of the signer's handwritten signature.*

Sec. 11.200 Electronic signature components and controls.

(a) Electronic signatures that are not based upon biometrics shall:

> *(1) Employ at least two distinct identification components such as an identification code and password.*

>> *(i) When an individual executes a series of signings during a single, continuous period of controlled system access, the first signing shall be executed using all electronic signature components; subsequent signings shall be executed using at least one electronic signature component that is only executable by, and designed to be used only by, the individual.*

>> *(ii) When an individual executes one or more signings not performed during a single, continuous period of controlled system access, each signing shall be executed using all of the electronic signature components.*

> *(2) Be used only by their genuine owners; and*

> *(3) Be administered and executed to ensure that attempted use of an individual's electronic signature by anyone other than its genuine owner requires collaboration of two or more individuals.*

(b) Electronic signatures based upon biometrics shall be designed to ensure that they cannot be used by anyone other than their genuine owners.

Sec. 11.300 Controls for identification codes/passwords.

Persons who use electronic signatures based upon use of identification codes in combination with passwords shall employ controls to ensure their security and integrity. Such controls shall include:

> *(a) Maintaining the uniqueness of each combined identification code and password, such that no two individuals have the same combination of identification code and password.*

X

(b) Ensuring that identification code and password issuances are periodically checked, recalled, or revised (e.g., to cover such events as password aging).

(c) Following loss management procedures to electronically deauthorize lost, stolen, missing, or otherwise potentially compromised tokens, cards, and other devices that bear or generate identification code or password information, and to issue temporary or permanent replacements using suitable, rigorous controls.

(d) Use of transaction safeguards to prevent unauthorized use of passwords and/or identification codes, and to detect and report in an immediate and urgent manner any attempts at their unauthorized use to the system security unit, and, as appropriate, to organizational management.

(e) Initial and periodic testing of devices, such as tokens or cards, that bear or generate identification code or password information to ensure that they function properly and have not been altered in an unauthorized manner.

Discussion of the Requirement

As discussed in Chapter 24, Part 11 includes both administrative and technical requirements. Key administrative requirements for electronic signatures include certifying electronic signatures and establishing a policy for electronic signatures. The administrative requirements for electronic signatures include all of the following:

- certification to FDA that electronic signatures are the legally binding equivalent of handwritten signatures,
- controls for electronic signatures,
- written policies to deter signature falsification, and
- written policies on individual accountability and responsibility with regard to electronic signatures.

Key technical requirements for electronic signatures cover the way in which electronic signatures are executed, the information that must be displayed as part of the electronic signature, and the process of linking signatures to their documents. Other technical requirements for electronic signatures include the following:

a. Base electronic signatures on biometric controls or two components such as a user identification code and a password.

b. Require the use of both components at the execution of the first electronic signature during a single uninterrupted signing session and use of one component for subsequent signings during the same session.

c. Implement biometric controls designed to be used only by their genuine owners.

d. Use electronic signatures that display the printed name of signer, date and time of the signature, and meaning of the signature.

e. Ensure that electronic and handwritten signatures are linked to their electronic records to prevent falsification of electronic records by ordinary means.

Certification of Electronic Signatures

Manufacturers using electronic signatures must certify to FDA that the electronic signatures in their system are the legally binding equivalent of traditional handwritten signatures. The certification must be on paper and signed with a traditional handwritten signature. Manufacturers should mail the electronic signature certification to the address specified in 21 CFR 11.100(c).

This is a one-time-only certification. The certification must be submitted before electronic signatures are used or at the time electronic signatures are first used. The certification covers all employees who are using electronic signatures, both when the certification is submitted and in the future. The certification can cover all the facilities in a company, even if those facilities are at various locations around the world. Manufacturers do not need to submit a new certification when employees leave or when new employees are hired, when the manufacturer moves from one facility to another, or when the manufacturer adds a new facility.

FDA may request that a manufacturer provide additional certification that a specific electronic signature is the legally binding equivalent of the signer's handwritten signature.

Executing Electronic Signatures

Electronic signatures may be biometric or based on two distinct components, such as a user identification code and a password. In either case, the user identification must be unique to each individual who will have the ability to execute an electronic signature.

When an individual executes an electronic signature or series of signatures that are based on two components, the system must require the signer to use both components to execute the first signing. The signer may use only one of the components to execute additional signings during the same single continuous period of controlled access. Manufacturers should take care to ensure that an individual is prevented from gaining access to a system once for an extended period (e.g., across several days or weeks). Typically, manufacturers have automated "logout" implemented to take effect after a predetermined period of inactivity on the system.

Discussions on policies for electronic signature integrity are included in Chapter 25.

Industry Practice on Electronic Signatures: Small Company Perspective

Only when electronic signatures are used to replace or be equivalent to handwritten signatures (or initials) will Part 11 apply. Therefore, those firms that maintain signed paper copies will not be affected by this requirement. Given the relative effort associated with validating electronic signatures, many small firms have chosen to establish a policy prohibiting the use of electronic signatures.

In other cases, firms have selected or adopted use of systems provided by software vendors that ensure compliance with Part 11 requirements for electronic signatures. These systems commonly include a "validation protocol" provided by the software vendor, to be executed by the manufacturer as part of the system installation effort. Manufacturers that choose to use such systems typically require proof from the vendor that each aspect of electronic signature compliance exists.

Industry Practice on Electronic Signatures: Large Company Perspective

The general approach that large firms have applied to electronic record-keeping systems also applies to electronic signature compliance efforts. This approach is described in detail in Chapter 25. As with small firms, the use of third-party software developed specifically to address FDA's electronic signature requirements is common.

Part 11 has clearly presented a new set of challenges to manufacturers. While small companies have restricted the potential cost of Part 11 compliance efforts by restricting use of electronic record-keeping and signature systems, many large manufacturers have established full-scale Part 11 offices to address pertinent issues while retaining their historic use of electronic record-keeping and signature systems.

Electronic signatures are more commonly used in large firms. In many cases, corporate IT departments have established relationships with software vendors to provide customization and validation support in light of Part 11 requirements. In other instances, specific sites are given latitude to establish electronic signature policies and validation programs under a corporate umbrella policy concerning validation of such systems before they are implemented.

Manufacturers are advised to remain aware of evolving regulatory issues for Part 11 by checking updates to the FDA's Part 11 web site: www.fda.gov/ora/compliance%5Fref/part11.

Other Electronic Record and Signature Issues for Manufacturers

Manufacturers that develop medical devices that provide electronic record-keeping for unique patient information may find that their customers are now subject to regulations based on the Health Insurance Portability and Accountability Act of 1996 (HIPAA). The final rule on health information privacy was published in 2000 (45 CFR 160 and 164), was updated in August 2002, and came into full effect in April 2003. This regulation is administered by the U.S. Department of Health and Human Services.

Devices that provide functions related to storage or transmission of unique patient health information may need to address electronic signature security and security requirements for electronic record transmission to meet user needs. Further information on the patient information privacy regulation is available at www.hhs.gov/ocr/hipaa.

X

NOTES:

X

"A fact in itself is nothing. It is valuable only for the idea attached to it, or for the proof which it furnishes."
C. Bernard (1813 – 1878)

NOTES:

X

"Let deeds match words."
             Titus Maccius Platutus (254 BC – 184 BC)

SECTION XI. EVOLVING REGULATORY AND INDUSTRY PRACTICE

CHAPTER 27. PROCESS VALIDATION IN A GLOBAL MARKETPLACE

This chapter presents an overview of a process validation guidance document implemented by the Center for Devices and Radiological Health (CDRH), discusses differences between this guidance document and previous Food and Drug Administration (FDA) publications, and describes the effect of current FDA inspection approaches on manufacturers' process validation programs. Material presented here supplements Chapter 15, "Process Validation."

Process Validation Guidance

In the *Guideline on General Principles of Process Validation* (May, 1987), FDA defined a series of activities necessary for validating production processes. This original guidance applied to medical device, drug, and biologic manufacturers. Subsequently, CDRH participated in Global Harmonization Task Force (GHTF) activities related to the development of new process validation guidance. The GHTF's Study Group 3 (Quality Systems group) began working on harmonized process validation guidance for medical device manufacturers in the late 1990s.

CDRH participated in Study Group 3 activities, as did other international regulatory bodies. In June 1999, the GHTF endorsed a document titled *Process Validation Guidance for Medical Device Manufacturers*. In January 2004, Study Group 3 issued an updated process validation guidance titled *Quality Management Systems – Process Validation Guidance*, edition 2. This guidance is intended to address more thoroughly the process validation and risk management requirements in the ISO 13485:2003 standard. CDRH has implemented the GHTF 2004 process validation guidance.

Manufacturers seeking to establish a single Quality System that addresses worldwide regulations for medical devices have found that the GHTF guidance supports this goal. Furthermore, if manufacturers ensure that various aspects of their Quality Systems are consistent with the GHTF guidance, medical device approvals and facility inspections may proceed more quickly.

The Center for Biologics Evaluation and Research (CBER) and the Center for Drug Evaluation and Research (CDER) still endorse FDA's 1987 guidance, however that guidance is currently being revised and updated by those centers. The primary difference between FDA's 1987 process validation guidance and GHTF's 2004 process validation guidance is in the terminology used to define the validation process. A comparison of the terminology is provided below, along with an overview of the GHTF guidance document.

Terminology Differences in Available Process Validation Guidance Documents

Process validation is a term used in the medical device industry to indicate that a process has been subject to such scrutiny that the result of the process (a product, a service or other outcome) can be practically guaranteed. This is vitally important if the predetermined requirements of the product can only be assured by destructive testing. [GHTF 2004 guidance]

Although the terminology differs in the two guidance documents, the principles of process validation remain the same. The process validation steps provided in the 2004 GHTF guidance are *Installation Qualification* (IQ), *Operational Qualification* (OQ), and *Performance Qualification* (PQ). The GHTF guidance provides the following key definitions:

Installation Qualification (IQ): establishing by objective evidence that all key aspects of the process equipment and ancillary system installation adhere to the manufacturers approved specification and that the recommendations of the supplier of the equipment are suitably considered.

Operational Qualification (OQ): establishing by objective evidence process control limits and action levels that result in product that meets all predetermined requirements.

Performance Qualification (PQ): establishing by objective evidence that the process, under anticipated conditions, consistently produces a product which meets all predetermined requirements. [GHTF 2004 guidance]

Some manufacturers have long-standing process validation programs based on FDA's 1987 guidance. Other manufacturers have adopted the GHTF process model. Table 27.1 provides a comparison of process validation terminology used in each guidance document.

Concept	Relevant Questions	FDA 1987 Guidance	GHTF 2004 Guidance
Equipment Capability	• Is the equipment installed correctly? • Does the equipment perform as expected?	Equipment Installation Qualification	Installation Qualification (**IQ**)
Process Characterization	• Are the process factors that influence resulting product quality understood? • Has "worst case" testing been performed to establish process control limits?	Preliminary Considerations	Operational Qualification (**OQ**)
Process Adequacy	• Is there consistent process output under normal operating conditions? • When the equipment is operated under controlled conditions, does the process deliver product that meets its specifications?	Process Performance Qualification/ Product Performance Qualification	Performance Qualification (**PQ**)

Table 27.1. Comparison of process validation terminology.

XI

Overview of GHTF Guidance

The GHTF 2004 guidance provides information on establishing an overall process validation program. Figure 27.1 provides an overview of this part of the guidance.

While the completion of process validation is a regulatory requirement, a manufacturer may decide to validate a process to improve overall quality, eliminate scrap, reduce costs, improve customer satisfaction, or other reasons. [GHTF 2004 guidance]

Manufacturers should establish validation responsibility within their organizations. They may find value in establishing a multifunctional validation team. Such a team can lend broad expertise to each validation effort. The validation team will also evaluate process changes to ensure that revalidation is considered and conducted when appropriate.

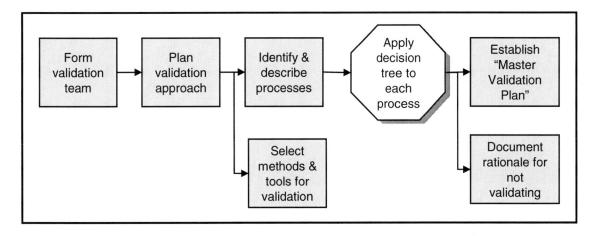

Figure 27.1. Establishing the process validation program.

As part of establishing the process validation program, manufacturers typically develop general process validation procedures that provide a framework for ongoing validation efforts. These general procedures define expectations and responsibilities for pursuing and documenting process validation and describe methods that may be employed. Some of the methods and tools typically used to support process validation include acceptance sampling plans, design of experiments, gauge repeatability and reproducibility studies, and control charts.

A decision tree provided in the GHTF 2004 guidance supports medical device manufacturers in determining which processes should be validated. Decisions are based on:
- whether process output is fully verifiable, and
- whether process output verification is sufficient and cost effective.

After determining which processes will be validated, manufacturers typically create a Master Validation Plan. The Master Validation Plan provides a roadmap for accomplishing many (possibly related) process validations.

Process validation is actually a series of qualifications; each qualification is based on an established protocol, with clear acceptance criteria. Figure 29.2 provides an overview of the GHTF guidance's descriptions of an individual process validation effort.

IQ focuses on correct installation of the equipment. A successful IQ will establish that the production equipment's design, installation conditions, safety features, and environmental conditions are adequate to ensure ongoing proper operation. As part of the IQ, the

XI

equipment is formally adopted into the equipment-related aspects of the manufacturer's Quality System. For example, IQ ensures that the equipment maintenance, cleaning, and calibration schedules are established, that related instructions are established, and that a spare parts list is available for maintenance personnel.

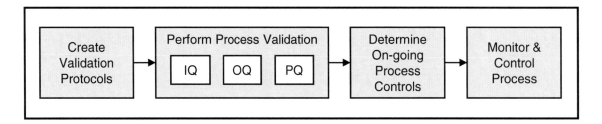

Figure 27.2. Individual process validation steps.

The OQ activities provide a clear understanding of key process parameters (i.e., those factors that are part of the process and that affect process outcomes). The process parameters are controllable factors or variables (such as temperature, time, and pressure). The OQ challenges process variables that may affect important quality attributes. In challenging a process, a manufacturer challenges typical day-to-day conditions that will be encountered in the manufacturing environment, including any probable worst-case conditions.   The challenges are repeated enough times to ensure meaningful, consistent results. By challenging process parameters the manufacturer will determine the worst-case conditions under which the process is still able to produce a product that meets its specifications. Process characterization establishes process control limits for key process parameters.

PQ demonstrates that the process will consistently produce acceptable product under normal operating conditions. Thus, the manufacturer establishes process repeatability and stability, essentially proving that the process control limits are valid during ongoing production activities. The process control limits are documented in standard operating procedures and used to support ongoing process operation, monitoring, and control. Because personnel often play a significant role in process outcomes, PQ typically includes the expected training and qualification activities for operators of the validated process.

OQ and PQ protocols should define the number of samples per run, the number of runs required, and the process or product characteristics that will be measured. Statistically valid techniques should be used in determining the sample size and run quantities to ensure that final validation results are defensible. In current practice, CDRH expects manufacturers to have a statistically valid rationale supporting the number of production runs and sample sizes used to complete the process validation activity.

Validation activities conclude with the preparation of a final report. This report should describe the statistical techniques and data collected and should state conclusions regarding the validation status of the process. The final report should be reviewed by the validation team, if one is appointed, and approved by appropriate members of management. A process that requires validation typically is not released for use in routine manufacturing until the validation report is approved. Such validation reports frequently include an executive summary to support future quality audit activities or regulatory submission preparation.

Ongoing monitoring and control of validated processes is essential. In some cases, a periodic, scheduled revalidation effort is appropriate. For example, sterilization processes are typically revalidated on a schedule that is based on an appropriate industry standard, regardless of whether known changes have occurred in the product or the process.

Revalidation based on planned product or process changes is expected when such changes could affect the process outcomes. Changes may not lead to a revalidation as extensive as the initial validation effort; each change should be evaluated as it is proposed. Examples of changes that could lead to revalidation include moving equipment, modifying a design, changing a raw material, or transferring a process to another facility.

The following list contains examples of typical production processes from the GHTF 2004 guidance. The guidance separates the processes on the basis of the likely need for validation, as follows:

a. Processes that should be validated:
    • sterilization processes,
    • clean room ambient conditions,
    • aseptic filling processes,
    • sterile package sealing processes,
    • lyophilization process,
    • heat treating processes,
    • plating processes, and
    • plastic injection molding processes.

b. Processes that may be satisfactorily covered by verification:
    • manual cutting processes;
    • testing for color, turbidity, total pH for solutions;
    • visual inspection of printed circuit boards; and
    • manufacturing and testing of wire harnesses.

c. Processes for which the GHTF decision tree may be useful in determining the need for validation:
    • cleaning processes,
    • certain human assembly processes,
    • numerical control cutting processes, and
    • filling processes.

The GHTF 2004 guidance provides a simple example of a heat-sealing process validation in Annex B.

Implications of the QSIT on Process Validation Programs

As discussed in Chapter 1, FDA's Quality System Inspection Technique (QSIT) focuses on four major subsystems. One is Production and Process Controls (P&PC). During the P&PC aspect of the inspection, an FDA investigator's selection of the process to evaluate is based on eight factors. Four of them relate directly to process validation:
    • use of the process in manufacturing higher-risk devices,

XI

- degree of risk that the process will cause device failures,
- use of the process in manufacturing multiple devices, and
- variety in process technologies.

The investigator pursues a series of objectives in determining whether the P&PC subsystem is adequate. Several QSIT questions relate directly to process validation activities and related documentation:

a. Is the process controlled and monitored?

b. Is the process operating within specified limits?

c. If the results of the selected process cannot be fully verified, was the process validated?

d. If the process is not operating within specified limits, has the process been adequately validated?

e. Are personnel appropriately qualified or trained to implement processes?

Thus, during a QSIT inspection, the process validation program, as implemented for a select process, may be subjected to significant scrutiny.

Process Validation, Design Validation, and Risk Management

Although there is a relationship between process validation and design validation, the purposes of the two activities are quite different. The Quality System regulation provides the following definitions:

> *Process Validation: Establishing by objective evidence that a process consistently produces a result or product meeting its predetermined specifications.* [21 CFR 820.3(z)(1)]

> *Design Validation: Establishing by objective evidence that the device specifications conform with user needs and intended use(s).* [21 CFR 820.3(z)(2)]

Manufacturers that have a mature risk management program often perform process Failure Modes and Effects Analysis (FMEA) or Hazard Analysis and Critical Control Points (HACCP) analysis in conjunction with initial process development. Although risk management is actually a required aspect of design controls under 21 CFR 820.30(g), "Design validation," it is also a valuable tool to support process validation.

The process risk management activity typically precedes any process validation OQ activity and is often integrated with the device design controls process. When manufacturers perform process FMEA or HACCP analysis, the results help identify candidates for process validation. Even if a process output is fully verifiable, manufacturers that have identified high-risk processes often choose to validate those processes to reduce overall business risk.

Manufacturers often use conforming devices produced during validation PQ manufacturing runs to support design validation activities. Because the PQ runs represent typical production based on approved product and process specifications and procedures, the PQ devices are production units and, therefore, valid design validation units, as per section 820.30(g).

XI

Design transfer is the element of design controls in which a manufacturer establishes procedures to ensure that the device design is correctly translated into production specifications. Process validation is completed during design transfer. This is because a part of ensuring correct translation of the design is demonstrating the capability to manufacture the finished device reliably.

Design controls are discussed in detail in Chapter 7; risk management is discussed further in Chapter 30.

XI

CHAPTER 28. COMBINATION PRODUCTS

Manufacturers are developing products that combine aspects of medical devices with drugs, medical devices with biologics, and drugs with biologics, as consumer needs change and science and technology advance to meet those needs. These "combination products" have the potential to provide significant advances in safe and effective treatments for patients. The products also present an array of challenges for manufacturers in terms of cost-effective product development, retaining adequately qualified personnel, identifying and qualifying appropriate suppliers, regulatory clearance and approval, and manufacturing controls.

Some examples of combination products include drug-eluting cardiovascular stents, dental floss coated with fluoride, wound dressings containing analgesics, metered-dose inhalers, and bone void filler with blood components. FDA's Office of Combination Products maintains a web site with current information and examples of regulated combination products: www.fda.gov/oc/combination.

FDA's Regulatory Approach

FDA established the Office of Combination Products in 2002, as required by the Medical Device User Fee and Modernization Act (MDUFMA). This office acts as an initial point of contact for manufacturers that are developing or manufacturing combination products. The Office of Combination Products supports both premarket review and postmarket regulation activities. It publishes an annual report concerning its performance; these reports are available on their web site.

To determine the appropriate jurisdiction for a given combination product, FDA relies on a determination of the product's "primary mode of action," which 21 CFR 3, "Product Jurisdiction," defines as follows:

> *Primary Mode of Action: The single mode of action of a combination product that provides the most important therapeutic action of the combination product. The most important therapeutic action is the mode of action expected to make the greatest contribution to the overall intended therapeutic effects of the combination product.* [21 CFR 3.2(m)]

After the primary mode of action is established, the appropriate FDA center[10] is assigned primary review responsibility for that product. When a new product is the first of its kind, a manufacturer can submit a Request for Designation so that the Office of Combination Products will determine which FDA center should have primary jurisdiction. The assigned center has primary jurisdiction for premarket review (i.e., product approval or clearance) and regulation.

The Office of Combination Products is also charged with ensuring that postmarket regulation of combination products is consistent and appropriate. After a product has been cleared or approved, manufacturers must establish a compliant manufacturing process.

XI

---

[10] Jurisdiction may be assigned to CDRH, CDER, or CBER.

FDA has activities under way to establish clear direction on the application of appropriate current good manufacturing practice (cGMP) regulations to combination products.

Development Challenges for Combination Product Manufacturers

No single development paradigm can address the breadth of combination products. Each manufacturer should evaluate the particular issues related to its product's particular constituent parts, its product's technological challenges, and its regulatory approach. Development approaches may differ significantly for the constituent parts. Nonetheless, the combined performance and safety aspects of the product must be addressed during the development process. Therefore, thorough design and development planning is essential to ensure a cost-effective and comprehensive product development approach. Consensus standards such as ISO 9001 and ISO 15378 may support the planning and conduct of development activities from a system perspective. Chapter 7 discusses design and development planning considerations.

For example, a manufacturer may have well-established, separate device design controls and drug development models. When considering a combination product, the manufacturer must also evaluate whether the drug combined with the device results in a safe and effective product. Therefore, significant developmental work and verification testing may be necessary to characterize and confirm performance of the combined product. This "systems view" of the product is required in order to establish essential outputs and product release criteria. A clear interface between the two development life cycle models and the specific activities therein is critical to ensuring product safety and efficacy.

In addition, potential adverse effects may occur when the constituent parts are combined. The extent to which and the time period in which the individual parts are combined could significantly affect safety or efficacy. Development efforts should evaluate the safety of the combination. Each product's potential constituent part interactions warrant substantial evaluation during development. A manufacturer may investigate issues and answer questions such as:

   a. Can the drug interact with the device or packaging materials, resulting in a degraded or impure drug?

   b. Can the drug adversely affect the device materials, resulting in improper or degraded performance?

   c. Will the drug be delivered as expected given its formulation, chemical properties, and physical characteristics?

Identifying and assigning the right personnel to the product development team is often a critical success factor for combination product manufacturers. Given the relatively new emphasis on combination products, few personnel are experienced in more than one cGMP regulation. Further, firms that have focused on one of the commodities tend to need skills in either engineering or various scientific disciplines for the product development efforts. The educational background, training, and developmental methods in these disciplines are often very different. Finding personnel with sufficient breadth of experience to support the development effort and help bridge gaps between developers of the constituent parts of the product is an on-going challenge. Establishing an experienced multi-disciplinary

XI

development team can be the key to ensuring that the development process is efficient and effective in developing a safe product along with a robust manufacturing process.

Expectations for concurrent development of product and manufacturing processes often vary widely among different commodity areas. This can also prove to be a significant challenge for combination product developers. While some commodities by their nature require a tightly coupled product-process development approach, others may be well-suited to hand-built prototyping, thereby delaying process development activities. Therefore, the planning and execution of a well-integrated development approach for product and manufacturing processes may either seem essential or superfluous to design and development personnel.

Further, establishment of a robust pre-production change control process may prove difficult for manufacturers accustomed to a single commodity area. Many combination products need clinical data to support the regulatory approval process. Developers may find that tighter pre-production change control is necessary earlier in the development life cycle, to ensure that a specific product "configuration" used in the clinical trial is representative of the finished product design. Defining the combination product pre-production change control methods can be a significant issue depending on the level of experience and expectations of the design and development personnel.

Another significant challenge presented during product development is determining the appropriate content of product labeling. Clearly defining the intended use and indications for the combination product is the first step. However, when the combination is based on previously approved individual constituent parts, confusion can easily arise. When used as approved separately, the labeling content requirements are clear. However, if the constituent product may also be used in combination with another, then the new intended use is probably not covered by existing label content. This issue is one example of a product development challenge that necessitates early, open communication with FDA, to help ensure that the product development plan will ultimately result in an approved or cleared product.

An area of potential concern is the identification and qualification of appropriate suppliers—particularly contract manufacturers. The issues that pertain to a firm's personnel, such as adequate experience in several commodity areas and understanding of terminology also relate to suppliers. While many suppliers have significant experience with a specific commodity, far fewer have experience with several. The level of control necessary to ensure that the combination product will continue to work as intended may be more extensive than the supplier is accustomed to. Thus, supplier selection activities, establishment of quality requirements, and definition of appropriate ongoing supplier monitoring may require significant effort during pre-production and may necessitate the use of different supplier control methods.

XI

FDA's *Early Development Considerations for Innovative Combination Products* guidance, published in September 2006, includes questions and suggestions that may support product development planning activities. This guidance also discusses issues related to clinical investigations and manufacturing process development.

Quality Systems and Combination Product Controls

Although each commodity (i.e., device, drug, or biologic) has a unique cGMP regulation, there is significant commonality among these regulations. For example, adequate qualification and training of personnel is a common requirement (see 21 CFR 211.25, 21 CFR 606.20, 21 CFR 820.25, and 21 CFR 1271.170). Similarly, common expectations exist concerning production process change control, document control, receiving acceptance, equipment cleaning and maintenance, handling, storage, and warehouse or store room controls. Thus, in many cases a single policy and related procedures could meet the requirements of any applicable regulation.

In other cases, one of the applicable cGMP regulations has unique or more specific requirements than the others. For example, yield calculation (21 CFR 211.103) and stability testing (21 CFR 211.166) requirements for drugs are more specific than device requirements. Similarly, device corrective and preventive action (21 CFR 820.100) requirements are more specific than drug or human tissue requirements. Further, the medical device GMP establishes a prescriptive development process requirement under design control (21 CFR 820.30) that does not have a corollary in the drug or biologic GMPs. The pre-production design and development activities for combination products often present a substantial challenge for manufacturers because the development paradigms are different for the various commodities. One of the complicating factors for manufacturers is a lack of a common understanding of terminology among personnel with different product perspectives. For example, the terms "prototype" and "verification" are often used in very different ways. These common terms with various meanings can lead to significant confusion and miscommunication during product development and manufacturing activities.

FDA's *Current Good Manufacturing Practice for Combination Products* draft guidance, published in September 2004, establishes a broad framework for combination product manufacturing regulation. The guidance stipulates that each constituent part (i.e., the device, drug, or biologic) is subject to its governing cGMP regulation before combination. During and after combination of the constituent parts, both cGMP regulations apply. For example, if a manufacturer designs a new class II device to deliver a drug that is already commercially available, design controls apply to the device design activity. If the combination product is combined and packaged as a single entity during manufacturing, then both the drug cGMP and the Quality System regulation apply to the manufacturing operations. However, if the drug is manufactured and distributed separately from the delivery device, then each constituent part needs to meet only the regulations that apply to that part, according to the draft guidance. A Notice of Proposed Rulemaking for combination product GMPs was published in the Federal Register in April 2007. The Notice states that the proposed rule would "clarify and streamline cGMP requirements for combination products" with an approach similar to that described in the draft guidance in September 2004.

The challenge for manufacturers is first to determine whether and when both regulations apply to a specific operation and then to establish a Quality System that addresses the regulations appropriately. This applies to both pre-production and post-market activities. Industry practice also differs because of the unique aspects of each commodity. For

XI

example, issues key to the adequate control of human tissue may not be relevant to the control of plastic components.

Many manufacturers currently developing or manufacturing combination products have taken one of two approaches to the design of their Quality System: a Quality System that is based on a consensus standard or a Quality System that is a superset of the primary cGMP regulation.

Option A: Quality System Based on a Quality Management System Standard

Some manufacturers that are developing or manufacturing combination products have based their Quality System on an ISO standard such as ISO 9001, ISO 13485, or ISO 15378. Using a consensus standard as a basis, their Quality System is comprehensive. Then, to achieve full compliance, they augment the ISO standard requirements with additional cGMP requirements for both aspects of the product. Figure 28.1 illustrates this approach and highlights the commonality among various cGMP regulations. Note that this model incorporates risk management in pre-production and post-market activities. Chapter 30 provides more details on risk management, including available standards and FDA guidance.

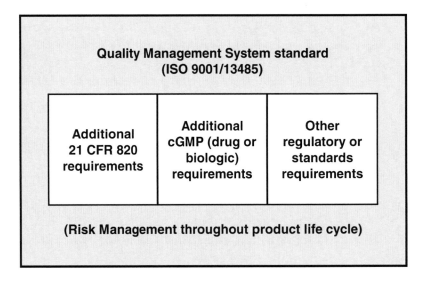

Figure 28.1. Combination product Quality System based on ISO standard.

This approach leverages the significant consensus standard activities in addressing typical issues for development and manufacture of products, while also addressing the FDA-specific expectations. This form of a Quality System is also likely to meet the expectations of other worldwide regulatory bodies. This approach benefits from the use of a lexicon that is more generic and well defined. Thus, training personnel in the standard facilitates a common understanding of key terminology. The Quality System becomes a superset of the base standard and all the applicable regulations, customized for the manufacturer's day-to-day operations.

XI

Option B: Quality System Based on the Primary cGMP Regulation

Some manufacturers that develop or manufacture combination products have established a Quality System based on the primary cGMP regulation that relates to the product. Using the cGMP as a basis, such a Quality System is designed to support the primary commodity (i.e., the device, drug, or biologic) in the product, with additional requirements applied to the secondary aspect of the product as required. The overlap between cGMP regulations provides for some commonality in expectations for operations related to each commodity. Figure 28.2 illustrates this approach and also highlights the commonality between various cGMP regulations. This model also incorporates risk management throughout the product life cycle.

This approach leverages significant knowledge within the company of the primary cGMP regulation. The resulting Quality System is clearly based on a single cGMP regulation, and terminology is consistent with that regulation as well. Manufacturers using this approach may encounter difficulties if the business focus changes (e.g., if they shift from a focus on biologics that need delivery to a focus on delivery devices for various biologics and drugs). In addition, introducing the product globally may result in the need for additional augmentation of the Quality System to meet other regulatory body requirements.

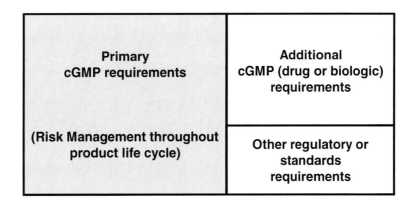

Figure 28.2. Combination product Quality System based on primary cGMP regulation.

FDA's final report on *Pharmaceutical CGMPs for the 21st Century – A Risk-Based Approach*, issued in September 2004, describes ongoing activities within the agency to streamline and harmonize various cGMP regulations. This document provides helpful insight into FDA's regulatory focus for drugs. In addition, FDA's guidance on *Quality Systems Approach to Pharmaceutical CGMP Regulations*, published in September 2006, describes a Quality System model that maps the existing drug cGMP regulations to a more "process-oriented" model.

XI

Inspections of Combination Product Manufacturers

FDA's *Investigations Operations Manual* describes a systems-based inspection approach for facilities subject to 21 CFR 820, 21 CFR 211, and 21 CFR 606. Various FDA Compliance Policy Guides provide additional information on inspectional approaches for each commodity. The current state of practice for many FDA inspections is to focus on higher-risk areas or products and to use a system-based inspectional approach.

FDA's *Quality Systems Approach to Pharmaceutical CGMP Regulations*, published in September 2006, describes an inspection approach that is based on a six-system inspection model. In this inspection approach, the Quality System provides a foundation for the five manufacturing systems: production, facilities and equipment, packaging and labeling, materials, and laboratory controls. Similarly, FDA's QSIT provides for a medical device Quality System inspection focused on four of the seven subsystems: Management Controls, Design Controls, Production and Process Controls, and Corrective and Preventive Actions (see Chapter 1). Thus, combination product manufacturers whose products are combined during manufacture or packaging can reasonably expect a system-based facility inspection that covers all applicable cGMP regulations.

XI

CHAPTER 29. NEW DIRECTIONS IN SOFTWARE VALIDATION

This chapter covers the availability of guidance from FDA on software validation and evolving industry practices in this area. It supplements discussions in Chapter 7, "Design Controls," in the section on "Design Verification and Validation" and in Chapter 13, "Production and Process Controls," in the section on "Automated Processes." This chapter does not address particular concerns for validation of electronic signature and electronic record-keeping systems, which are covered separately (see Chapters 24–26).

Summary of Available Guidance from FDA

FDA has published several key guidance documents covering various aspects of software validation. These guidance documents provide a more detailed perspective for FDA staff and industry on essential aspects of software validation for various types of software. One guidance document provides a general discussion on good software validation practices; two others provide details on premarket submissions (i.e., PMAs or 510(k)s) when devices include software.

In addition to the generally applicable software guidance documents described below, FDA also publishes product-specific guidance where appropriate. For example, there is a guidance document for software used in clinical trials and there are others for blood establishment computer software. A search of the CDRH and CBER web sites can assist manufacturers in identifying product-specific guidance documents that pertain to their particular medical devices.

General Principles of Software Validation

In 1997, FDA released draft guidance for comment on *General Principles of Software Validation*. CDRH and CBER issued the final version, *General Principles of Software Validation; Final Guidance for Industry and FDA Staff*, in January 2002. This guidance is the broadest in scope of the three guidance documents described here because it applies both to medical device software and to automated process software.

As a guiding principle, *General Principles of Software Validation* asserts that the design and development activities related to software, including the methodologies used, are an important aspect of overall validation of the software. Software validation is not restricted to the formal testing of the software but encompasses software engineering practices as well. This is because of the breadth of knowledge and experience gained over years of evaluating software-related medical device failures in the field. In many cases, inadequate software design activities or inadequate software change controls have contributed substantially to medical device recalls.

General Principles of Software Validation provides a detailed explanation of terms related to software validation and addresses the use of process validation terms in the context of software validation. This guidance describes software validation concepts (e.g., defect prevention and software life cycle), as well as activities and tasks (e.g., software design and coding). Throughout these sections, the guidance provides references to the specific regulatory requirements related to each topic.

This guidance provides a thorough description of software test planning, reasons for testing different levels of software (i.e., unit-, integration-, and system-level software), and various types of software testing, including the following:

a. Structural testing, also called "white box" testing, demonstrates that the software's decision control points result in appropriate system behavior. This testing relies on knowledge gained from evaluating the source code and software design.

b. Functional testing, also called "black box" testing, demonstrates that the software meets specified requirements.

c. User site testing, demonstrates that the software meets its requirements when installed on the target hardware in the users' environment.

Because software may be changed over time, owing to a need to resolve problems or to upgrade features, this guidance discusses the concept of software maintenance and good practices for software change control. In particular, it describes revalidation of software.

General Principles of Software Validation includes a section that specifically covers validation of automated process equipment and Quality System software. The following concepts are particularly important for these types of software:

a. The extent of validation required is commensurate with the risk involved with using the software.

b. The scope of the validation effort should be defined according to the manufacturer's intended use, not necessarily the full potential functionality inherent in the software.

c. System-level or functional validation may be the only practical approach for some off-the-shelf (OTS) software products (e.g., software development tools such as compilers).

This guidance concludes with an extensive bibliography of FDA and government references, as well as software industry standards and general software references. Manufacturers seeking to adopt good software validation practices can use *General Principles of Software Validation* as a basis for understanding terminology, common industry practices, and FDA expectations.

Premarket Submissions for Medical Devices with Software

The Office of Device Evaluation issued *Guidance for the Content of Premarket Submissions for Software Contained in Medical Devices* on May 29, 1998. This guidance, which has since been superseded, focused on the approach and documentation for a premarket submission (i.e., PMA or 510(k))—for devices that contain software. In other words, the guidance related to medical devices that are subject to design controls and the software that is a part of the device, is an accessory to the device, or is the device (i.e., stand-alone software). In May 2005, the guidance was reissued by CDRH and CBER. The updated content combines the original content with earlier guidance on blood establishment software.

The 2005 version of *Guidance for the Content of Premarket Submissions for Software Contained in Medical Devices* provides a definition and explanation of "level of concern," a term used to describe the most significant risk associated with a software failure. By defining the software's level of concern, a manufacturer provides a summary of the risk (or hazard) analysis that is specifically focused on the software. Three potential concern levels—major, moderate, and minor—are described in the guidance. Furthermore, a decision tree is provided with examples to aid both reviewers and manufacturers in reaching a determination of the software's level of concern. This determination is key when deciding on the amount of documentation to include in the premarket submission package.

The 2005 guidance describes various types of software documentation that may be required in the premarket submission package. A table in the guidance summarizes the documentation required in a premarket submission for devices with software of each level of concern. In some cases, the information is required for all levels of concern (e.g., Device Hazard Analysis, Traceability Analysis). In other cases, only software with a major level of concern would require the information (e.g., unit- and integration-level test protocols, test results, and test summaries).

As an alternative to following the guidance verbatim, manufacturers may choose to declare conformance to ANSI/AAMI/IEC 62304:2006 *Medical device software—Software life cycle processes*. By declaring conformity, the submission burden can be reduced according to FDA's consensus standards database:

> *The attached table defines the relationship between the standard IEC 62304 and the FDA Guidance for the Content of Pre-market Submissions for Medical Devices Containing Software. ... If the manufacturer declares conformance to this standard, the manufacturer is NOT required to submit the indicated software documentation. Whenever IEC 62304 is used, the medical device manufacturer must document all conformance declaration information in the pre-market submission.* [FDA Consensus Standards Database, effective 03-Nov-2006]

The *Guidance for the Content of Premarket Submissions for Software Contained in Medical Devices* provides a high-level overview of risk assessment and management activities throughout the software life cycle; however, it also refers to the ISO 14971 consensus standard for further information on risk management techniques. The 2005 version of guidance concludes with brief discussions on some special topics and references.

Although the guidance is focused on medical device software, some of the general principles in it may be helpful for automated process software validation. For example, conducting a risk analysis and determining the relative risk posed by the software are valid activities for automated process software validation.

Premarket Submissions for Off-The-Shelf Software in Medical Devices

The Office of Device Evaluation issued *Off-The-Shelf Software Use in Medical Devices — Guidance for Industry, FDA Reviewers, and Compliance* in September 1999. This version supersedes the version issued in June 1997. The purpose of this guidance is to augment the expectations for premarket submissions, as described in the previous section, specifically when a manufacturer incorporates off-the-shelf (OTS) software in a medical device. The most common example of OTS software used in medical devices is an operating system. Medical devices often use operating systems either on personal computers and workstations or as embedded real-time systems operating within a device.

XI

As with the guidance discussed in the previous section, *Off-The-Shelf Software Use in Medical Devices — Guidance for Industry, FDA Reviewers, and Compliance* uses software risk in determining the type and extent of documentation required in the premarket submission package. This OTS software guidance provides a safety-oriented perspective on the use of OTS software in medical devices. Rather than focusing on failure likelihood, analysis should focus on the severity of the harm related to a failure. The subtle distinction is that software failures do not happen in the same generally predictable manner over the device's lifetime as hardware failures (i.e., software does not "wear out"). Therefore, analyzing the potential harm from a software failure is more meaningful than analyzing the likelihood of software failure.

This OTS software guidance uses a decision schematic to aid manufacturers in determining which activities and documentation pertain to the premarket submission package. Again, this information expands on the general software submission guidance. For OTS software with a major level of concern, manufacturers are advised to evaluate the OTS developer's design and development methodology, possibly through an audit. Ultimately, manufacturers that use OTS software with a major level of concern must be able to demonstrate safety in the use of the software through appropriate risk mitigation and software verification and validation tests.

Off-The-Shelf Software Use in Medical Devices — Guidance for Industry, FDA Reviewers, and Compliance provides several examples of medical devices that incorporate OTS software and the related level of concern. It also addresses specific issues with:
- changes to devices that use OTS software and are subject to premarket notification (510(k)) requirements,
- investigational device exemptions for devices that use OTS software,
- PMA issues,
- device labeling issues, and
- special considerations for artificial intelligence software such as expert systems.

This OTS software guidance concludes with an appendix that provides background on various types of OTS software (e.g., operating systems and local area networks) and application of general software engineering concepts to OTS software.

Off-The-Shelf Software Use in Medical Devices — Guidance for Industry, FDA Reviewers, and Compliance is focused on medical device software. Nonetheless, some of the principles are generally applicable to automated process software validation. For example, the appendix coverage of maintenance and obsolescence of OTS medical device software could also apply to OTS manufacturing process software.

To address the increasing use of networks in user facilities, FDA issued *Cybersecurity for Networked Medical Devices Containing Off-the-Shelf (OTS) Software* in January 2005. The guidance provides recommendations for devices that contain OTS software and that can be connected to an intranet or the Internet. The document's specific focus is security for the software system in light of vulnerabilities that can develop from network access. Unauthorized system access could lead to unanticipated changes in the software, ultimately resulting in compromised safety or effectiveness of a finished device.

XI

Evolving Software Validation Practices

"Software validation" is used in industry as a general term that applies to design and development of the software product, as well as to testing performed to confirm that the software meets its requirements. Software validation practices in the medical device industry may vary for medical device software and other automated process software, primarily because of different regulatory requirements for these two software categories.

There are basic principles that apply in each software validation effort. The general software validation approach involves a sequence of steps, as illustrated in Figure 29.1. The variability in applying this approach for medical device software and other software types stems from the regulatory requirements that apply in each case.

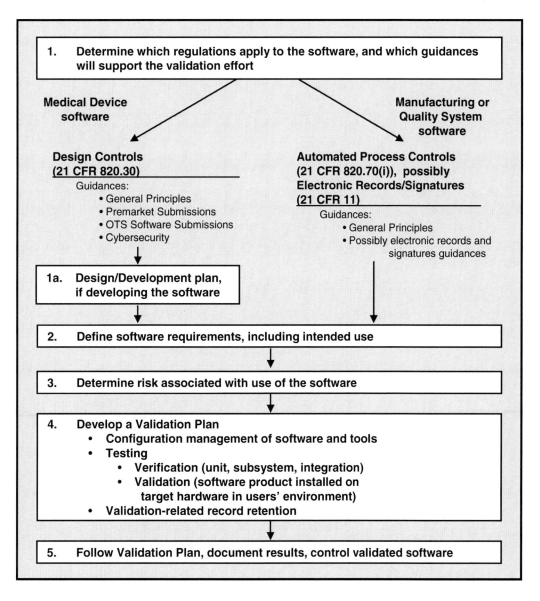

Figure 29.1. General software validation process.

Some large medical device manufacturers have two departments involved in software validation activities: a software quality assurance group focused on medical device software, and an Information Technology (IT) group focused on automated process software validation. In other firms a single group handles all software validation activities. Regardless of the organizational responsibilities for validation of automated processes software and device software, the same principles apply.

The automated process software validation requirements include expectations of defining intended use, determining software risk, and conducting formal testing based on pre-approved protocols. Furthermore, *General Principles of Software Validation,* which applies equally to device and automated process software (refer to section 2.1 of that guidance), identifies several essential concepts in the validation approach:

  a. Use risk analysis as a preliminary step in determining the extent of validation appropriate for the software.

  b. Maintain independence in software evaluation (i.e., someone other than the developer is involved in determining whether the software meets its intended use).

  c. Institute software change control.

Thus, although the additional rigors of design controls are not required for automated process software, many design controls principles could (and often do) help improve the quality of such software.

To help illustrate the application of generally accepted good practice in software validation to automated processes, a case study on a simple spreadsheet validation is included at the end of this chapter. Given the prolific use of spreadsheets at some device firms, this case study may help in establishing basic principles for approaching both prospective and retrospective validations.

Software Validation Practices for Medical Device Software

The four available general FDA software guidance documents all pertain to medical device software. This software, subject to the requirements of Design Controls, is often developed similarly to the finished device itself. Even though the requirement for software validation is embedded in 21 CFR 820.30(g), "Design validation," manufacturers typically conduct software-related development activities in parallel with other product development tasks, as described in the guidance in *General Principles of Software Validation.*

Manufacturers apply each aspect of the Design Control requirements to the design and development of the device software. Table 29.1 illustrates the relationship between design control terminology (as per 21 CFR 820.30) and terms used in *General Principles of Software Validation.* Typically manufacturers establish an explicit software design and development plan to describe the software life cycle model and related development activities.

XI

Quality System Regulation Design Control Terminology	General Principles of Software Validation Terminology
Design and development planning	Quality planning
Design input	Requirements
Design output	Software design specification, source code
Design verification	Testing by developer
Design validation	User site testing
Design review	Independent review
Risk Analysis	Preliminary and updated risk analysis

Table 29.1. Comparison of terminology.

Various industry standards exist to support manufacturers who are establishing software life cycle models. For example, the IEEE has a series of software-related standards, the International Society of Pharmaceutical Engineering (ISPE) produced the *Good Automated Manufacturing Practice (GAMP®)*, IEC has ISO/IEC 16085:2006 *Systems and software engineering—Life cycle processes—Risk management*, and AAMI has published ANSI/AAMI/IEC 62304:2006 *Medical device software—Software life cycle processes*.

In addition, organizations such as AAMI, ISO, and IEC have on-going efforts to update existing standards and create new standards applicable to medical device software development and controls. In some cases the standards are being developed to work in concert with current standards for risk management (e.g., ANSI/AAMI/IEC 62304) or product safety. Standards organizations have also increased their focus on development of medical devices connected to IT networks.

General Principles of Software Validation also recommends an integrated model for software development and risk management, and many manufacturers have adopted this approach. By considering the risk to users and patients starting from the initial establishment of software requirements, developers can adopt a defensible, scaled development plan consistent with the risk presented or mitigated by the software. In other words, the amount of development rigor and documentation can be adjusted to address the risk to users and patients. *Guidance for the Content of Premarket Submissions for Software Contained in Medical Devices* contains a specific risk assessment rating scheme (i.e., level of concern) to apply to medical device software. Additional information on risk management is available in Chapter 30.

Design review is often applied to the software requirements, software design, and software code (i.e., source code review). Knowledgeable software practitioners should carry out the source code reviews.

Independence in testing is common industry practice. Thus, the software developer is not typically the software tester. Depending on the target market and the regulatory submission strategy, software testing may be based on applicable industry standards. FDA's consensus standards database provides a list of potential standards. This database can be found at: www.fda.gov/cdrh/stdsprog.html.

Design history files (DHFs) often include an explicit area for the software-related documentation. The total documentation package (requirements, risk analysis, design, reviews, test protocols, and results) supports a conclusion of successful validation of medical device software, as required by 21 CFR 820.30(g), "Design validation."

Software Validation Practices for Automated Processes

The requirements for validation of automated processes apply to production software and to Quality System software. Medical device industry production software is often one of two types: software that controls production equipment or software that supports the production operation. Table 29.2 provides examples of software subject to requirements for validation under 21 CFR 820.70(i), "Automated Processes."

Production Equipment Control	Production Operation Support	Quality System Support
Wave-soldering process software	Material resource planning (MRP) software	Internal audit or supplier audit tracking software
Milling machine control software	Automated lot traveler printing software	Corrective and preventive action database
Injection molding control software	Statistical Process Control software	Complaint tracking database
Formulation and mixing control software	Automated Heating, Ventilation, and Air Conditioning (HVAC) control software	Electronic document repository

Table 29.2. Common examples of automated process software per 21 CFR 820.70(i).

Typically, the software that controls production equipment is validated as part of the process validation activity, although it may also be validated separately if the software is user configurable or modified by the manufacturer as part of the equipment installation process. Refer to Chapters 15 and 27 for more details on Process Validation.

The examples in Table 29.2 illustrate the diversity in production support software. Software of this type is often validated explicitly (i.e., not as part of a larger process validation). In some cases, a large software system may support many activities, some of which are not subject to FDA regulations. For example, a material tracking function may be part of a larger accounting system that supports customer billing and supplier invoice payment. Although the material tracking functions are subject to 21 CFR 820.70(i), the accounting functions are not. When production support software covers a very broad scope that exceeds FDA compliance concerns, manufacturers often focus on validating the particular functions that are subject to Quality System regulation requirements rather than validating the entire system.

Finally, Quality System software ranges from simple spreadsheets developed in-house directly by users, to OTS specialized databases, to custom-developed applications. Quality System software is almost always subject to explicit software validation, because it is not typically part of a process that is subject to process validation.

Note that the common examples of Quality System software in Table 29.2 did not include calculators. The significant distinction between using a spreadsheet and using a calculator is that someone (the user or an independent developer) "programs" the spreadsheet to perform a particular calculation. Whether the formulas used to calculate given data are hard coded or created ad hoc, the accuracy of the formula directly affects the final result. Thus, a calculator is not typically considered to be an "automated process," whereas a spreadsheet is an "automated process" in the context of 21 CFR 820.70(i).

Completion of automated process software validation results in a validation package that contains all the documentation created during the validation effort, as well as the software itself. These items are typically part of the Quality System Record (QSR), although special-purpose software (and its validation package) may be part of a device master record (DMR) in some cases. Retention of software validation records in either case is required by 21 CFR 820.180.

Case Study Example: Validating a Spreadsheet[11]

The use of simple software applications to collect or evaluate quality data is widespread, thanks to the ready availability of PC-based tools that provide surprisingly sophisticated data analysis and user interface capabilities. These tools are easy for the computer user to configure, which encourages their use. The use of software applications in the Quality System, based on spreadsheets or databases, often falls under 21 CFR 820.70(i), Production and process controls - Automated processes.

It is actually straightforward to validate these simple Quality System applications. The key to validating these applications is to follow, on a much smaller scale, the same good practices that might be performed for large systems. Like all development projects, a basic methodology exists:

1. Define the requirements (i.e., the intended use).

2. Determine the potential "risk" of using the system.

3. Design and implement the system (i.e., create the software or application).

4. Establish a test protocol (to demonstrate that the software meets the requirements defined in step 1).

5. Create a test record-keeping format to capture test results.

6. Perform the validation and document the results.

7. Control the validated system to prevent inadvertent changes.

These seven steps are the key to validating simple Quality System applications. Taken together these steps provide the basis for showing that the application has been successfully validated. The simple case study example on the following pages illustrates the validation of a common automated process implemented with a spreadsheet.

Case Study Example: Consider a simple spreadsheet application used to calculate the average daily complaints received each month. Such a spreadsheet might be a tool to evaluate trends and provide a monthly status report to management. This example application is presented with the seven validation steps highlighted. Each step discusses which tasks are needed and what documentation would be created to support the software validation effort.

In this example, the complaint data are formally recorded in a different system; the spreadsheet is used only to calculate an average each month. This example spreadsheet is not an electronic record-keeping system and is not subject to Part 11 requirements for electronic records. Thus, the validation scope is restricted to the correct calculation of the monthly average (i.e., the intended use of the spreadsheet). The validation will not include considerations for Part 11 or for the general functions the spreadsheet program enables, only the specific implementation and intended use of the particular spreadsheet application as defined here.

XI

---

[11] Case study example © Copyright *The St. Vrain Group, Inc*, 2001. Reprinted with permission.

1. Define the Requirements.

The requirements define "what" the application does. Requirements should define the basic functions of the application and any features or protections the application needs. Also, any specific data should be identified, including data formats, data storage, and any access limitations.

Requirements – Daily Complaint Average Application

Purpose:
- Calculate daily average of complaints received over a calendar month.

Requirements:
- Use a spreadsheet that is stored on a server to facilitate access within the Regulatory Department.
- Allow several employees to manually enter and to review data.
- Calculate the average complaints received per day over the calendar month.
- Store the previous month's average at the start of each month.
- Provide basic instructions in the spreadsheet for users.

Assessment:
- Does this spreadsheet need validation?
  - Yes—it is Quality System software:
    - It is part of complaint-handling system (21 CFR 820.198), and
    - It is providing data trending as a part of the corrective and preventive action (CAPA) system (21 CFR 820.100(a)(1)).

---

2. Determine the Potential "Risk" of Using the System (Perform Software Risk Analysis).

The risk analysis needs to determine a "risk index". Software with "moderate" to "high" risk will require more formalized verification and validation. Many Quality System software applications cannot adversely affect patients or users and thus are low risk. Refer to *Guidance for the Content of Premarket Submissions for Software Contained in Medical Devices* for guidance on this assessment process.

Risk Analysis – Daily Complaint Average Application

Analysis:
- Will failure of the software have a direct impact on patient or user safety?
  - No—it is Quality System software, not device software.

- Will failure of the software have an indirect impact on patient or user safety?
  - No—the software does not involve testing or release of devices.

- Will failure of the software have a direct impact on effectiveness of the Quality System?
  - Yes—failure of the software could lead to inability to detect a changing trend in complaints.

Determination:
- Software level of concern: Minor
  - Severity of failure: Minor
  - Software risk index: Low

XI

3. Design and Implement the System.

The design of a system defines "how" the requirements are met. This design can be descriptive (text) or in a picture format. In this case, both techniques are used to define the application.

The design is specific to the application being developed. Provide as many details as are reasonably possible. A detailed design shows how the requirements are met, and it provides documentation for any future changes that might need to be made to the application.

When the design is done, use it to create the spreadsheet application.

Design – Daily Complaint Average Application

- Application and location:
  - Use Excel, from Microsoft Office XP.
  - Call the file "Daily Complaint Avg.XLS."
  - Store the file on the server under Quality_System/quality_tools.

- Detailed design:
  - Label each data entry cell.
  - Prevent editing of cell formulas by users.
  - Ensure calculation is based on the correct number of days in the month.
  - Restrict daily complaint values to whole numbers.
  - Present the monthly average with accuracy to the hundredths.
  - Present pull-down options for the "Month of" field.
  - Prefill the number of days in the month in accordance with the user's entries for the "Year of" and "Month of" fields.
  - Layout as follows:

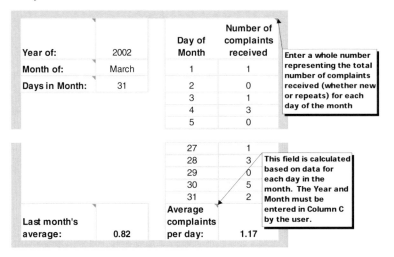

---

4. Establish a Test Protocol.

A test protocol provides step-by-step instructions on how to "test" the application. These are often written so that an end user could complete the validation testing. The protocol steps should trace back to the requirements and design, to ensure that important features of the Quality System software application are tested.

The goal for the test protocol is to be able to assert that the system meets its intended use.

Test Protocol – Daily Complaint Average Application

1. Confirm the calculation is based on the correct number of days:
   - Fill in "0" for days 1–27.
   - Fill in nonzero values for days 28–31.
   - Confirm that the average changes appropriately for a 28-day, 30-day, and 31-day month by comparing the result to data from a handheld calculator.

2. Verify the accuracy of the calculation by comparing the spreadsheet data to a hand-held calculator, as follows, for 28-day, 30-day, and 31-day months:
   - Enter a 0 for each even day of the month, a 1 for each odd day of the month, and a 10 for days 30 and 31, and then calculate the average.
   - Determine highest daily complaint count for past three years, enter twice this value for each even day of month, and calculate average.

3. Confirm that the calculated average formula and the "Days in Month" field cannot be edited.

4. Confirm that "Days in Month" is calculated correctly for
   - 2/2002: 28; 4/2002: 30; 5/2002: 31

5. Verify that user instructions exist for key data entry fields.

5. Create a Test Record.

A test record is a form that can be completed as the validation test is performed. Usually, the test record follows the same order (and even numbering) as the test protocol. This format helps the tester follow the protocol and document the test results accurately. Although a particular format is not "required" per se, it is very helpful in ensuring that the first validation effort is appropriately documented (thereby reducing likelihood of needing to repeat the validation).

As in the case of all forms, providing a "data entry field" makes it easy for the tester to fill-in test results as the test is performed. The pass/fail determination for each test case is based on the test protocol.

Two key items on the record include the date on which the testing was performed and the signature of the tester.

<u>Test Record – Daily Complaint Average Application</u>

Spreadsheet Name/Location: _____

Test Date: _____   Tester Name: _____

1.   Data is 0 for days 1 – 27, _____ for days 28 – 31;

       Year: _____

       Feb avg: _____;   April avg: ____;   May avg: _____;

       Test Case 1: ☐ Pass ☐ Fail

2.   28-day month average:

	Spreadsheet value	Calculator
0/1:	_____	_____
___/1:	_____	_____

       30-day month average:

	Spreadsheet value	Calculator
0/1/10:	_____	_____
___/1:	_____	_____

       31-day month average:

	Spreadsheet value	Calculator
0/1/10:	_____	_____
___/1:	_____	_____

       Test Case 2: ☐ Pass ☐ Fail

3.   Able to edit averaging formula? ☐ Yes ☐ No

       Able to edit "Days in Month" field? ☐ Yes ☐ No

       Test Case 3: ☐ Pass ☐ Fail

4.   No. of Days in 2/2002: _____; 4/2002: _____; 5/2002: _____;

       Test Case 4: ☐ Pass ☐ Fail

5.   Are data entry (user) instructions available? ☐ Yes ☐ No

Test Result: ☐ Pass ☐ Fail ☐ Other: _____

Signature/Date: _____ _____

XI

6. Perform Validation and Document Results.

Use the test protocol and test record to perform validation testing and to document the test results. Note that if testing uncovers any system defects or test protocol anomalies, the test record would typically be augmented by a summary report that explains the issues and actions taken to resolve them.

Once testing is complete, the entire validation package (requirements, design, risk analysis, protocol, and completed test records) should be retained in the Quality System Record.

7. Control the Validated System.

The final step is confirming appropriate file protections are in place, that the system is covered by backup procedures, and that the software is revalidated if it is changed.

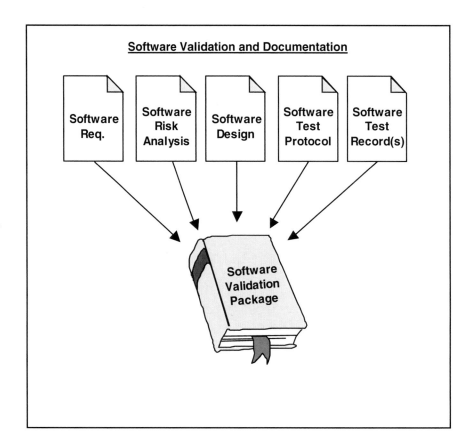

Software Validation and Documentation

Software Req. · Software Risk Analysis · Software Design · Software Test Protocol · Software Test Record(s)

Software Validation Package

System Control

- Software location is appropriate for use and desired controls.
- Software is protected from inadvertent changes or deletion.
- Software backup procedures allow recovery from inadvertent changes or deletion.
- Software change control exists to ensure that changes are validated before they are used: repeat steps 1–7 as appropriate.

The seven steps above, using the Daily Complaint Averaging spreadsheet example, illustrate how to approach the validation of a spreadsheet application, in relation to the requirements of 21 CFR 820.70(i). None of these steps are overly burdensome, and most of the documentation associated with a given step could easily fit on a single sheet of paper. The important point to remember is that software validation demonstrates that a system meets user needs. Thus, it is necessary first to document the user needs (requirements) and then to document testing that shows that the system meets the requirements.

For a retrospective validation, meaning that the spreadsheet already exists and is in use, the same seven steps apply. Instead of defining the requirements and designing the spreadsheet, however, it is necessary to retrospectively document what requirements were established and how the spreadsheet was designed. In some cases, the retrospective requirements assessment may result in identification of new requirements! The remaining validation steps proceed as described above. ▣

CHAPTER 30. RISK MANAGEMENT FOR MEDICAL DEVICES

This chapter discusses the state of medical device industry practice in estimating and managing product risk. Particularly for manufacturers who distribute devices in Europe, a comprehensive risk management program has become common practice. This chapter does not cover particular issues related to software risk management; Chapter 29, "New Directions in Software Validation," addresses software risk management.

Purpose of Risk Management

Generally, risk is a measure of the possibility of loss or harm. The regulatory context for medical device risk management is the risk inherent in the use of the device—the risks presented to product users and patients. "Risk management" in this context does not apply to business risks, such as financial risks associated with product development or introduction, or project development risks, such as scope creep or variable resource levels.

Product risk involves the combination of two factors, which each play a role in defining the level of risk. Both factors relate to harm, which is a physical injury or damage to the health of a patient or user or to the surrounding environment or property. A hazard exists relative to each harm (i.e., a hazard is a potential source of harm). For the harm to occur, a scenario or hazardous situation must unfold. The hazardous situation is the sequence of circumstances that must exist to expose people, property, or the environment to one or more hazards. Product risk involves the probability (or likelihood) that a particular harm will occur and the severity of that harm. Note that product risk may be defined with qualitative or quantitative measures of probability and severity.

Product risk is the inverse of product safety. As risk decreases, safety increases. Thus, a risk management program is, in fact, also a product safety program. The goal of such a program is to ensure that the product is as safe as practical and that the safety of the product is acceptable for a given intended use. The actual use of any medical device always includes some measure of risk to users or patients—no medical device is ever 100% safe.

Working with applicable regulatory authorities, each manufacturer must determine how much risk is acceptable. Establishing an acceptable level of risk depends on the intended use of the device. Intended use includes definitions of:
- particular health condition of the patient population,
- general cognitive abilities of the patient population,
- skill level of the health practitioners involved,
- their level of direct supervision of the product's use, and
- the use environment.

All these aspects of intended use play a role in determining the level of product risk. For example, pediatric or seriously ill adult patients may have less ability to detect a product malfunction and to notify a health practitioner when a malfunction occurs. Furthermore, a consumer-controlled device generally gets less knowledgeable oversight than a clinic-based device. Thus, a product that is used in both a clinic environment and a home environment may have two different risk levels, given its two different intended uses.

Risk management is the systematic application of policies, procedures, and practices to the tasks of analyzing, evaluating, controlling, and monitoring risk. In other words, managing risk involves proactive evaluation, control and monitoring of product risk, and reactive response to actual situations that may indicate new or changing product risk.

Standards That Support the Risk Management Program

The most significant standard to support a manufacturer's risk management program is ISO 14971:2007, *Medical devices—Application of risk management to medical devices*. The standard applies to all medical devices, including *in vitro* diagnostics, and covers the entire life cycle of a product from concept through final decommissioning and disposal.

FDA first recognized ISO 14971:2000 as a consensus standard in May 2001, adopting the complete standard. In September 2007 FDA updated their consensus standards database to recognize ISO 14971:2007 in its entirety. In the database entry FDA outlines the extent of recognition for ISO 14971:2007:

> *A declaration of conformity means that (1) a process appropriate for medical devices and their accessories, including in vitro diagnostic devices, has been used to identify hazards and hazardous situations, estimate and evaluate the risks, control those risks including overall residual risk, and monitor the effectiveness of the controls, and (2) criteria based upon applicable national or regional regulations, relevant international Standards, information such as the generally accepted state of the art, and known stakeholder concerns was used to determine risk acceptability.* [FDA Consensus Standards Database, effective 12-Sep-2007]

ISO 14971:2007 provides an example of a risk management process, describes the essential aspects of a risk management program, and specifies particular activities and documentation that must be established. The general approach described by the standard includes establishing a clear statement of intended use for the device, considering risk under normal use scenarios and considering misuse such as incorrect use by a user. Figure 30.1 depicts the overall risk management process. The numerous annexes in the standard provide substantial additional information and nonbinding guidance to support the effective use of risk management techniques and principles.

In addition to ISO 14971:2007, numerous technical standards exist to support risk analysis using techniques such as fault tree analysis, FMEA, and other analytical tools (see IEC and ISO in Appendix A). For manufacturers of electro-medical devices, IEC 60601-1 requires the use of an ISO 14971-compliant risk management process in meeting its requirements and the IEC 60601-1-1 and IEC 60601-1-2 family of safety standards for individual products. A number of other standards require or recommend the use of the ISO 14971 risk management process, such as ANSI/AAMI/IEC 62304.

Basis for the Risk Requirement

For manufacturers that distribute medical devices in the U.S., the Quality System regulation, 21 CFR 820, is the source of the requirement for conducting risk analysis. Section 21 CFR 820.30(g), "Design validation," stipulates, "Design validation shall include software validation and risk analysis, where appropriate." Further details concerning this requirement are provided in the Preamble to the Final Rule of the Quality System Regulation (see Appendix C). Preamble comment 83 refers manufacturers to pertinent risk management standards for guidance on conducting risk analysis (see text on standards and guidance below).

Comments in the Preamble also relate to FDA's expectation for risk-based decision making. For example, comment 4 states, "In fact the new regulation is less prescriptive and gives the manufacturer the flexibility to determine the controls that are necessary commensurate with risk." Furthermore, Preamble comment 13 states, "The extent of documentation necessary to meet the regulation requirements may vary based on ... risk associated with the failure of the device, among other factors." Thus, the Quality System regulation includes a general expectation for risk-based decision making and a specific requirement for conducting risk analysis.

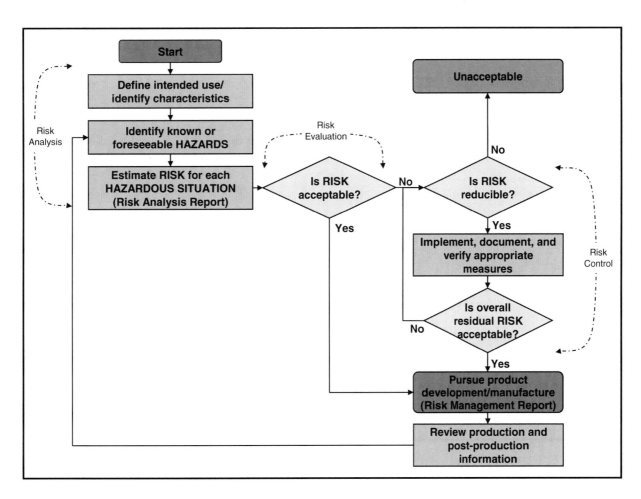

Figure 30.1. Overview of risk management process (modified from ISO 14971:2007).

For manufacturers that rely on registration to ISO 13485:2003 to allow distribution of their medical devices—for example, if CE marking is based on ISO 13485:2003—that standard defines two requirements related to risk management:

    a. Under "Planning of Product Realization" (section 7.1): "The organization shall establish documented requirements for risk management throughout product realization. Records arising from risk management shall be maintained."

b. Under "Design and Development Inputs" (section 7.3.2): "These inputs shall include ... output(s) of risk management."

Therefore, under ISO 13485:2003, there is a requirement for a risk management program, and an explicit requirement to consider risk management when establishing the design inputs.

Implementing a Risk Management Program

Risk management is typically implemented as an integral aspect of the Quality System. Risk-based decisions occur throughout various Quality System processes, and a cohesive approach to risk management exists across the manufacturer's organization. Risk management during product design, during production, and after product release are discussed below.

Risk Management during Product Design

Effective risk management usually starts in conjunction with the design and development planning process, to ensure that the risk management approach fits within the overall project plan. The key to proactive risk management is initiating the risk management process at a point in the development life cycle when the results of analyses can affect the design process. Starting too late typically means that designers have progressed past a point where reasonable risk mitigation features could have been included in the design itself. The possible approaches for reducing risk are typically described as a prioritized list:
- inherent design safety,
- protective measures in the design or manufacturing processes (e.g., alarms), and
- user notifications (e.g., labeled warnings).

Establishing the intended use of the product often happens in the context of developing design inputs. Intended use is a required input to risk analysis according to the ISO 14971 standard. Intended use includes definition of the patient population, product use environment, involvement of knowledgeable practitioners, and so forth. When design inputs are developed, specific safety requirements may be included on the basis of early risk management activities. These early activities might include risk analysis, review of legacy products' performance, or evaluation of public data concerning competitor product safety.

A preliminary hazard analysis or risk analysis can be very helpful in ensuring that design inputs are comprehensive and address user needs. Risk analysis often starts with identification of potential hazards, definition of hazardous situations, estimation of the related risks, and evaluation to determine whether the risk is acceptable. For risks that are deemed unacceptable, control measures are planned and implemented.

As the design matures, more detailed risk analysis of the actual design features may be required. Some techniques, such as Fault Tree Analysis (FTA) and FMEA, are better suited to analysis at this stage when design details are available. A part of early design verification may include performing traceability analysis to confirm that the risk control measures that were planned have actually been implemented in the design.

The use of risk analysis techniques also aids in identifying design outputs that are "essential for proper functioning of the device" as required by 21 CFR 820.30(d), "Design output." These "essential outputs" should be considered when selecting supplier controls and also can aid in identifying the "critical control points" in the production process. Design outputs are discussed in detail in Chapter 7, "Design Controls."

Moreover, before design transfer can commence, design verification must include confirmation that the risk control measures are effective in controlling or reducing risk. For example, suppose a design included a safety feature to ensure that a heater unit stays within a safe temperature range. A verification test could be designed to try to force an overheating situation and confirm that the product effectively maintains the desired temperature range (i.e., that the safety feature is effective). Risk control verification is key to ensuring that the design is as safe as practical.

Risk Management during Production

As a part of the design transfer process, production processes are typically planned and developed. Evaluation of potential failure modes, or critical control points, is often part of the process development effort. From a risk management perspective, when the production process is under development, evaluation of potential hazards that could be introduced or exacerbated by the production process itself is essential. Risk analysis also applies for analyzing production process hazards; however, different analytical tools may be used than those used in analyzing the design. For example, a HACCP analysis or process FMEA may be used. Performing proactive assessment before production begins is akin to starting risk analysis early in the design effort.

After the manufacturing processes are defined and their potential effect on product risk is determined, the internal controls related to the processes themselves may be established proactively, to support the release of products that are safe. In addition, this information supports the establishment of other internal controls, such as the type, extent, and frequency of acceptance activities, equipment calibration and maintenance intervals, environmental controls, and personnel controls.

Furthermore, during design transfer the manufacturer often determines the type and extent of supplier controls, particularly for suppliers that provide products or services that are related to the essential outputs. Again, an understanding of the relationship between supplied items and product risk supports sound decisions with respect to purchasing controls.

Risk Management after Product Release

Risk management continues from the time the product is introduced into commercial distribution until the time the product is decommissioned. Each proposed product change, including design, labeling, and production process changes, must be assessed to evaluate the effect of the change on the product risk. Incorporating consideration of risk into the change control process provides an opportunity to ensure that the level of risk inherent in the product remains within acceptable levels throughout its commercial life cycle.

One of the difficulties here may be accessing the knowledge of the original designers to better understand the effect of changes to the product or process. A good risk management file would include the rationale for the assessment of and acceptability of risk-related aspects of the design. The information in this file must then be accessible to those proposing changes to design, packaging, labeling, production processes, or acceptance activities. Some manufacturers ensure access to the risk analysis by including it in the DMR.

Many but not all of the post-release risk activities are reactive rather than proactive. The reactive activities are based on the ongoing assessment of quality data to determine (a) whether initial risk probability estimates were accurate and (b) whether any new, unforeseen hazards or hazardous situations have developed during actual device use. In either event, additional risk analysis, evaluation, control, or monitoring activities may be necessary.

Table 30.1 lists some of the key areas that generate quality data potentially related to product risk. Routine assessment of these and other pertinent data may uncover new information relevant to the risk management program. Given that 21 CFR 820.100(a), "Corrective and preventive action," requires routine monitoring of key quality data for the purpose of identifying actual or potential quality problems, ensuring that the monitoring process also considers product risk provides for a well-integrated monitoring program.

Key Quality System Area	Examples of Risk-Related Data
Purchasing controls	Supplier performance over time
Acceptance activities	Nonconformances by part number per supplier
Nonconforming product evaluations	Root causes of nonconformances
Change control	Scope, extent, and quantity of changes
Complaints	Root causes of product failures by model; failure rates per model and product family
Corrective and preventive action	Quality System failure types (based on root causes) and failure rates
Servicing	Root causes of product failures by model; failure rates

Table 30.1. Quality data related to risk management after product release.

On the basis of analysis of pertinent quality data, the manufacturer may choose to enact new or more stringent internal controls, external controls (e.g., additional supplier-related controls) or design changes to maintain an acceptable level of product risk. Changes to the risk management file may indicate a need to improve the Risk Management process. Such changes may be due to:
- different severity of harm or probability of harm estimates or actual results, or
- previously unidentified risks discovered during the production and postproduction phases that may indicate a need for improving the Risk Management process.

ISO 14971 requires that the Risk Management process be reviewed periodically for effectiveness. Review of the effectiveness of the Risk Management process is usually addressed during a Management Review.

FDA Inspections and the Focus on Risk Management

Manufacturing facility inspections are based on the QSIT, which is discussed extensively in Chapter 1, "FDA's Organization and Regulatory Strategies." Within the instructions to investigators, some specific questions directly refer to or relate to risk management. Table 30.2 summarizes the pertinent subsystems and risk-related questions.

QSIT Subsystem	Risk-Related QSIT Inspection Objectives
Design controls	3. Review the design plan for the selected project to understand the layout of the design and development activities including assigned responsibilities and interfaces. Note: Evaluate the firm's conduct of risk analysis while proceeding through the assessment of the firm's Design Control system. 11. Confirm that risk analysis was performed.
Corrective and preventive actions	6. Determine if failure investigation procedures are followed. Determine if the degree to which a quality problem or nonconforming product is investigated is commensurate with the significance and risk of the nonconformity. ...
Production and process controls	1. Select a process for review based on: ... c) degree of risk of the process to cause device failures; ...

Table 30.2. Risk-related questions during FDA inspections.

Note that the QSIT narrative section includes numerous references to product risk in the subsystems included in Table 30.2. For example, in the detailed "Narrative for Design Controls," the investigator is advised, "While the requirement for the conduct of risk analysis appears in Section 820.30(g) Design Validation, a firm should not wait until they are performing design validation to begin risk analysis. Risk analysis should be addressed in the design plan and risk should be considered throughout the design process. Risk analysis must be completed in design validation." Manufacturers may find a review of the QSIT helpful when establishing or revising the Risk Management program.

Additional Guidance for Manufacturers

FDA's focus on risk management principles has been evident in guidance documents since the mid-1990s. Hazard analysis as an aspect of human factors engineering is presented in the *Do It By Design* guidance, issued in December 1996. *Medical Device Use Safety: Incorporating Human Factors Engineering into Risk Management*, issued in July 2000, provides comprehensive guidance on anticipating, analyzing, and controlling use-related hazards. FDA's *Guidance on Medical Device Patient Labeling*, issued in April 2001, describes the types of information on proper device use, risks, and benefits that should be included in device labeling provided to lay caregivers.

The GHTF issued its guidance, *Implementation of risk management principles and activities within a Quality Management System*, in May 2005. This guidance illustrates the

XI

links between various Quality System processes and risk management. It also includes examples of various risk management documents.

Additional standards and standards-based guidance documents are under development by various organizations to aid manufacturers in the use of risk management in areas such as biocompatibility, clinical trials, software lifecycles, and the use of medical devices in IT networks.

XI

NOTES:

XI

> "Change has become both pervasive and persistent. It *is* normality."
>   M. Hammer & J. Champy, *Reengineering the Corporation: A Manifesto for Business Revolution*, 1994

NOTES:

XI

"A fixation on what 'was' can blind us to what 'is', blocking the recognition of change."
R. Reich, *The Work of Nations: Preparing Ourselves for 21st Century Capitalism*, 1992

APPENDICES

APPENDIX A. BIBLIOGRAPHY

This bibliography identifies specific relevant documents related to industry practices in complying with the Quality System regulation. For generic references on a specific topic, see Appendix B, "Web Links".

AMERICAN NATIONAL STANDARDS INSTITUTE:

American National Standard Guide for Electrostatic Discharge Test Methodologies and Criteria for Electronic Equipment. ANSI C63.16:1993.

AMERICAN SOCIETY FOR QUALITY:

American National Standard for Calibration Systems. ANSI/ASQC M1:1996.

Environmental management systems—General guidelines on principles, systems and support techniques. ANSI/ISO/ASQ E14004:2004.

Environmental management systems—Requirements with guidance for use. ANSI/ISO/ASQ E14001:2004.

Guidelines for quality and/or environmental management systems auditing. ANSI/ISO/ASQ QE19011:2002. <u>Note</u>: This Standard replaces ISO/ASQ 10011-1, ISO/ASQ 10011-2, ISO/ASQ 10011-3, ISO 14010, ISO 14011 and ISO 14012.

Measurement management systems—Requirements for measurement processes and measuring equipment. ANSI/ISO/ASQ Q10012:2003.

Quality Management and Quality Assurance—Vocabulary. ANSI/ISO/ASQC A8402:1994. <u>Note</u>: This standard is obsolete. It is superseded by ANSI/ISO/ASQ Q9000:2005.

Quality management systems—Fundamentals and vocabulary. ANSI/ISO/ASQ Q9000:2005. <u>Note</u>: This standard supersedes ANSI/ISO/ASQ Q9000:2000 and ANSI/ISO/ASQC A8402:1994.

Quality management systems—Requirements. ANSI/ISO/ASQ Q9001:2000. <u>Note</u>: This standard supersedes ANSI/ISO/ASQ Q9001:1994, ANSI/ISO/ASQ Q9002:1994, and ANSI/ISO/ASQ Q9003:1994.

Quality management systems—Guidelines for performance improvements. ANSI/ISO/ASQ Q9004:2000.

Quality systems—Model for Quality Assurance in Design, Development, Production, Installation, and Servicing. ANSI/ISO/ASQC Q9001:1994. <u>Note</u>: This standard is obsolete. It is superseded by ANSI/ISO/ASQ Q9001:2000.

Sampling Procedures and Tables for Inspection by Attributes. ANSI/ASQ Z1.4:2003.

Sampling Procedures and Tables for Inspection by Variables for Percent Nonconforming. ANSI/ASQ Z1.9:2003.

ASSOCIATION FOR THE ADVANCEMENT OF MEDICAL INSTRUMENTATION:

Guidance for ANSI/AAMI/ISO 11607, Packaging for terminally sterilized medical devices—Part 1 and Part 2:2006. AAMI TIR22:2007.

Human factors design process for medical devices. ANSI/AAMI HE74:2001.

Human factors engineering guidelines and preferred practices for the design of medical devices. ANSI/AAMI HE48:1993.

Medical device software risk management. AAMI TIR32:2004.

Medical device software—Software life cycle processes. ANSI/AAMI/IEC 62304:2006. This standard supersedes ANSI/AAMI SW68:2001.

Medical devices—Application of risk management to medical devices. ANSI/AAMI/ISO 14971:2007.

Medical devices—Quality management systems—Guidance on the application of ISO 13485:2003. ANSI/AAMI/ISO TIR14969:2004.

Medical devices—Quality management systems—Requirements for regulatory purposes. ANSI/AAMI/ISO 13485:2003. <u>Note</u>: This standard supersedes ANSI/ISO/ASQ 13485:1996.

Medical devices—Symbols to be used with medical device labels, labeling, and information to be supplied—Part 1: General requirements. ANSI/AAMI/ISO 15223-1:2007.

Medical electrical equipment—Part 1: General requirements for basic safety and essential performance. ANSI/AAMI ES60601-1:2005.

Medical electrical equipment—Part 1-2: General requirements for basic safety and essential performance—Collateral standard: Electromagnetic compatibility—Requirements and tests. ANSI/AAMI/IEC 60601-1-2:2007.

Packaging for terminally sterilized medical devices—Part 1: Requirements for materials, sterile barrier systems, and packaging, 3rd edition. ANSI/AAMI/ISO 11607-1:2006.

Packaging for terminally sterilized medical devices—Part 2: Validation requirements for forming, sealing, and assembly processes. ANSI/AAMI/ISO 11607-2:2006.

Sterilization of health care products—Ethylene oxide—Part 1: Requirements for the development, validation and routine control of a sterilization process. AAMI/ISO 11135-1:2007.

Sterilization of health care products—Moist heat—Part 1: Requirements for development validation, and routine control of a sterilization process for medical devices. ANSI/AAMI/ISO 17665-1:2006. <u>Note</u>: This standard replaces ANSI/AAMI/ISO 11134:1993.

Sterilization of health care products—Radiation—Part 1: Requirements for the development, validation, and routine control of a sterilization process for medical devices. ANSI/AAMI/ISO 11137-1:2006.

Sterilization of health care product—Radiation—Part 2: Establishing the sterilization dose. ANSI/AAMI/ISO 11137-2:2006.

Sterilization of health care product—Radiation—Part 3: Guidance on dosimetric aspects. ANSI/AAMI/ISO 11137-3:2006.

ELECTROSTATIC DISCHARGE ASSOCIATION:

Protection of Electrical and Electronic Parts, Assemblies and Equipment (Excluding Electrically Initiated Explosive Devices). ANSI/ESD S20.20:2007.

Garments. ANSI/ESD STM2.1:1997.

Grounding. ANSI/ESD S6.1:2005.

Ionization. ANSI/ESD STM3.1:2006.

Packaging Materials for ESD Sensitive Items. ANSI/ESD S541:2003.

Resistive Characterization of Materials-Floor Materials. ANSI/ESD S7.1:2005.

Wrist Straps. ANSI/ESD S1.1:2006.

EUROPEAN COUNCIL:

Active implantable medical device directive. EC directive 90/385/EEC, 20 June 1990.

Amending Council Directive 90/385/EEC on the approximation of the laws of the Member States relating to active implantable medical devices, Council Directive 93/42/EEC concerning medical devices and Directive 98/8/EC concerning the placing of biocidal products on the market. EC directive 2007/47/EC, 5 September 2007.

Electromagnetic compatibility directive. EC directive 2004/108/EC, 15 December 2004.

In vitro diagnostic medical devices directive. EC Directive 98/79/EC, 27 October 1998.

Medical device directive. EC Directive 93/42/EEC, 14 June 1993.

Medicinal products for human use directive.   2001/83/EC, 6 November 2001.

Placing of biocidal products on the market directive. 98/8/EC, 16 February 1998.

FOOD AND DRUG ADMINISTRATION:

Laws and Regulations

Federal Food, Drug, and Cosmetic Act, US Code, Title 21, Chapter 9.

   Safe Medical Devices Act of 1990, Public Law 101-629.

   Food and Drug Administration Amendments Act of 2007, Public Law 110-85.

   Food and Drug Administration Modernization Act of 1997, Public Law 105-115.
      21 CFR Part 3 – Product Jurisdiction
      21 CFR Part 11 – Electronic Records; Electronic Signatures
      21 CFR Part 20 – Public Information
      21 CFR Part 211 – Current Good Manufacturing Practice for Finished Pharmaceuticals
      21 CFR Part 606 – Current Good Manufacturing Practice for Blood and Blood
            Components
      21 CFR Part 801 – Labeling
      21 CFR Part 803 – Medical Device Reporting
      21 CFR Part 806 – Medical Devices; Reports of Corrections and Removals
      21 CFR Part 807 – Establishment Registration and Device Listing for Manufacturers and
            Initial Importers of Devices
      21 CFR Part 809 – In Vitro Diagnostic Products for Human Use
      21 CFR Part 812 – Investigational Device Exemptions
      21 CFR Part 820 – Quality System Regulation[12]
      21 CFR Part 821 – Medical Device Tracking Requirements
      21 CFR Part 1271 – Human Cells, Tissues, and Cellular and Tissue-Based Products

---

[12] See Appendix C for the full text of this regulation.

Medical Device User Fee and Modernization Act of 2002 (MDUFMA), Public Law 107-250.

Health Insurance Portability and Accountability Act of 1996 (HIPAA), Public Law 104-191.
    45 CFR Part 162 – Health Insurance Reform: Standards for Electronic Transactions
    45 CFR Part 164 – Standards for Privacy of Individually Identifiable Health Information

General Guidances and FDA Topics

Changes in Enforcement of FDA's Requirements for Single Use Devices, CDRH, September 2001 (www.fda.gov/cdrh/reprocessing/letter-092501.html).

Compliance Program Guidance Manual, FDA, June 2006 (www.fda.gov/ora/cpgm/default.htm).

FDA Export Certificates, Guidance for Industry, FDA, April 2005 (www.fda.gov/cber/gdlns/exprtcert.pdf).

Guideline on General Principles of Process Validation, CDRH/Center for Drugs and Biologics, May 1987 (www.fda.gov/cdrh/ode/425.pdf).

Guide to Inspections of Quality Systems, Quality System Inspection Technique (QSIT), ORA, August 1999 (www.fda.gov/ora/inspect_ref/igs/qsit/qsitguide.htm).

Implementation of the Inspection by Accredited Persons Program Under The Medical Device User Fee and Modernization Act of 2002; Accreditation Criteria — Guidance for Industry, FDA Staff, and Third Parties, CDRH/CBER, October 2004 (www.fda.gov/cdrh/mdufma/guidance/1200.pdf).

Investigations Operations Manual, ORA (www.fda.gov/ora/inspect_ref/iom/default.htm).

Medical Device Quality Systems Manual: A Small Entity Compliance Guide, First Edition, HHS Publication: FDA 97-4179, CDRH, December 1996 (www.fda.gov/cdrh/dsma/gmpman.html).

Medical Device Reporting for Manufacturers, CDRH, March 1997 (www.fda.gov/cdrh/manual/mdrman.pdf).

Medical Device Reporting for User Facilities, CDRH, April 1996 (www.fda.gov/cdrh/mdruf.pdf).

Medical Device Tracking — Guidance for Industry and FDA Staff, CDRH, November 2007 (www.fda.gov/cdrh/comp/guidance/169.pdf).

Medical Device User Fee and Modernization Act of 2002, Validation Data in Premarket Notification Submissions (510(k)s) for Reprocessed Single-Use Medical Devices — Guidance for Industry and FDA Staff, CDRH, September 2006 (www.fda.gov/cdrh/ode/guidance/1216.pdf).

Note Concerning the March 27, 2000 Amendments to the MDR Regulation to Implement FDAMA Changes, CDRH, September 2000 (www.fda.gov/cdrh/postsurv/note_932700.html).

Procedures for Handling Post-Approval Studies Imposed by PMA Order — Guidance for Industry and FDA Staff, CDRH, August 2007 (www.fda.gov/cdrh/osb/guidance/1561.pdf).

Protecting the Public Health: FDA Pursues an Aggressive Enforcement Strategy, FDA White Paper, June 2003 (www.fda.gov/oc/whitepapers/enforce.html).

Quality System Information for Certain Premarket Application Reviews — Guidance for Industry and FDA Staff, CDRH, February 2003 (www.fda.gov/cdrh/comp/guidance/1140.pdf).

Third Party Programs Under the Sectoral Annex on Medical Devices to the Agreement on Mutual Recognition Between the United States of America and the European Community (MRA) — Guidance for Staff, Industry and Third Parties CDRH, January 1999 (www.fda.gov/cdrh/modact/eurma.pdf).

Combination Product Topics

Current Good Manufacturing Practice for Combination Products — Draft Guidance for Industry and FDA, OCP, September 2004 (www.fda.gov/oc/combination/OCLove1dft.pdf).

Pharmaceutical CGMPs for the 21ˢᵗ Century – A Risk-Based Approach, Final Report, FDA, September 2004 (www.fda.gov/ohrms/dockets/ac/04/briefing/2004-4078B1_08_CGMP-Report.pdf).

Quality Systems Approach to Pharmaceutical CGMP Regulations — Guidance for Industry, FDA, September 2006 (www.fda.gov/cder/guidance/7260fnl.pdf).

Design Topics

Deciding When to Submit a 510(k) for a Change to an Existing Device, CDRH, January 1997 (www.fda.gov/cdrh/ode/510kmod.pdf).

Design Control Guidance For Medical Device Manufacturers, CDRH, March 1997 (www.fda.gov/cdrh/comp/designgd.pdf).

Do It By Design: An Introduction to Human Factors in Medical Devices, CDRH, December 1996 (www.fda.gov/cdrh/humfac/doitpdf.pdf).

Early Development Considerations for Innovative Combination Products — Guidance for Industry and FDA Staff, OCP, September 2006 (www.fda.gov/oc/combination/innovative.pdf).

Guidance on Medical Device Patient Labeling — Final Guidance for Industry and FDA, CDRH, April 2001 (www.fda.gov/cdrh/ohip/guidance/1128.pdf).

In Vitro Diagnostic (IVD) Device Studies – Frequently Asked Questions — Draft Guidance for Industry and FDA Staff, CDRH/CBER, October 2007 (www.fda.gov/cdrh/oivd/guidance/1587.pdf).

Medical Device Use-Safety: Incorporating Human Factors Engineering into Risk Management — Guidance for Industry and FDA Premarket and Design Control Reviewers, CDRH, July 2000 (www.fda.gov/cdrh/humfac/1497.pdf).

Medical Devices with Sharps Injury Prevention Features — Guidance for Industry and FDA Staff, CDRH, August 2005 (www.fda.gov/cdrh/ode/guidance/934.pdf).

Modifications to Devices Subject to Premarket Approval (PMA) - The PMA Supplement Decision-Making Process — Draft Guidance for Industry and FDA Staff , CDRH/CBER, March 2007 (www.fda.gov/cdrh/ode/guidance/1584.pdf).

Radio-Frequency Wireless Technology in Medical Devices — Draft Guidance for Industry and FDA Staff, CDRH, January 2007 (www.fda.gov/cdrh/osel/guidance/1618.pdf).

Recognition and Use of Consensus Standards — Final Guidance for Industry and FDA Staff, CDRH, June 2001 (www.fda.gov/cdrh/ost/guidance/321.pdf).

Statistical Guidance on Reporting Results from Studies Evaluating Diagnostic Tests — Guidance for Industry and FDA Staff, CDRH, March 2007 (www.fda.gov/cdrh/osb/guidance/1620.pdf).

The New 510(k) Paradigm: Alternate Approaches to Demonstrating Substantial Equivalence in Premarket Notifications", CDRH, March 1998 (www.fda.gov/cdrh/ode/parad510.pdf).

Updated 510(k) Sterility Review Guidance K90-1 — Guidance for Industry and FDA, CDRH, August 2002 (www.fda.gov/cdrh/ode/guidance/361.pdf).

Write it Right: Recommendations for Developing User Instruction Manuals for Medical Devices Used in Home Health Care, CDRH, August 1993 (www.fda.gov/cdrh/dsma/897.pdf).

Software and Part 11 Topics

Computerized Systems Used in Clinical Investigations — Guidance for Industry, FDA, May 2007 (www.fda.gov/cder/guidance/7359fnl.pdf).

Cybersecurity for Networked Medical Devices Containing Off-the-Shelf (OTS) Software — Guidance for Industry, CDRH, January 2005 (www.fda.gov/cdrh/comp/guidance/1553.pdf).

General Principles of Software Validation — Final Guidance for Industry and FDA Staff, CDRH,/CBER, January 2002 (www.fda.gov/cdrh/comp/guidance/938.pdf).

Glossary of Computerized System and Software Development Terminology, ORA, August 1995 (www.fda.gov/ora/inspect_ref/igs/gloss.html).

Guidance for the Content of Premarket Submissions for Software Contained in Medical Devices — Guidance for Industry and FDA Staff, CDRH(ODE & OIVD)/CBER, May 2005 (www.fda.gov/cdrh/ode/guidance/337.pdf).

Part 11, Electronic Records; Electronic Signatures – Scope and Application — Guidance for Industry, FDA, August 2003 (www.fda.gov/cder/guidance/5667fnl.pdf).

Off-The-Shelf Software Use in Medical Devices — Guidance for Industry, FDA Reviewers, and Compliance, CDRH, September 1999 (www.fda.gov/cdrh/ode/guidance/585.pdf).

GLOBAL HARMONIZATION TASK FORCE:

Essential Principles of Safety and Performance of Medical Devices, GHTF/SG1/N41R9:2005 (www.ghtf.org/sg1/inventorysg1/sg1n41r92005.pdf).

Guidelines for Regulatory Auditing of Quality Management Systems of Medical Device Manufacturers, Part 1 – General Requirements, GHTF/SG4/28:1999 (www.ghtf.org/sg4/inventorysg4/99-28genreq.pdf).

Guidelines for Regulatory Auditing of Quality Management Systems of Medical Device Manufacturers, Part 2 – Regulatory Auditing Strategy, GHTF/SG4/N30R20:2006 (www.ghtf.org/sg4/inventorysg4/SG4N30R20-2006_auditing_strategy_FINAL.pdf).

Implementation of risk management principles and activities within a Quality Management System, GHTF/SG3/N15R8:2005 (www.ghtf.org/sg3/inventorysg3/sg3n15r82005.pdf).

Quality Management Systems – Process Validation Guidance, Edition 2, GHTF/SG3/N99-10:2004 (www.ghtf.org/sg3/inventorysg3/sg3_fd_n99-10_edition2.pdf).

Role of Standards in the Assessment of Medical Devices, GHTF/SG1/N012R10:2000 (www.ghtf.org/sg1/inventorysg1/sg1-n12r10.pdf).

GODFREY, A. B. and JURAN, J. M., _Juran's Quality Handbook, Fifth Edition_, 1999, McGraw-Hill, 1936 pgs.

INSTITUTE FOR ELECTRICAL AND ELECTRONICS ENGINEERS:

Recommended Practice for Software Acquisition. IEEE 1062:1998.

Recommended Practice for Software Design Descriptions. IEEE 1016:1998.

Recommended Practice for Software Requirements Specifications. IEEE 830:1998.

Standard for Developing a Software Project Life Cycle Process. IEEE 1074:2006.

Standard for Software Configuration Management Plans. IEEE 828:2005.

Standard for Software Project Management Plans. IEEE 1058:1998.

Standard for Software Quality Assurance Plans. IEEE 730:2002.

Standard for Software Reviews. IEEE 1028:1998.

Standard for Software Test Documentation. IEEE 829:1998.

Standard for Software User Documentation. IEEE 1063:2001.

Standard for Software Verification and Validation. IEEE 1012:2004.

INTERNATIONAL ELECTROTECHNICAL COMMISSION:

Analysis techniques for system reliability—Procedure for failure mode and effects analysis (FMEA). IEC 60812:2006.

Design review. IEC 61160:2006.

Fault tree analysis (FTA). IEC 61025:2006.

General requirements for the competence of testing and calibration laboratories. ISO/IEC 17025:2005.

Hazard and operability studies (HAZOP studies) – Application guide. IEC 61882:2001.

INTERNATIONAL ORGANIZATION FOR STANDARDIZATION:

Aseptic processing of health care products—Part 1: General requirements. ISO 13408-1:1998.

Guidance on statistical techniques for ISO 9001:2000. ISO/TR 10017:2003.

Guidelines for quality management system documentation. ISO/TR 10013:2001.

Guidelines for the selection of quality management system consultants and use of their services. ISO 10019:2005.

Primary packaging materials for medicinal products—Particular requirements for the application of ISO 9001:2000, with reference to Good Manufacturing Practice (GMP). ISO 15378:2006.

Quality management—Customer satisfaction—Guidelines for complaints handling in organizations. ISO 10002:2004.

Quality management—Guidelines for training. ISO 10015:1999.

Quality management systems—Guidelines for configuration management. ISO 10007:2003.

Quality management systems—Guidelines for quality management in projects. ISO 10006:2003.

Quality management systems—Guidelines for quality plans. ISO 10005:2005.

Systems and software engineering—Life cycle processes—Risk management. ISO/IEC 16085:2006.

Software engineering—Guidelines for the application of ISO 9001:2000 to computer software. ISO/IEC 90003:2004.

INTERNATIONAL SOCIETY OF PHARMACEUTICAL ENGINEERS:

Good Automated Manufacturing Practice (GAMP®) Guide for Validation of Automated Systems – GAMP4, December 2001.

GAMP® Good Practice Guide: Electronic Data Archiving, July 2007.

GAMP® Good Practice Guide: Global Information Systems, November 2005.

GAMP® Good Practice Guide: IT Infrastructure Control and Compliance, September 2005.

GAMP® Good Practice Guide: Risk-Based Approach to Electronic Records & Signatures, February 2005.

GAMP® Good Practice Guide: Testing of GxP Systems, December 2005.

GAMP® Good Practice Guide: Validation of Laboratory Computerized Systems, April 2005.

GAMP® Good Practice Guide: Validation of Process Controls Systems, October 2003.

LINK, D. M. and MCDONNELL, E. J. (eds.), *Current Issues in Medical Device Quality Systems*, 1997, AAMI, 256 pgs.

NATIONAL INSTITUTE OF STANDARDS AND TECHNOLOGY:

Risk Management Guide for Information Technology Systems, Recommendations from the National Institute of Standards and Technology, NIST, Special Pub. 800-30, July 2002, 54 pgs.

TRAUTMAN, K. A., *The FDA and Worldwide Quality System Requirements Guidebook for Medical Devices*, 1997, ASQC Quality Press, 210 pgs.

WOMACK, J. P. and JONES, D. T., *Lean Thinking*, 2003, Free Press, 396 pgs.

APPENDIX B. WEB LINKS

The table below provides links to useful sites on the Worldwide Web. These are divided into FDA resources (FDA), other government resources (Gov), organizations that support medical device development (Org), and standards organizations (Stds).

Type	Name	Address
FDA	510(k) Information and Releasable Database	www.accessdata.fda.gov/scripts/cdrh/cfdocs/cfpmn/pmn.cfm
FDA	510(k) Paradigm	www.fda.gov/cdrh/ode/parad510.html
FDA	CBER Guidance Documents	www.fda.gov/cber/guidelines.htm
FDA	CDER Guidance Documents	www.fda.gov/cder/guidance/index.htm
FDA	CDRH Consumer Information	www.fda.gov/cdrh/consumer/index.html
FDA	CDRH Device Advice	www.fda.gov/cdrh/devadvice
FDA	CDRH Guidance Documents	www.accessdata.fda.gov/scripts/cdrh/cfdocs/cfggp/search.cfm
FDA	CDRH Industry Support (formerly DSMA)	www.fda.gov/cdrh/industry/support/index.html
FDA	CDRH Referral List	www.accessdata.fda.gov/scripts/cdrh/cfdocs/cfReferral/referral.cfm
FDA	CDRH Standards Program (Consensus Standards)	www.fda.gov/cdrh/stdsprog.html
FDA	CDRH "What's New"	www.accessdata.fda.gov/scripts/cdrh/cfdocs/cfTopic/cdrhnew.cfm
FDA	Center for Biologics Evaluation and Research (CBER)	www.fda.gov/cber
FDA	Center for Devices and Radiological Heath (CDRH)	www.fda.gov/cdrh
FDA	Center for Drug Evaluation and Research (CDER)	www.fda.gov/cder
FDA	Code of Federal Regulations (CFR)	www.gpoaccess.gov/cfr/index.html
FDA	Combination Products	www.fda.gov/oc/combination
FDA	Commissioner's Office	www.fda.gov/oc
FDA	Compliance Program Manuals	www.fda.gov/ora/cpgm/default.htm
FDA	Device Listing Searchable Database	www.accessdata.fda.gov/scripts/cdrh/cfdocs/cfRL/listing.cfm
FDA	DSMICA—Staff Directory	www.fda.gov/cdrh/dsma/dsmastaf.html
FDA	Electronic Records Information	www.fda.gov/ora/compliance_ref/part11/Default.htm
FDA	Establishment Registration and U.S. Agent	www.fda.gov/cdrh/devadvice/341.html
FDA	FDA Modernization Act	www.fda.gov/cdrh/modact/modern.html
FDA	FDA Web Page	www.fda.gov
FDA	Federal Food, Drug, and Cosmetic Act	www.fda.gov/opacom/laws/fdcact/fdctoc.htm
FDA	Federal Register	www.gpoaccess.gov/fr/index.html
FDA	Freedom of Information Reading Room (Warning Letters)	www.fda.gov/foi/warning.htm
FDA	Guide to Inspection of Quality Systems	www.fda.gov/ora/inspect_ref/igs/qsit/qsitguide.htm
FDA	Health Insurance Portability and Accountability Act (HIPAA)	www.hhs.gov/ocr/hipaa
FDA	Inspection References	www.fda.gov/ora/inspect_ref/default.htm
FDA	International Program	www.fda.gov/cdrh/international
FDA	Investigations Operations Manual (IOM)	www.fda.gov/ora/inspect_ref/iom/default.htm
FDA	Medical Device Exemptions	www.fda.gov/cdrh/devadvice/315.html

Type	Name	Address
FDA	Medical Device Reporting Home Page	www.fda.gov/cdrh/mdr/index.html
FDA	MEDWATCH	www.fda.gov/medwatch/revise.htm
FDA	Office of Regulatory Affairs	www.fda.gov/ora
FDA	Premarket Approval Database	www.accessdata.fda.gov/scripts/cdrh/cfdocs/cfPMA/pma.cfm
FDA	Product Classification Database	www.accessdata.fda.gov/scripts/cdrh/cfdocs/cfPCD/classification.cfm
FDA	Quality System Inspection Technique (QSIT)	www.fda.gov/ora/inspect_ref/igs/qsit/qsitguide.htm
FDA	Radiological Health Program	www.fda.gov/cdrh/radhealth
FDA	Reengineering Efforts in CDRH	www.fda.gov/cdrh/reengine.html
FDA	Registration Searchable Database	www.accessdata.fda.gov/scripts/cdrh/cfdocs/cfRL/registration.cfm
FDA	Third Party Review Program	www.fda.gov/cdrh/thirdparty
FDA	Title 21 of CFR (Direct Link)	www.fda.gov/cdrh/devadvice/365.html
FDA	Warning Letters	www.fda.gov/foi/warning.htm
Gov	Agency for HealthCare Research and Quality (U.S.)	www.ahcpr.gov
Gov	Australia Therapeutic Goods Authority (TGA)	www.tga.gov.au
Gov	Australian Institute of Health and Welfare (AIHW)	www.aihw.gov.au/index.cfm
Gov	Canadian Medical Devices	www.hc-sc.gc.ca/dhp-mps/md-im/index_e.html
Gov	CDC (Centers for Disease Control and Prevention)	www.cdc.gov
Gov	CMS (Centers for Medicare and Medicaid Services)	www.cms.hhs.gov
Gov	Danish Medicines Agency	www.dkma.dk
Gov	European Commission—Medical Devices	ec.europa.eu/enterprise/medical_devices/index_en.htm
Gov	European Union Directives	eur-lex.europa.eu/en/index.htm
Gov	Federal Register Online	www.gpoaccess.gov/fr/index.html
Gov	Japanese Ministry of Health, Labour and Welfare	www.mhlw.go.jp/english/index.html
Gov	New Zealand Medicines and Medical Devices Safety Authority (MedSafe)	www.medsafe.govt.nz
Gov	NIH (National Institutes of Health)	www.nih.gov
Gov	NIST (National Institute of Standards and Technology)	www.nist.gov
Gov	NTIS (National Technical Information Service)—MIL-Standards	www.ntis.gov
Gov	U.K. Medical Devices Agency	www.medical-devices.gov.uk
Gov	U.S. Code (general and permanent laws of the United States)	www.law.cornell.edu/uscode
Gov	U.S. Department of Commerce	www.commerce.gov
Gov	U.S. Department of Health and Human Services	www.os.dhhs.gov
Gov	U.S. House of Representatives	www.house.gov
Gov	U.S. Public and Private Laws	www.gpoaccess.gov/plaws/index.html
Gov	U.S. Senate	www.senate.gov

Type	Name	Address
Org	AAMI (Association for the Advancement of Medical Instrumentation)	www.aami.org
Org	AdvaMed (Advanced Medical Technology Association, Formerly HIMA)	www.advamed.org
Org	AMA (American Medical Association)	www.ama-assn.org
Org	Biotechnology Industry Organization	www.bio.org
Org	DIMDE—German Institute of Medical Documentation and Information	www.dimdi.de/dynamic/en/index.html
Org	FDLI (Food and Drug Law Institute)	www.fdli.org
Org	Global Harmonization Task Force	www.ghtf.org
Org	HIDA (Health Industry Distributors Association)	www.hida.org
Org	ISPE (International Society for Pharmaceutical Engineers)	www.ispe.org
Org	Medical Device Link	www.devicelink.com
Org	Medtech Insight (Formerly Medical Data International)	www.medtechinsight.com
Org	NEMA (National Electrical Manufacturers Association)	www.nema.org
Org	Project Management Institute (Project Management Resources)	www.pmi.org
Org	RAPS (Regulatory Affairs Professionals Society)	www.raps.org
Stds	AAMI (Association for the Advancement of Medical Instrumentation)—Medical Device, Sterilization, and Other Standards	www.aami.org
Stds	AFNOR (French Association for Standardization)	www.afnor.fr
Stds	ANSI (American National Standards Institute)—Wide Range of Standards, Often Cross-listed with Standards From Other Organizations	www.ansi.org
Stds	ASQ (American Society for Quality)	www.asq.org
Stds	ASTM (American Society for Testing and Materials)	www.astm.org
Stds	BSI (British Standards Institution)	www.bsi-global.com
Stds	CEN (European Committee for Standardization)	www.cen.eu/cenorm/homepage.htm
Stds	CENELEC (European Committee for Electrotechnical Standardization)	www.cenelec.be
Stds	CSA International (Canadian Standards Association)	www.csa-international.org
Stds	DIN (German Standards Institute)	www.din.de

Type	Name	Address
Stds	DS (Danish Standards)	www.en.ds.dk
Stds	ESD Association	www.esda.org
Stds	IEC (International Electrotechnical Commission)—Electrical Safety Standards	www.iec.ch
Stds	IEEE (Institute of Electrical and Electronics Engineers)—Software Development Standards	www.ieee.org
Stds	IEST (Institute of Environmental Sciences and Technology)—Cleanroom Standards	www.iest.org
Stds	ISA (Instrument Society of America)—Measurement/Control and Gas Quality Standards	www.isa.org
Stds	ISO (International Organization for Standardization)—Worldwide Standards Organization, Standards Often Co-listed	www.iso.ch
Stds	ISPE (International Society for Pharmaceutical Engineers)	www.ispe.org
Stds	JSA (Japanese Standards Association)	www.jsa.or.jp/default_english.asp
Stds	NCCLS (National Committee for Clinical Laboratory Standards)	www.nccls.org
Stds	NNI (Netherlands Standards Institute)	www.nen.nl
Stds	Norway Standards	www.standard.no
Stds	NSAI (National Standards Authority of Ireland)	www.nsai.ie
Stds	PDA (Parenteral Drug Association)—Sterilization Validation, Aseptic Filling, Filtration, Closure Integrity, etc.	www.pda.org
Stds	SCC (Standards Council Canada)	www.scc.ca
Stds	SFS (Finnish Standards Association)	www.sfs.fi
Stds	SIS (Swedish Standards Institute)	www.sis.se
Stds	SNV (Swiss Association for Standardization)	www.snv.ch
Stds	TAPPI (Technical Association of the Pulp and Paper Industry)—Test methods for paper/labels	www.tappi.org
Stds	USP (United States Pharmacopeia)	www.usp.org

APPENDIX C. FINAL RULE FOR THE QUALITY SYSTEM REGULATION

21 CFR 820: *Quality System Regulation, Final Rule*
Federal Register, Part VII, Department of Health and Human Services
Volume 61, Number 195, Pages 52601–52662, October 7, 1996

The Final Rule for the Quality System regulation, including the Preamble, is reproduced on the following pages. This is the original publication found in the *Federal Register*. Since its initial publication in 1996, there have been a small number of technical amendments to the Quality System regulation, which are described below.

Technical Amendment	Federal Register Citation
65 FR 17136 (31-Mar-2000) Change removed paragraphs (e) and (f) from 820.1 Scope.	PART 820—QUALITY SYSTEM REGULATION 7. The authority citation for 21 CFR part 820 continues to read as follows: Authority: 351, 352, 360, 360c, 360e, 360h, 360i, 360j, 360l, 371, 374, 381, 383. 8. Amend § 820.1 by removing paragraphs (e) and (f).
65 FR 66636 (07-Nov-2000) Change restored paragraph (e) to 820.1 Scope.	PART 820—QUALITY SYSTEM REGULATION 5. The authority citation for 21 CFR part 820 continues to read as follows: Authority: 21 U.S.C. 351, 352, 360, 360c, 360d, 360e, 360h, 360i, 360j, 360l, 371, 374, 381, 383. 6. Section 820.1 is amended by adding paragraph (e) to read as follows: § 820.1 Scope. * * * * * (e) Exemptions or variances. (1) Any person who wishes to petition for an exemption or variance from any device quality system requirement is subject to the requirements of section 520(f)(2) of the act. Petitions for an exemption or variance shall be submitted according to the procedures set forth in § 10.30 of this chapter, the FDA's administrative procedures. Guidance is available from the Center for Devices and Radiological Health, Division of Small Manufacturers Assistance (HFZ–220), 1350 Piccard Dr., Rockville, MD 20850, U.S.A., telephone 1–800–638–2041 or 1–301–443–6597, FAX 301–443–8818. (2) FDA may initiate and grant a variance from any device quality system requirement when the agency determines that such variance is in the best interest of the public health. Such variance will remain in effect only so long as there remains a public health need for the device and the device would not likely be made sufficiently available without the variance.
69 FR 11313 (10-Mar-2004) Change removed reference to 21 CFR 804, which was deleted from the CFR.	PART 820—QUALITY SYSTEM REGULATION 14. The authority citation for 21 CFR part 820 continues to read as follows: Authority: 21 U.S.C. 351, 352, 360, 360c, 360d, 360e, 360h, 360i, 360j, 360l 371, 374, 381, 383. 15. Section 820.198(d) is revised to read as follows § 820.198 Complaint files. * * * * * (d) Any complaint that represents an event which must be reported to FDA under part 803 of this chapter shall be promptly reviewed, evaluated, and investigated by a designated individual(s) and shall be maintained in a separate portion of the complaint files or otherwise clearly identified. In addition to the information required by § 820.198(e), records of investigation under this paragraph shall include a determination of: (1) Whether the device failed to meet specifications; (2) Whether the device was being used for treatment or diagnosis; and (3) The relationship, if any, of the device to the reported incident or adverse event. * * * * *

Technical Amendment	Federal Register Citation
	16. Section 820.200(c) is revised to read as follows: § 820.200 Servicing. * * * * * (c) Each manufacturer who receives a service report that represents an event which must be reported to FDA under part 803 of this chapter shall automatically consider the report a complaint and shall process it in accordance with the requirements of § 820.198.
69 FR 29829 (25-May-2004) Changed to specifically note applicability of 21 CFR 820 to tissue products, under newly released 21 CFR 1271. Also, the Quality System regulation contains a typographic error: it has a date of 2005, but 2004 is the correct date.	PART 820—QUALITY SYSTEM REGULATION 6. The authority citation for 21 CFR part 820 is revised to read as follows: Authority: 21 U.S.C. 351, 352, 360, 360c, 360d, 360e, 360h, 360i, 360j, 360l, 371, 374, 381, 383; 42 U.S.C. 216, 262, 263a, 264. 7. Section 820.1 is amended by adding two sentences to the end of paragraph (a)(1), and by revising paragraph (b) to read as follows: § 820.1 Scope. (a) Applicability. (1) * * * Manufacturers of human cells, tissues, and cellular and tissue-based products (HCT/Ps), as defined in § 1271.3(d) of this chapter, that are medical devices (subject to premarket review or notification, or exempt from notification, under an application submitted under the device provisions of the act or under a biological product license application under section 351 of the Public Health Service Act) are subject to this part and are also subject to the donor-eligibility procedures set forth in part 1271 subpart C of this chapter and applicable current good tissue practice procedures in part 1271 subpart D of this chapter. In the event of a conflict between applicable regulations in part 1271 and in other parts of this chapter, the regulation specifically applicable to the device in question shall supersede the more general. * * * * * (b) The quality system regulation in this part supplements regulations in other parts of this chapter except where explicitly stated otherwise. In the event of a conflict between applicable regulations in this part and in other parts of this chapter, the regulations specifically applicable to the device in question shall supersede any other generally applicable requirements.
71 FR 16228 (31-Mar-2006) Change removed reference to 21 CFR 804, which was deleted from the CFR.	PART 820—QUALITY SYSTEM REGULATION 3. The authority citation for 21 CFR part 820 continues to read as follows: Authority: 21 U.S.C. 351, 352, 360, 360c, 360d, 360e, 360h, 360i, 360j, 360l, 371, 374, 381, 383. 4. Amend paragraph (a)(3) of § 820.198 by removing "or 804".
72 FR 17397 (09-Apr-2007) Change updated title, address, and phone numbers for DSMICA.	PART 820—QUALITY SYSTEM REGULATION 6. FDA is revising Sec. 820.1(e) and replacing "Division of Small Manufacturers Assistance (HFZ-220), 1350 Piccard Dr., Rockville, MD 20850, U.S.A., telephone 1-800-638-2041 or 1-301-443-6597, FAX 301-443-8818" with "Division of Small Manufacturers, International and Consumer Assistance (HFZ-220), 1350 Piccard Dr., Rockville, MD 20850, U.S.A., telephone 1-800-638-2041 or 240-276-3150, FAX 240-276-3151."

**Monday
October 7, 1996**

Part VII

Department of Health and Human Services

Food and Drug Administration

21 CFR Parts 808, 812, and 820
Medical Devices; Current Good
Manufacturing Practice (CGMP); Final
Rule

R

DEPARTMENT OF HEALTH AND HUMAN SERVICES

Food and Drug Administration

21 CFR Parts 808, 812, and 820

[Docket No. 90N–0172]

RIN 0910–AA09

Medical Devices; Current Good Manufacturing Practice (CGMP) Final Rule; Quality System Regulation

AGENCY: Food and Drug Administration, HHS.

ACTION: Final rule.

SUMMARY: The Food and Drug Administration (FDA) is revising the current good manufacturing practice (CGMP) requirements for medical devices and incorporating them into a quality system regulation. The quality system regulation includes requirements related to the methods used in, and the facilities and controls used for, designing, manufacturing, packaging, labeling, storing, installing, and servicing of medical devices intended for human use. This action is necessary to add preproduction design controls and to achieve consistency with quality system requirements worldwide. This regulation sets forth the framework for device manufacturers to follow and gives them greater flexibility in achieving quality requirements.

DATES: The regulation is effective June 1, 1997. For more information on compliance with 21 CFR 820.30 see section IV. of this document.

Written comments on the information collection requirements should be submitted by December 6, 1996.

ADDRESSES: Submit written comments on the information collection requirements to the Dockets Management Branch (HFA–305), Food and Drug Administration, 12420 Parklawn Dr., rm. 1–23, Rockville, MD 20857. All comments should be identified with the docket number found in brackets in the heading of this document.

FOR FURTHER INFORMATION CONTACT: Kimberly A. Trautman, Center for Devices and Radiological Health (HFZ–341), Food and Drug Administration, 2098 Gaither Rd., Rockville, MD 20850, 301–594–4648.

SUPPLEMENTARY INFORMATION:

I. Background

Manufacturers establish and follow quality systems to help ensure that their products consistently meet applicable requirements and specifications. The quality systems for FDA-regulated products (food, drugs, biologics, and devices) are known as CGMP's. CGMP requirements for devices in part 820 (21 CFR part 820) were first authorized by section 520(f) of the Federal Food, Drug, and Cosmetic Act (the act) (21 U.S.C. 360j(f)), which was among the authorities added to the act by the Medical Device Amendments of 1976 (Pub. L. 94–295).

Under section 520(f) of the act, FDA issued a final rule in the Federal Register of July 21, 1978 (43 FR 31 508), prescribing CGMP requirements for the methods used in, and the facilities and controls used for the manufacture, packing, storage, and installation of medical devices. This regulation became effective on December 18, 1978, and is codified under part 820. Except for editorial changes to update organizational references in the regulation and revisions to the list of critical devices that was included in the preamble to the final regulation, the device CGMP requirements have not been revised since 1978. This final rule is the result of an extensive effort begun in 1990 to revise this regulation.

The Safe Medical Devices Act of 1990 (the SMDA) (Pub. L. 101–629), enacted on November 28, 1990, amended section 520(f) of the act, providing FDA with the authority to add preproduction design controls to the CGMP regulation. This change in law was based on findings that a significant proportion of device recalls were attributed to faulty design of product. Specifically, in January 1990, FDA published the results of an evaluation of device recalls that occurred from October 1983 through September 1989, in a report entitled "Device Recalls: A Study of Quality Problems" (Ref. 1). (See 55 FR 21108, May 22, 1990, where FDA announced the availability of the report.) FDA found that approximately 44 percent of the quality problems that led to voluntary recall actions during this 6-year period were attributed to errors or deficiencies that were designed into particular devices and may have been prevented by adequate design controls. These design-related defects involved both noncritical devices (e.g., patient chair lifts, in vitro diagnostics, and administration sets) and critical devices (e.g., pacemakers and ventilators). Also in 1990, the Department of Health and Human Services' Inspector General conducted a study entitled "FDA Medical Device Regulation From Premarket Review to Recall" (Ref. 2), which reached similar conclusions. With respect to software used to operate medical devices, the data were even more striking. A subsequent study of software-related recalls for the period of fiscal year (FY) 1983 through FY 1991 indicated that over 90 percent of all software-related device failures were due to design-related errors, generally, the failure to validate software prior to routine production (Ref. 3).

The SMDA also added new section 803 to the act (21 U.S.C. 383) which, among other things, encourages FDA to work with foreign countries toward mutual recognition of CGMP requirements. FDA undertook the revision of the CGMP regulation to add the design controls authorized by the SMDA to the CGMP regulation, as well as because the agency believed that it would be beneficial to the public and the medical device industry for the CGMP regulation to be consistent, to the extent possible, with the requirements for quality systems contained in applicable international standards, primarily, the International Organization for Standards (ISO) 9001:1994 "Quality Systems—Model for Quality Assurance in Design, Development, Production, Installation, and Servicing" (Ref. 4), and the ISO committee draft (CD) revision of ISO/CD 13485 "Quality Systems—Medical Devices—Supplementary Requirements to ISO 9001" (Ref. 5).

This action is being taken under those provisions of the SMDA and in response to the following: (1) Notices that appeared in the Federal Register of April 25, 1990 (55 FR 17502), and in the Federal Register of April 17, 1991 (56 FR 15626), that announced meetings of the agency's Device Good Manufacturing Practice Advisory Committee (GMP Advisory Committee), at which the need for revisions to the CGMP regulation was explored; (2) an advance notice of proposed rulemaking (ANPRM) that appeared in the Federal Register of June 15, 1990 (55 FR 24544), that announced the agency's intent to revise the CGMP regulation; (3) a notice of availability of a document that appeared in the Federal Register of November 30, 1990 (55 FR 49644), entitled "Medical Devices; Current Good Manufacturing Practices (CGMP) Regulations Document; Suggested Changes; Availability" (Ref. 6) and comments solicited from the public about the document; (4) a proposed rule in the Federal Register of November 23, 1993 (58 FR 61952), (Ref. 7) and comments solicited from the public about the proposal; (5) a notice of availability that appeared in the Federal Register of July 24, 1995 (60 FR 37856), announcing the availability of the "Working Draft of the Current Good Manufacturing Practice (CGMP) Final Rule" (hereinafter referred to as the Working Draft) (Ref. 8) and comments solicited from the public about the Working Draft; (6) testimony at an August 23, 1995, open public meeting announced in the Federal Register (60 FR 37856); (7) and testimony and advisory committee recommendations from the September 13 and 14, 1995, meeting of the GMP Advisory Committee announced in the Federal Register of August 24, 1995 (60 FR 44036). Thus, FDA's decision to revise the CGMP regulation is based on changes in the law made by the SMDA, the agency's discussions with others including its GMP Advisory Committee, responses to the Federal Register notices on this matter, FDA's analysis of recall data, its experience with the regulatory application of the original CGMP regulation, and its assessment of international quality standards.

The agency's final rule embraces the same "umbrella" approach to the CGMP regulation that is the underpinning of the original CGMP regulation. Because this regulation must apply to so many different types of devices, the regulation does not prescribe in detail how a manufacturer must produce a specific device. Rather, the regulation provides the framework that all manufacturers must follow by requiring that manufacturers develop and follow procedures and fill in the details that are appropriate to a given device according to the current state-of-the-art manufacturing for that specific device. FDA has made changes to the proposed regulation and the Working Draft, as the final rule evidences, to provide manufacturers with even greater flexibility in achieving the quality requirements.

The Supreme Court recently addressed the preemptive effect, under section 521 of the act (21 U.S.C. 360k), of the original CGMP regulation and other FDA requirements for medical devices on State tort actions. In *Medtronic, Inc.* v. *Lohr,* 116 S. Ct. 2240 (1996), the Supreme Court gave substantial deference to the agency's interpretation of section 521 of the act found at § 808.1 (21 CFR 808.1). The Court noted that CGMP requirements are general rather than "specific requirements applicable to a particular device," and that State common law remedies are similarly general, and do not establish a "substantive requirement for a specific device." (*Lohr* at 2257; see also § 808.1(d) and (d)(6)(ii).) Moreover, the Court drew a distinction between remedies and requirements, noting that while common law tort actions may provide remedies different from those available under the act, no preemption occurs unless the substantive requirements of the State law are

"different from, or in addition to," those imposed by the act. (See *Lohr* at 2255.) Under the Supreme Court's analysis in *Lohr,* the requirements imposed by the original CGMP regulation would rarely have preemptive effect.

FDA believes that the reasoning of *Medtronic* v. *Lohr* applies equally to the new quality system regulation, which, as does the original CGMP regulation, prescribes requirements that apply to medical devices in general, rather than to any particular medical device. Therefore, FDA has concurrently amended part 808 (21 CFR part 808) to make clear the new quality system regulation does not preempt State tort and common law remedies.

II. Decision to Make a Working Draft Available for Comment

In the Federal Register of November 23, 1993, the agency issued the proposed revisions to the CGMP regulation, entitled "Medical Devices; Current Good Manufacturing Practice (CGMP) Regulations; Proposed Revisions; Request for Comments," and public comment was solicited. After the proposal issued, FDA met with the Global Harmonization Task Force (the GHTF) Study Group in early March 1994, in Brussels, to compare the provisions of the proposal with the provisions of ISO 9001:1994 and European National Standard (EN) 46001 "Quality Systems—Medical Devices— Particular Requirements for the Application of EN 29001" (Ref. 9). ISO 9001:1994 and EN 46001:1994 are written as voluntary standards, but when used to fulfill the requirements of the European Medical Device Directives, or other national regulations, these standards are mandatory requirements similar to the CGMP requirements. The GHTF includes: Representatives of the Canadian Ministry of Health and Welfare, the Japanese Ministry of Health and Welfare, FDA, and industry members from the European Union (EU), Australia, Canada, Japan, and the United States. The participants at the GHTF meeting favorably regarded FDA's effort toward harmonization with international standards. The GHTF submitted comments, however, noting where FDA could more closely harmonize to achieve consistency with quality system requirements worldwide. Since the proposal published, FDA has also attended numerous industry and professional association seminars and workshops, including ISO Technical Committee (TC) 210 "Quality Management and Corresponding General Aspects for Medical Devices" meetings, where the proposed revisions were discussed.

The original period for comment on the proposal closed on February 22, 1994, and was extended until April 4, 1994. Because of the heavy volume of comments and the desire to increase public participation in the development of the quality system regulation, FDA decided to publish the notice of availability in the Federal Register to allow comment on the Working Draft before issuing a final regulation.

The Working Draft represented the agency's views at the time on how it would respond to the many comments received, and on how the agency believed a final rule should be framed. FDA solicited public comment on the Working Draft until October 23, 1995, to determine if the agency had adequately addressed the many comments received and whether the agency had framed a final rule that achieved the public health goals to be gained from implementation of quality systems in the most efficient manner.

III. Open Public Meeting and GMP Advisory Committee Meeting

FDA held an open public meeting on the quality system regulation on August 23, 1995. The public meeting consisted of prepared presentations followed by an open discussion period. Both the agency and the participants found the meeting to be very productive in focusing attention on the few main areas of concern in the Working Draft. The main issues were: The application of the regulation to component manufacturers; the application of the regulation to third party servicers and refurbishers; and the implementation timeframe of the final rule. A transcript of the proceedings of the public meeting, as well as data and information submitted to FDA during the public meeting, are available from the Dockets Management Branch (HFA–305), Food and Drug Administration, 12420 Parklawn Dr., rm. 1–23, Rockville, MD 20857, between 9 a.m. and 4 p.m., Monday through Friday.

There also was a meeting of the GMP Advisory Committee on the Working Draft on September 13 and 14, 1995. A notice of the meeting was published in the Federal Register of August 24, 1995. FDA made a brief presentation to the committee on the changes from the 1993 proposal to the 1995 Working Draft and discussed some changes that FDA was recommending as a result of the August 1995 meeting. Two consultants also made presentations to the committee, one a representative from ISO TC 176 (the TC that authored the ISO 9000 series) and the other a representative from the European Committee for Standardization (CEN). The remainder of the meeting consisted of prepared

R

presentations from the public and the committee's discussion on the main issues.

The overwhelming majority of the committee members believed that the Working Draft met the public health needs, gave manufacturers sufficient flexibility to comply with the regulation, and met the agency's goal of harmonizing the quality system requirements with those of other countries. The GMP Advisory Committee strongly supported FDA's recommendation, in response to the August 1995 public meeting, to not include component manufacturers under this final rule. However, the GMP Advisory Committee was clearly divided on several issues related to the proposed regulation of third party servicers and refurbishers. A transcript of the proceedings of the GMP Advisory Committee meeting, as well as data and information submitted to FDA during the meeting, are available from the Dockets Management Branch (address above).

After considering the written comments and the views expressed at meetings with the GHTF, at the August 1995 public meeting, and at the September 1995 GMP Advisory Committee meeting, FDA is publishing this final rule. A summary of changes from the July 1995 Working Draft to the final rule is contained at the end of this preamble.

IV. Implementation of the Final Rule

FDA has decided, in response to the many comments and concerns expressed about the need for more time to implement design controls, to implement the final rule in two stages. Under stage one, on June 1, 1997, approximately 1 year after this rule is published in the Federal Register, all elements of the final rule become effective. However, with respect to the design control requirements in § 820.30, as long as manufacturers are taking reasonable steps to come into compliance, FDA will implement a special 1-year transition program, with a midcourse review, during which official agency action will not be initiated, including FDA Form 483 observations, warning letters, or enforcement cases, based on failure to comply with § 820.30. Under stage two, beginning June 1, 1998, FDA will treat noncompliance with design control requirements in § 820.30 the same as noncompliance with other provisions of the CGMP regulation.

To prepare for stage one of this implementation plan, FDA intends to develop, by April of 1997, a strategy for inspecting the design control requirements. Both industry and FDA field investigators will then be trained on this inspectional strategy for design controls during April and May 1997. Starting June 1, 1997, manufacturers will be inspected for compliance with all the new quality system requirements, including design controls, in the manner described in the inspectional strategy. However, as part of the transition program, from June 1, 1997, for a period of 1 year, although FDA will inspect firms for compliance with the design control requirements, the field will issue any observations to the manufacturer on a separate design control inspectional strategy report, not on FDA Form 483. The design control inspectional strategy report will be made a part of the manufacturer's establishment inspection report (EIR), but the observations relating to § 820.30 will not be included in any warning letters or regulatory actions during this initial 1-year period. FDA notes that it can, at any time, take action against unsafe or adulterated medical devices under different regulatory or statutory authorities. FDA wants to emphasize that *manufacturers are required to take reasonable steps to come into compliance with the design control requirements during the June 1, 1997, to June 1, 1998, period.*

FDA also emphasizes that this transition period relates only to the design control requirements of § 820.30, and that beginning June 1, 1997, the agency will issue observations on FDA Form 483's, issue warning letters, and take any necessary regulatory action for violations of all other provisions of the CGMP final rule. The time period from June 1, 1997, to June 1, 1998, is intended to allow both the industry and FDA field investigators time to become familiar with the design control requirements and the enforcement aspects of this new area.

Finally, as described elsewhere in this preamble, FDA intends to conduct a midcourse review of the new design control requirements during the transition year (June 1997 to June 1998). Specifically, the results of the first several months of design control inspections will be reviewed by early 1998. FDA will review all of the completed design control inspectional strategy reports that were given to manufacturers from between June 1, 1997, through December 1, 1997. The completed strategy reports will be reviewed with particular attention paid to clarity of information obtained, the appropriateness of the information collected with respect to the design control requirements, the appropriateness of the questions on the inspectional strategy, the manner in which the investigators are writing out their observations, and any requirements that seem to be giving manufacturers a problem or where there might be misunderstandings as to what the regulation requires. FDA will then hold an open public meeting in early 1998 to discuss with industry these findings and to further explore any concerns industry might be having in implementing the new design control requirements. As a result of the midcourse review and open public meeting, FDA might hold additional workshops, meetings, and/or training sessions.

Any midcourse adjustments to the inspectional strategy will be instituted and made public by the spring of 1998. Also during this midcourse review, FDA will evaluate the information gathered at that point and determine if the design control requirements as written in this final rule are appropriate to obtain the goals expressed in this preamble. FDA will consider minor or even major changes, based on experience to date. Any necessary adjustments or proposed revisions will be published in the Federal Register and comments will be solicited as necessary during the spring of 1998. This implementation strategy is responsive to requests by industry for FDA to harmonize the quality system regulation's implementation with the mandatory date for implementation of the EU's Medical Device Directive, which is June 1998. However, if during the midcourse review of stage one it is determined that the industry and/or FDA needs more time to fully implement the design control requirements, FDA will publish an extension of the regulatory implementation date for design control requirements prior to June 1, 1998.

V. Response to Comments and Rationale for Changes

Approximately 280 separate individuals or groups commented on the proposal published in the Federal Register of November 23, 1993, and approximately 175 separate individuals or groups commented on the Working Draft that was announced in a notice of availability published in the Federal Register on July 24, 1995. FDA made many changes in response to the comments. Most of the changes were made in response to specific comments, in response to comments for clarity, understanding, and readability, or to further harmonize FDA requirements with international standards, as many comments requested.

Numerous comments stated that industry was very pleased with FDA's

Working Draft and the effort that was made to harmonize with ISO, as well as to engage industry in commenting on the Working Draft through the open public meeting and the GMP Advisory Committee meeting that were held in August and September 1995, respectively.

FDA's responses to the comments received on the proposal and the Working Draft, as well as explanations for the changes made, follow.

A. General Provisions (Subpart A)

i. Scope (§ 820.1)

1. The title of the regulation, as reflected in this section, has been changed from the "Current Good Manufacturing Practices (CGMP)" regulation to the "Quality System" regulation. This revision follows the suggestion underlying many comments on specific provisions that FDA generally harmonize the CGMP requirements and terminology with international standards. ISO 9001:1994, ISO/CD 13485, and EN 46001 employ this terminology to describe the CGMP requirements. In addition, this title accurately describes the sum of the requirements, which now include the CGMP requirements for design, purchasing, and servicing controls. CGMP requirements now cover a full quality system.

FDA notes that the principles embodied in this quality system regulation have been accepted worldwide as a means of ensuring that acceptable products are produced. While the regulation has been harmonized with the medical device requirements in Europe, Australia, and Japan, as well as the requirements proposed by Canada, it is anticipated that other countries will adopt similar requirements in the near future.

FDA, however, did not adopt ISO 9001:1994 verbatim for two reasons. First, there were complications in dealing with the issue of copyrights and, second, FDA along with health agencies of other governments does not believe that for medical devices ISO 9001:1994 alone is sufficient to adequately protect the public health. Therefore, FDA has worked closely with the GHTF and TC 210 to develop a regulation which is consistent with both ISO 9001:1994 and ISO/CD 13485. FDA made several suggestions to TC 210 on the drafts of the ISO/CD 13485 document in order to minimize differences and move closer to harmonization. In some cases, FDA has explicitly stated requirements that many experts believe are inherent in ISO 9001:1994. Through the many years of experience enforcing and evaluating

compliance with the original CGMP regulation, FDA has found that it is necessary to clearly spell out its expectations. This difference in approach does not represent any fundamentally different requirements that would hinder global harmonization. In fact, numerous comments expressed their approval and satisfaction with FDA's effort to harmonize the quality system requirements with those of ISO 9001:1994 and ISO/CD 13485.

2. One comment suggested that the term "purchasing" in the scope be deleted because it could be interpreted to mean the purchase of finished medical devices by health care institutions and medical professionals, instead of the purchase of components and manufacturing materials as intended.

FDA agrees and has deleted the term "purchasing" throughout the regulation when used in this context.

3. Several comments suggested that § 820.1(a)(1) should not state that the regulation establishes the "minimum" requirements because it implies that compliance with the stated requirements may be insufficient. They asked that FDA delete the word "minimum," to avoid having auditors search for additional requirements.

FDA does not believe that the provision would have required that manufacturers meet additional requirements not mandated by the regulation but has modified the section to clarify its intent by stating that the regulation establishes the "basic" requirements for manufacturing devices. The quality system regulation provides a framework of basic requirements for each manufacturer to use in establishing a quality system appropriate to the devices designed and manufactured and the manufacturing processes employed. Manufacturers must adopt current and effective methods and procedures for each device they design and manufacture to comply with and implement the basic requirements. The regulation provides the flexibility necessary to allow manufacturers to adopt advances in technology, as well as new manufacturing and quality system procedures, as they become available.

During inspections, FDA will assess whether a manufacturer has established procedures and followed requirements that are appropriate to a given device under the current state-of-the-art manufacturing for that specific device. FDA investigators receive extensive training to ensure uniform interpretation and application of the regulation to the medical device industry. Thus, the agency does not believe that FDA investigators will cite

deviations from requirements not contained in this part. However, as noted above, FDA has altered the language of the scope to make clear that additional, unstated requirements do not exist.

4. A few comments suggested eliminating the distinction between critical and noncritical devices, thus eliminating the need for distinct requirements for critical devices. Other comments disagreed, asserting that eliminating the distinction would increase the cost of production of low-risk devices without improving their safety and effectiveness.

FDA agrees in part with the comments that suggest eliminating the distinction between critical and noncritical devices and has eliminated the term "critical device" from the scope, definitions, and regulation in §§ 820.65 *Critical devices, traceability* and 820.165 *Critical devices, labeling.* However, FDA has retained the concept of distinguishing between devices for the traceability requirements in § 820.65. As addressed in the discussion under that section, FDA believes that it is imperative that manufacturers be able to trace, by control number, any device, or where appropriate component of a device, that is intended for surgical implant into the body or to support or sustain life whose failure to perform when properly used in accordance with instructions for use provided in the labeling can be reasonably expected to result in a significant injury to the user.

The deletion of the terminology will bring the regulation in closer harmony with ISO 9001:1994 and the quality system standards or requirements of other countries.

Finally, FDA notes that eliminating the term "critical device" and the list of critical devices does not result in the imposition of new requirements. In fact the new regulation is less prescriptive and gives the manufacturer the flexibility to determine the controls that are necessary commensurate with risk. The burden is on the manufacturer, however, to describe the types and degree of controls and how those controls were decided upon. Such determinations are made in accordance with standard operating procedures (SOP's) established by the manufacturer.

5. In response to numerous comments, FDA has added the sentence "If a person engages in only some operations subject to the requirements in this part, and not in others, that person need only comply with those requirements applicable to the operations in which he or she is engaged." This sentence was added to clarify the scope of the regulation and

R

the responsibility of those who fall under this regulation. The wording is the same as that used in the drug CGMP.

6. Several comments recommended that the short list of class I devices subject to design control requirements be deleted from the regulation and be placed in the preamble, to allow additions or deletions without requiring a change to the entire regulation. Others commented that the list of class I devices should be entirely eliminated to harmonize with Europe and Japan.

FDA disagrees that the list of devices subject to design control requirements should be deleted from the regulation. FDA has experienced problems or has concerns with the class I devices listed and has determined that design controls are needed for the listed devices. Further, placing the list in the regulation establishes the requirements related to those devices, and is convenient for use by persons who are not familiar with, or who do not have access to, the preamble. Further, FDA notes that individual sections of a regulation may be revised independent of the remainder of the regulation.

7. Numerous written comments and persons who testified at the August and September 1995 meetings stated that application of the regulation to component manufacturers would increase product cost, with questionable value added to device safety and effectiveness, and that many component suppliers would refuse to supply components or services to the medical device industry. This would be especially likely to occur, it was suggested, where medical device manufacturers account for a small fraction of the supplier's sales.

FDA believes that because of the complexity of many components used in medical devices, their adequacy cannot always be assured through inspection and testing at the finished device manufacturer. This is especially true of software and software-related components, such as microprocessors and microcircuits. Quality must be designed and built into components through the application of proper quality systems.

However, FDA notes that the quality system regulation now explicitly requires that the finished device manufacturer assess the capability of suppliers, contractors, and consultants to provide quality products pursuant to § 820.50 *Purchasing controls.* These requirements supplement the acceptance requirements under § 820.80. Manufacturers must comply with both sections for any incoming component or subassembly or service, regardless of the finished device

manufacturer's financial or business affiliation with the person providing such products or services. FDA believes that these purchasing controls are sufficient to provide the needed assurance that suppliers, contractors, and consultants have adequate controls to produce acceptable components.

Therefore, balancing the many concerns of the medical device industry and the agency's public health and safety concerns, FDA has decided to remove the provision making the CGMP regulation applicable to component manufacturers and return to the language in the original CGMP regulation. This approach was unanimously endorsed by the members of the GMP Advisory Committee at the September 1995 meeting. FDA will continue to focus its inspections on finished device manufacturers and expects that such manufacturers will properly ensure that the components they purchase are safe and effective. Finished device manufacturers who fail to comply with §§ 820.50 and 820.80 will be subject to enforcement action. FDA notes that the legal authority exists to cover component manufacturers under the CGMP regulation should the need arise.

8. One comment stated that proposed § 820.1(a)(2) should be revised to include the District of Columbia and the Commonwealth of Puerto Rico, as in the original CGMP regulation.

FDA agrees with the comment. These localities were inadvertently omitted and have been added to the regulation.

9. FDA added § 820.1(a)(3) on how to interpret the phrase ''where appropriate'' in the regulation, as recommended by the GMP Advisory Committee. This section is consistent with the statement in ISO/CD 13485.

10. Some comments on proposed § 820.1(c) recommended that the section be deleted as it already appears in the act. Others stated that the provision implies that FDA will subject devices or persons to legal action, regardless of the level of noncompliance. Still others suggested that only intentional violations of the regulation should give rise to regulatory action.

FDA disagrees with these comments. The consequences of the failure to comply, and the legal authority under which regulatory action may be taken, are included in the regulation so that the public may be fully apprised of the possible consequences of noncompliance and understand the importance of compliance. FDA notes that the agency exercises discretion when deciding whether to pursue a regulatory action and does not take enforcement action for every violation it

encounters. Further, FDA generally provides manufacturers with warning prior to initiating regulatory action and encourages voluntary compliance. The agency also notes, however, that violations of this regulation need not be intentional to place the public at serious risk or for FDA to take regulatory action for such violations.

In response to the concerns regarding the tone of the section, however, the title has been changed. FDA has also deleted the specific provisions referenced in the proposed section with which the failure to comply would render the devices adulterated. The term ''part'' includes all of the regulation's requirements.

11. A few comments on proposed § 820.1(c)(2), now § 820.1(d), requested that the agency clarify what is meant by requiring that foreign manufacturers ''schedule'' an inspection. A few comments stated that FDA was adding new requirements for foreign manufacturers in this section. Others stated that the proposed language would prohibit global harmonization because it would limit third party audits in place of FDA inspections.

FDA has moved the provision related to foreign manufacturers into a separate section and has modified the language. The language in the regulation reflects the language in section 801(a) of the act (21 U.S.C. 381(a)). FDA disagrees that it is adding new requirements for foreign manufacturers in § 820.1(d) because the section recites the current requirement and standard used, and is consistent with current agency policy. The agency believes that it is imperative that foreign facilities be inspected for compliance with this regulation and that they be held to the same high standards to which U.S. manufacturers are held. Otherwise, the U.S. public will not be sufficiently protected from potentially dangerous devices, and the U.S. medical device industry will be at a competitive disadvantage.

FDA intends to continue scheduling inspections of foreign manufacturers in advance to assure their availability and avoid conflicts with holidays and shut down periods. However, the language pertaining to the ''scheduling'' of such inspections has been deleted to allow flexibility in scheduling methods.

FDA disagrees that, as written, the language would prohibit inspections by third parties. FDA may use third party inspections, as it uses other compliance information, in setting its priorities and utilizing its resources related to foreign inspections. In this regard, FDA looks forward to entering into agreements with foreign countries related to CGMP inspections that would provide FDA with reliable inspectional information.

12. Two comments stated that the section on "Exemptions or variances," now § 820.1(e), should require that FDA provide a decision on petitions within 60 days of receipt and state that the agency will take no enforcement action with respect to the subject of the petition until a decision is rendered. The comments said that the petition process is long, arduous, and not practical.

FDA disagrees with the comments. Currently, FDA is required by section 520(f)(2)(B) of the act to respond within 60 days of receipt of the petition, unless the petition is referred to an advisory committee. When the 1978 CGMP regulation was published, there was a prediction that FDA would be overwhelmed with petitions for exemption and variance from the regulation. Over the past 18 years, since the CGMP regulation first became effective, FDA has only received approximately 75 petitions. It is FDA's opinion that few petitions have been received because of the flexible nature of the CGMP regulation. FDA has attempted to write the current regulation with at least the same degree of flexibility, if not more, to allow manufacturers to design a quality system that is appropriate for their devices and operations and that is not overly burdensome.

Guidelines for the submission of petitions for exemption or variance are available from the Division of Small Manufacturers Assistance (the DSMA). The petition guidelines state that FDA will not process a petition for exemption or variance while an FDA inspection of a manufacturer is ongoing. Until FDA has approved a petition for an exemption or variance, a manufacturer should not deviate from the requirements of this regulation. FDA must first have the opportunity to ensure that the manufacturer has established that an exemption or variance is warranted, to carry out its obligation of ensuring that devices are safe and effective.

13. Several comments stated that the proposed requirements are not necessary for all manufacturers, particularly small manufacturers with few employees and low-risk devices. Other comments stated that the documentation requirements are excessive.

FDA generally disagrees with these comments. The regulation provides the "basic" requirements for the design and manufacture of medical devices. And, as noted in the previous response, the requirements are written in general

terms to allow manufacturers to establish procedures appropriate for their devices and operations. Also, as discussed above, a manufacturer need only comply with those requirements applicable to the operations in which he or she is engaged. However, because the regulation requirements are basic, they will apply in total to most manufacturers subject to the regulation. The extent of the documentation necessary to meet the regulation requirements may vary with the complexity of the design and manufacturing operations, the size of the firm, the importance of a process, and the risk associated with the failure of the device, among other factors. Small manufacturers may design acceptable quality systems that require a minimum of documentation and, where possible, may automate documentation. In many situations, documentation may be kept at a minimum by combining many of the recordkeeping requirements of the regulation, for example, the production SOP's, handling, and storage procedures. When manufacturers believe that the requirements are not necessary for their operations, they may petition for an exemption or variance from all or part of the regulation pursuant to section 520(f)(2) of the act.

In addition, FDA has added a variance provision in § 820.1(e)(2) under which the agency can initiate a variance when it is in the best interest of the public health. Under this provision, for instance, the agency may initiate and grant a variance to manufacturers of devices during times of product shortages, where the devices are needed by the public and may not otherwise be made available, if such manufacturers can adequately assure that the resulting devices are safe and effective. The agency envisions this provision as a bridge, providing a manufacturer with the time necessary to fulfill the requirements in the regulation while providing important and needed devices to the public. Thus, the variance would only be granted for a short period of time, and only while the devices remained necessary and in short supply. Under this provision, FDA will require a manufacturer to submit a plan detailing the action it is taking to assure the safety and effectiveness of the devices it manufactures and to meet the requirements of the regulation.

This agency initiated variance provision is in accordance with section 520(f) of the act which permits, but does not require, FDA to promulgate regulations governing the good manufacturing practices for devices and section 701(a) of the act (21 U.S.C.

371(a)), which permits FDA to promulgate regulations for the efficient enforcement of the act. Because the statute does not mandate that the agency establish any requirements for device CGMP's, the agency has the authority to determine that the manufacturers of certain devices need not follow every requirement of the regulation.

Further, the agency initiated variance provision is in keeping with the intent of Congress that FDA prevent hazardous devices from reaching the marketplace, H. Rept. 853, 94th Cong., 2d sess. 25–26 (1976), and the general intent of the act that the agency undertake to protect the public health. The agency will only initiate such a variance where the devices are needed and may not otherwise be made available, and the manufacturer can assure the agency that its procedures are likely to be adequate and that it is actively pursuing full compliance. The variances will only be in effect for a limited time.

Section 820.1(e) has been modified to include the above addition, to reflect the title change of the regulation, and to provide the most current address for the DSMA.

ii. Definitions (§ 820.3)

14. Several comments were received regarding the definition of "complaint." Comments generally believed that the definition was unclear and could be interpreted to include routine service requests, communications from customers unrelated to the quality, safety, or effectiveness of the device, and internal communications.

FDA agrees with the comments in part and has modified the definition to make clear that a communication would be considered a "complaint" only if the communication alleged some deficiency related to the identity, quality, durability, reliability, safety, effectiveness, or performance of the device after it is released for distribution. The definition is now very similar to the definition used in ISO/CD 13485.

The regulation addresses service requests and in-house indications of dissatisfaction under § 820.100 *Corrective and preventive action.* This section requires manufacturers to establish procedures to identify quality problems and process the information received to detect and correct quality problems. Information generated in-house relating to quality problems should be documented and processed as part of this corrective and preventive action program.

With respect to service requests, § 820.200 *Servicing* states that a service report that represents an event which

R

must be reported to the FDA under part 803 or 804 (21 CFR part 803 or 804) shall automatically be considered a complaint. All other service reports must be analyzed for trends or systemic problems and when found, these trends or systemic problems must be investigated according to the provisions of § 820.100 *Corrective and preventive action.*

15. One comment suggested that the agency delete the phrase "used during device manufacturing" in the definition of "component" because it was confusing and may cause problems with certain aspects of distributor operations.

FDA agrees and has deleted the words "used during device manufacturing" from the definition because it was not intended to differentiate between distributors and manufacturers. Further, FDA deleted the term "packaging" to clarify that every piece of packaging is not necessarily a component. Only the materials that are part of the "finished, packaged, and labeled device" are considered to be components.

16. Several comments stated that the term "complete history" in the definition of "control number" should be clarified or deleted because it is unclear what a complete production history is, and the term could be construed to require full traceability for all component lots of any product containing a control number.

FDA agrees in part with the comments. The control number is the means by which the history of the device, from purchase of components and materials through distribution, may be traced, where traceability is required. The definition does not require that a manufacturer be able to trace the device whenever control numbers are used. In fact, the definition itself does not establish any requirements. The agency notes, however, that the manufacturer's traceability procedures should ensure that a complete history of the device, including environmental conditions which could cause the device to fail to conform to its specified requirements, can be traced and should facilitate investigation of quality problems and corrective action. FDA notes, however, that the level of detail required for this history is dependent on the nature of the device, its intended use, and its complexity. Therefore, FDA has removed the term "complete" in the definition for clarity and flexibility.

FDA has also amended the definition for added flexibility, to state that symbols may be used and has included the term "unit" for any device that is not manufactured as a lot or batch.

17. The definition of "critical device" has been deleted for the reasons discussed above.

18. Several comments stated that the term "design history record" should be changed because the acronym for the term is the same as that for device history record (the DHR). Other comments said the "design history record" should not need to contain documentation of a "complete" design history. One comment stated that the definition should allow reference to records containing the design history of the device. A few comments stated that the term should be deleted altogether because it is redundant with the definition of device master record (the DMR).

FDA agrees in part with these comments and has changed the term "design history record" to "design history file." In addition, FDA has amended the provisions to require that the file describe the design history, as it may not be necessary to maintain a record of every step in the design phase, although the "entire history" should be apparent from the document. Section 820.30(j) further delineates what should be in the design history file (the DHF), specifically records sufficient to verify that the design was developed in accordance with the design and development plan and other applicable design requirements of the regulation.

FDA does not agree that the definitions of the DHF and the DMR are redundant. The DHF for each type of device should include, for example, the design and development plan, design review results, design verification results, and design validation results, as well as any other data necessary to establish compliance with the design requirements. The DMR should contain all of the procedures related to each type of device as required by this part and the most current manufacturing specifications of the device, once the design specifications have been transferred into production.

19. One comment on "design input" stated it was confused by the term "requirements" and wanted to know whose requirements are encompassed in this definition.

The term "requirement" is meant in the broadest sense, to encompass any internally or externally imposed requirements such as safety, customer-related, and regulatory requirements. All of these requirements must be considered as design inputs. How these requirements are handled and dealt with is up to the manufacturer.

20. Two comments stated that the definition of "design output" should be revised because it is not necessary, and

would be burdensome, to keep records of and review the "results of a design effort at each design phase and at the end." Other comments suggested that the design output definition should be restricted to physical characteristics of the device.

FDA agrees in part, but has not deleted the phrase "results of a design effort at each design phase and at the end" from the definition. The intent was not to dictate when design phases would occur. Such phases will be defined in the design and development plan. For example, a manufacturer may only have a few design phases for a new type of syringe. Thus, design output would be the results of those few efforts. The results of each design phase constitute the total design output. The definition has been amended, however, to clarify that the finished design output is the basis for the DMR.

FDA disagrees with the comments that suggest that the design output should be restricted to physical characteristics of the device. Design output is more than just the device specifications. Design output includes, among other things, the specifications for the manufacturing process, the quality assurance testing, and the device labeling and packaging. It is important to note that the design effort should not only control the design aspects of the device during the original development phase, but also all subsequent design and development activities including any redesign or design changes after the original design is transferred to production.

21. A few comments on the definition of "design review" stated that proposing solutions to problems is not part of the design review activity. Two other comments expressed concern that the definition would require that *each design review be "comprehensive."*

In response to the comments on the proper role of design review, FDA agrees that the design review participants are typically not responsible for establishing solutions, although they may do so in many small operations. The definition has been amended, but FDA wants to make clear that although the design review participants need not propose solutions, they should ensure that solutions to any identified problems are adequate and implemented appropriately.

Regarding the scope of design review, each design review need not be "comprehensive" for the entire design process but must be "comprehensive" for the design phase being reviewed. However, at the end of the design process when the design is transferred to production, all aspects of the design process should have been reviewed.

A few other changes were made to harmonize with the definition in ISO 8402:1994 "Quality—Vocabulary."

22. Comments on the definition of "device master record" pointed out that the definition is not consistent with the requirements of § 820.181 *Device master record.* Other comments stated that the definition should allow reference to records. One comment stated that "all" procedures related to a specific finished device need not be included in the DMR, such as the procedures for the design and development, since they may be in the DHF.

FDA agrees in part with the comments that found the DMR definition and requirements to be inconsistent and has amended the definition to be consistent with the requirements set forth in § 820.181. FDA does not believe, however, that it is necessary to modify the definition to include the referencing of records because the DMR requirements in § 820.181 state that the DMR "shall include or refer to the location of" the required information. FDA agrees that the term "all" is not necessary and has deleted it in order to give manufacturers the necessary flexibility.

23. The definition for the term "end-of-life" was added to the Working Draft because this term was used in the definitions for "refurbisher" and "servicing" to help distinguish the activities of refurbishing from those of servicing. FDA determined that such a distinction was necessary, due to comments and ongoing confusion regarding the difference between the two functions, and the different requirements applicable to the functions.

Many written comments and persons who testified at the August and September 1995 meetings stated that the term was confusing, unnecessary, and introduced many new legal and liability issues. FDA agrees with these comments and has deleted the term throughout the regulation. FDA has also deleted definitions for "refurbisher" and "servicing" for the reasons discussed below.

24. The few comments received on the definition of "establish" indicated a concern that the regulation requires too much documentation and is more onerous than ISO 9001 requirements.

FDA disagrees with the comments. The term "establish" is only used where documentation is necessary. FDA also notes that the quality system regulation is premised on the theory that adequate written procedures, which are implemented appropriately, will likely ensure the safety and effectiveness of the device. ISO 9001:1994 relies on the same premise. The 1994 version of ISO 9001 broadly requires the manufacturer to "establish, document, and maintain a quality system," which includes documenting procedures to meet the requirements.

The definition has been amended, however, in response to general comments received, to clarify that a "document" may be in writing or on electronic media, to allow flexibility for any type of recorded media.

25. FDA received comments questioning the inclusion of a device that is intended to be sterile, but that is not yet sterile, in the definition of "finished device." A few comments stated that "capable of functioning" is ambiguous, and "suitable for use" is not necessary. Another comment requested that the term "accessory" be defined.

FDA disagrees with the comments, but has amended the definition for clarification. Since the 1978 CGMP regulation was promulgated, FDA has been repeatedly asked whether devices intended to be sold as sterile are considered subject to the CGMP requirements, even though they have not yet been sterilized. The agency had intended the new definition to make explicit the application of the regulation to the manufacture of sterile devices that have yet to be sterilized. Although FDA believes it should be obvious that such devices are subject to CGMP requirements, some manufacturers have taken the position that the regulation does not apply because the device is not "finished" or "suitable for use" until it has been sterilized.

To better clarify its intent, FDA has amended the definition to add that all devices that are capable of functioning, including those devices that could be used even though they are not yet in their final form, are "finished devices." For example, devices that have been manufactured or assembled, and need only to be sterilized, polished, inspected and tested, or packaged or labeled by a purchaser/manufacturer are clearly not components, but are now in a condition in which they could be used, therefore meeting the definition of "finished device."

The distinction between "components" and "finished devices" was *not* intended to permit manufacturers to manufacture devices without complying with CGMP requirements by claiming that other functions, such as sterilization, incoming inspection (where sold for subsequent minor polishing, sterilization, or packaging), or insertion of software, will take place. The public would not be adequately protected in such cases if a manufacturer could claim that a device was not a "finished" device subject to the CGMP regulation because it was not in its "final" form.

The phrase "for commercial distribution" was deleted from the proposed definition of "finished device" because it is not necessary for a device to be in commercial distribution to be considered a finished device. Further, FDA notes that the term "accessory" is described in § 807.20(a)(5) (21 CFR 807.20(a)(5)).

26. Two comments on the definition of "lot or batch" requested that the definition be clarified: One to reflect that single units may be produced for distribution, the other to indicate that what constitutes a lot or a batch may vary depending on the context.

In response to the comments, FDA has modified the definition to make clear that a lot or batch may, depending on circumstances, be comprised of one finished device. Whether for inspection or for distribution, a lot or batch is determined by the factors set forth in the definition; of course, a manufacturer may determine the size of the lot or batch, as appropriate.

27. Several comments received on the definition of "executive management" objected that the definition is inconsistent with ISO 9001. Others thought that FDA should better define the level of management the term was intended to describe.

FDA agrees with both concerns and has modified the definition by deleting the second half, which appeared to bring executive authority and responsibility too far down the organization chart. The term was intended to apply only to management that has the authority to bring about change in the quality system and the management of the quality system. Although such management would clearly have authority over, for example, distribution, those who may have delegated management authority over distribution would not necessarily have authority over the quality system and quality policy. Accordingly, the definition has been modified to include only those who have the authority and responsibility to establish and make changes to the quality policy and quality system. It is the responsibility of top management to establish and communicate the quality policy. In addition, the term "executive management" has been changed to "management with executive responsibility," to harmonize with ISO 9001:1994.

28. Several comments in response to the proposed definition of

"manufacturer" stated that refurbishers and servicers should be added to the definition of a "manufacturer." Other comments recommended adding the term "remanufacturer." Other comments requested deletion of contract sterilizers, installers, specification developers, repackagers, relabelers, and initial distributors from the definition. One comment stated that the phrase "processes a finished device" should be explained in the definition of manufacturer.

FDA's Compliance Policy Guide (CPG) 7124.28 contains the agency's policy regarding the provisions of the act and regulations with which persons who recondition or rebuild used devices are expected to comply. This CPG is in the process of being revised in light of FDA's experience in this area. FDA is not including the terms "servicer" or "refurbisher," as they relate to entities outside the control of the original equipment manufacturer, in this final regulation, even though it believes that persons who perform such functions meet the definition of manufacturer. Because of a number of competitive and other issues, including sharply divided views by members of the GMP Advisory Committee at the September 1995 meeting, FDA has elected to address application of the CGMP requirements to persons who perform servicing and refurbishing functions outside the control of the original manufacturer in a separate rulemaking later this year, with another opportunity for public comment.

FDA agrees that the term "remanufacturing" should be added to the definition of "manufacturer" and has separately defined the term. A remanufacturer is defined as "any person who processes, conditions, renovates, repackages, restores, or does any other act to a finished device that significantly changes the finished device's performance or safety specifications, or intended use."

However, FDA disagrees that contract sterilizers, installers, specification developers, repackagers, relabelers, and initial distributors should be deleted from the definition, primarily because all such persons may have a significant effect on the safety and effectiveness of a device and on the public health. All persons who perform these functions meet the definition of manufacturer, and therefore should be inspected to ensure that they are complying with the applicable provisions. For example, a specification developer initiates the design requirements for a device that is manufactured by a second party for subsequent commercial distribution. Such a developer is subject to design

controls. Further, those that perform the functions of contract sterilization, installation, relabeling, remanufacturing, and repacking have routinely been considered to be manufacturers under the original CGMP definition, and the agency has treated them as such by inspecting them to ensure that they comply with the appropriate portions of the original CGMP. By explicitly including them in the definition of "manufacturer" the agency has simply codified its longstanding policy and interpretation of the original regulation.

The phrase "processes a finished device" applies to a finished device *after* distribution. Again, this phrase has been part of the CGMP regulation definition of "manufacturer" for 18 years.

29. A number of comments on the definition of "manufacturing material," and on other parts of the proposal containing requirements for "manufacturing material," stated that while the control of manufacturing material is important, it need not be as extensive as required throughout the regulation. Other comments stated that the meaning of the phrase "or other byproducts of the manufacturing process" is unclear, and should be deleted. One comment suggested that the definition be modified to separate the definition from the examples.

FDA agrees that, depending on the manufacturing material and the device, the degree of control that is needed will vary. FDA believes that manufacturing materials must be assessed, found acceptable for use, and controlled. Therefore, the regulation requires manufacturers to assess, assure acceptability of, and control manufacturing materials to the degree necessary to meet the specified requirements. The agency notes that international standards such as ISO 8402:1994 include manufacturing material in their definition of "product," to which all requirements apply, and notes that FDA has added the same definition in § 820.3(r) in its effort toward harmonization.

FDA amended the definition of manufacturing material to read "a concomitant constituent, or a byproduct constituent produced during the manufacturing process" to help clarify this definition. These terms refer to those materials or substances that naturally occur as a part of the material or during the manufacturing process which are intended to be removed or reduced in the finished device. For example, some components, such as natural rubber latex, contain allergenic proteins that must be reduced or

removed from the finished devices. The definition has been modified to include "concomitant constituents" to clarify the meaning.

In addition to clarifying the definition, FDA has deleted the specific examples. Therefore, FDA notes that cleaning agents, mold release agents, lubricating oils, latex proteins, and sterilant residues are just some examples of manufacturing materials.

30. The comments received on the definition for "nonconforming" conveyed a general sense that the definition was confusing, with various comments suggesting that different parts of the definition should be deleted and one suggesting that the definition be deleted altogether.

In response to these comments, the definition of "nonconforming" has been deleted. However, the definition from ISO 8402:1994 for "nonconformity" was added to ensure that the requirements in the regulation, especially those in §§ 820.90 *Nonconforming product* and 820.100 *Corrective and preventive action* are understood. FDA emphasizes that a "nonconformity" may not always rise to the level of a product defect or failure, but a product defect or failure will typically constitute a nonconformity.

31. Several comments requested various revisions to the definition of "production" to make it more clear, and one thought that it was a common term and should be deleted.

In response, FDA has deleted the definition for "production" because it should be commonly understood.

As noted in response to comments on the definition of manufacturing material, FDA has added a definition of "product" to conform to the definition in ISO 8402:1994 and to avoid the necessity of repeating the individual terms throughout the regulation. Whenever a requirement is not applicable to all types of product, the regulation specifically states the product(s) to which the requirement is applicable.

It should be noted that the regulation has acceptance requirements for incoming "product" and other requirements for "product," which by definition includes manufacturing materials. Manufacturing materials should be controlled in a manner that is commensurate with their risk as discussed above. However, for manufacturing materials that are "concomitant constituents," FDA realizes that incoming acceptance, identification, etc., may not be feasible. The important control measure for "concomitant constituents" is the reduction or removal requirement found in § 820.70(h).

32. A few comments stated that the definition of "quality" should be changed to be identical to ISO 8402. Others stated that the terminology adopted from ISO 8402, "that bear on," is too broad and could cover every potential and imaginable factor. Still others wanted to add the phrase, "as defined by the manufacturer" to the end of the sentence.

FDA disagrees with the comments and believes that the definition is closely harmonized to that in ISO 8402:1994. FDA believes that the definition appropriately defines quality in the context of a medical device and believes that the phrase from ISO 8402:1994, "stated and implied needs," has the same meaning as the phrase "fitness-for-use, including safety and performance" in the context of the Quality System regulation. Further, "quality" is not just "defined by the manufacturer" but is also defined by customer need and expectation.

33. Many comments received on the "quality audit" definition suggested that the definition should not state that it is an examination of the "entire" quality system because that would require that every audit include the "entire" quality system. Other comments on "quality audit" stated that it is unclear what is meant by the last sentence of the proposed definition, namely, that "'[q]uality audit' is different from * * * other quality system activities required by or under this part."

FDA agrees that while the quality audit is an audit of the "entire" quality system, audits may be conducted in phases, with some areas requiring more frequent audits than other areas, and that each audit need not review the whole system. The frequency of internal quality audits should be commensurate with, among other things, the importance of the activity, the difficulty of the activity to perform, and the problems found. To avoid any misunderstanding, the word "entire" before quality system has been deleted.

FDA emphasizes that if conducted properly, internal quality audits can prevent major problems from developing and provide a foundation for the management review required by § 820.20(c), "Management review."

In response to the confusion about the last sentence of the proposed definition, FDA has deleted the last sentence. The purpose of the sentence was to clarify that the internal audit requirement is different from, and in addition to, the requirements for establishing quality assurance procedures and recording results. On occasion, manufacturers

have attempted to prevent FDA investigators from reviewing such quality assurance procedures and results (for example, trend analysis results) by stating that they are part of the internal quality audit report and not subject to review during a CGMP inspection. FDA disagrees with this position. To clarify which records are exempt from routine FDA inspection, FDA has added § 820.180(c).

34. One comment said that the word "executive" should be deleted from the definition of "quality policy" because quality policy should be supported by all personnel, not just those in executive management. A few comments stated that "formally expressed" should be deleted because it is incompatible with the requirements in § 820.20(a) and (c) which require that the quality policy be "established." Other comments stated that the "quality" before "intentions" was tautological.

FDA agrees that all company personnel must follow the quality policy. However, the definition is intended to make clear that the quality policy must be established by top management. Therefore it has been retained. The term "executive management" has been modified to "management with executive responsibility" to be consistent with the revised ISO 9001:1994. FDA agrees with the remaining comments and has changed "formally expressed" to "established" for consistency and has deleted the "quality" before "intentions."

35. A few comments suggested using the definition of "quality systems" from ISO 8402 and 9001. Other comments on the definition of "quality system" said that the term "quality management" should be defined.

FDA agrees in part with the comments. The term "specifications" has been deleted to harmonize the definition with ISO 8402:1994. FDA does not agree that the term "quality management" must be defined. A definition can be found in ISO 8402:1994 that is consistent with FDA's use of the term.

36. Many comments on the definition of "record" were received. Some thought the term was too broad, giving FDA access to all documents and exceeding FDA's inspection authority. Others thought that the definition of "record" would tremendously increase the recordkeeping burden. Several comments recommended that FDA adopt the ISO definition.

The definition of "record" was deleted because it seemed to add more confusion than clarity. The definition was intended to clarify that "records"

may include more than the traditional hardcopy procedures and SOP's, for example, plans, notes, forms, data, etc. FDA was trying to clarify that "records" could be written, electronic, optical, etc., as long as they could be stored and controlled. FDA could not adopt the ISO 8402:1994 definition because of how the term "record" is used in the act, which is broader than the ISO definition. Therefore, FDA will allow the act and case law to continue to define the term.

37. The definition in the Working Draft of "refurbisher" was deleted and will be addressed in the separate rulemaking described above.

38. FDA added the definition of "remanufacturer" to codify FDA's longstanding policy and interpretation of the original CGMP. The language is consistent with the 510(k) provisions and the premarket approval amendment/supplement requirements, because FDA has always considered remanufacturers in fact to be manufacturers of a new device.

39. Several comments on the definition of "reprocessing" requested clarification of the difference between that term and "refurbishing." Several other comments on the definition of "reprocessing" stated that FDA should clarify that "reprocessing" is an activity performed before a device is distributed. Others commented that the term "rework" should be used instead of the term "reprocessing," to be consistent with ISO terminology.

FDA agrees with the comments and has changed the term to "rework," adopted the ISO 8402:1994 definition, and added that "rework" is performed according to specified DMR requirements before the device is released for distribution.

40. A few comments stated that including the term "maintenance" in the proposed definition of "servicing" implies that preventative maintenance would be subject to the regulation. Other comments said that it may not be desirable to return old devices or devices that have received field modifications to the original specifications. Therefore, the comments suggested deleting the last part of the definition that states that "servicing" is returning a device to its specifications.

FDA has deleted the definition of "servicing" and has not added a definition of "servicer" because this will be covered in the separate rulemaking discussed above. FDA notes, however, that servicing performed by manufacturers and remanufacturers is subject to the requirements in § 820.200 *Servicing.* These requirements are a codification of longstanding interpretations of the original CGMP,

§ 820.20(a)(3), and current agency policy.

41. Several comments were received on the proposed definition of "special process." Many asked for clarification or adoption of the ISO definition. Some stated that it is impossible to completely verify processes in every instance.

FDA has deleted the definition because the term "special process" is no longer used in ISO 9001:1994, except in a note. FDA has, however, modified the requirements of the regulation to reflect that, in many cases, testing and inspecting alone may be insufficient to prove the adequacy of a process. One of the principles on which the quality systems regulation is based is that all processes require some degree of qualification, verification, or validation, and manufacturers should not rely solely on inspection and testing to ensure processes are adequate for their intended uses.

42. Several comments on the definition of "specification" suggested that the term should not apply to quality system requirements. One comment suggested that the phrase "other activity" be deleted because it is too broad. Another comment noted that the definition in ISO 9001 pertains to requirements, not only documents.

In response, FDA has amended the definition to make clear that it applies to the requirements for a product, process, service, or other activity. The reference to the quality system has been deleted. FDA disagrees that the definition is too broad and has not deleted the term "other activity" because a specification can be developed for anything the manufacturer chooses. FDA notes, however, that ISO 9001:1994 does not contain a definition for "specification" but uses the definition found in ISO 8402:1994.

43. Numerous comments were received on the definitions of "validation" and "verification." Almost all stated that the two definitions overlapped and that there was a need to rewrite the definitions to prevent confusion. Many suggested that the ISO definitions be adopted. Others stated that there was a need to distinguish between design validation and process validation.

FDA agrees with the comments and has rewritten the two definitions to better reflect the agency's intent. FDA has adopted the ISO 8402:1994 definition of validation. "Validation" is a step beyond verification to ensure the user needs and intended uses can be fulfilled on a consistent basis. FDA has further distinguished "process validation" from "design validation" to

help clarify these two types of "validation." The "process validation" definition follows from FDA's "Guidelines on General Principles of Process Validation" (Ref. 10). The definition for "design validation" is consistent with the requirements contained in § 820.30 *Design controls.*

The ISO 8402:1994 definition of "verification" has been adopted. "Verification" is confirmation by examination and provision of objective evidence that specified requirements for a particular device or activity at hand have been met.

iii. Quality System (§ 820.5)

44. Several comments suggested that the requirement should be more general, in that the requirement that devices be safe and effective is covered elsewhere in the regulation. The comments recommended that the quality system requirements be harmonized with international standards and focus on requiring that a system be established that is appropriate to the specific device and that meets the requirements of the regulation.

FDA agrees in part with the comments and has modified the language as generally suggested by several comments to require that the quality system be "appropriate for the specific medical device(s) designed or manufactured, and [] meet[] the requirements of this part." This is essentially the requirement of the original CGMP regulation with the added reference to design control.

The requirements that effective quality system instructions and procedures be established and effectively maintained are retained; however, they were moved to § 820.20(b)(3)(i). As previously noted, the quality system regulation is premised on the theory that the development, implementation, and maintenance of procedures designed to carry out the requirements will assure the safety and effectiveness of devices. Thus, the broad requirements in § 820.5 are in a sense the foundation on which the remaining quality system requirements are built.

B. Quality System Requirements (Subpart B)

i. Management Responsibility (§ 820.20)

45. Several comments on § 820.20(a), "Quality policy," related to the use of the term "executive management." A few comments stated that quality system development and implementation are the responsibility of the chief executive officer, but how he or she chooses to discharge the responsibility should be

left to the discretion of the manufacturer. Other comments stated that the requirement that executive management ensure that the quality policy is understood is impossible and should be deleted or rewritten.

FDA agrees in part with the comments. In response to the comments, FDA has deleted the term "executive management" and replaced it with "management with executive responsibility," which is consistent with ISO 9001:1994. Management with executive responsibility is that level of management that has the authority to establish and make changes to the company quality policy. The establishment of quality objectives, the translation of such objectives into actual methods and procedures, and the implementation of the quality system may be delegated. The regulation does not prohibit the delegation. However, it is the responsibility of the highest level of management to establish the quality policy and to ensure that it is followed. (See *United States* v. *Dotterweich,* 320 U.S. 277 (1943), and *United States* v. *Park,* 421 U.S. 658 (1975).)

For this reason, FDA disagrees that the requirement that management ensure that the quality policy is understood should be deleted. It is without question management's responsibility to undertake appropriate actions to ensure that employees understand management's policies and objectives. Understanding is a learning process achieved through training and reinforcement. Management reinforces understanding of policies and objectives by demonstrating a commitment to the quality system visibly and actively on a continuous basis. Such commitment can be demonstrated by providing adequate resources and training to support quality system development and implementation. In the interest of harmonization, the regulation has been amended to be very similar to ISO 9001:1994.

46. A few comments stated that the words "adequate" and "sufficient" should be deleted from § 820.20(b) "Organization," as they are subjective and too difficult to define. One comment thought that the general requirements in the paragraphs are addressed by § 820.25 *Personnel.* Another comment stated that "designed" should be added prior to "produced" for consistency with the scope.

FDA agrees that the requirement for "sufficient personnel" is covered in §§ 820.20(b)(2), "Resources," and 820.25 *Personnel,* both of which require manufacturers to employ sufficient personnel with the training and experience necessary to carry out their assigned activities properly. The phrase is, therefore, deleted. However, FDA has retained the requirement for establishing an "adequate organizational structure" to ensure compliance with the regulation, because such an organizational structure is fundamental to a manufacturer's ability to produce safe and effective devices. The organizational structure should ensure that the technical, administrative, and human factors functions affecting the quality of the device will be controlled, whether these functions involve hardware, software, processed materials, or services. All such control should be oriented towards the reduction, elimination, or ideally, prevention of quality nonconformities. Further, the agency does not believe that the term is ambiguous. The organizational structure established will be determined in part by the type of device produced, the manufacturer's organizational goals, and the expectations and needs of customers. What may be an "adequate" organizational structure for manufacturing a relatively simple device may not be "adequate" for the production of a more complex device, such as a defibrillator. FDA has also added "designed" prior to "produced" to be consistent with the scope of the regulation.

47. A number of comments on proposed § 820.20 (b)(1)(i) through (b)(1)(v), "Responsibility and authority," objected to the section, stating that it was too detailed and confusing and that the wording was redundant with other sections of the proposal.

FDA agrees generally with the comments in that the proposed paragraphs set forth examples of situations in which independence and authority are important. Therefore, the examples provided in § 820.20 (b)(1)(i) through (b)(1)(v) are deleted. However, FDA has retained the broad requirement that the necessary independence and authority be provided as appropriate to every function affecting quality. FDA emphasizes that it is crucial to the success of the quality system for the manufacturer to ensure that responsibility, authority, and organizational freedom (or independence) is provided to those who initiate action to prevent nonconformities, identify and document quality problems, initiate, recommend, provide, and verify solutions to quality problems, and direct or control further processing, delivery, or installation of nonconforming product. Organizational freedom or independence does not necessarily require a stand-alone group,

but responsibility, authority, and independence should be sufficient to attain the assigned quality objectives with the desired efficiency.

48. Several comments on proposed § 820.20(b)(2), "Verification resources and personnel," stated that requiring "adequately" trained personnel was subjective and that the section was not consistent with ISO 9001.

FDA agrees that the section is not consistent with ISO 9001, and has adopted the language used in ISO 9001:1994, section 4.1.2.2, "Resources," and has renamed the section "Resources." The provision is now a broad requirement that the manufacturer provide adequate resources for the quality system and is not restricted to the verification function. FDA acknowledges that § 820.25(a), "General," requires that sufficiently trained personnel be employed. However, § 820.20(b)(2), "Resources," emphasizes that *all* resource needs must be provided for, including monetary, supplies, etc., as well as personnel resources. In contrast, § 820.25(a) specifically addresses education, background, training, and experience requirements for personnel.

49. Comments on § 820.20(b)(3), "Management representative," stated that the management representative should not be limited to "executive" management. A few comments stated that the appointment should be documented. In addition, a few comments from proposed § 820.5 stated that the terms "effective" and "effectively" should be defined.

The agency agrees that the responsibility need not be assigned to "executive" management and has modified the requirement to allow management with executive responsibility to appoint a member of management. When a member of management is appointed to this function, potential conflicts of interest should be examined to ensure that the effectiveness of the quality system is not compromised. In addition, in response to many comments, the requirement was amended to make clear that the appointment of this person must be documented, moving the requirement up from § 820.20(b)(3)(ii). The amended language is consistent with ISO 9001:1994. Further, FDA has amended this section to change "executive management" to "management with executive responsibility" for consistency with the definition.

The terms "effective" and "effectively" are no longer used in § 820.5 but "effectively" is found in § 820.20(b)(3)(i). FDA does not believe that these terms require a definition.

Instructions and procedures must be defined, documented, implemented, and maintained in such a way that the requirements of this part are met. If they are, they will be "effective."

50. A few comments stated that the improvement of the quality system is not a requirement under the act and the reference to such improvement in § 820.20(b)(3)(ii) should, therefore, be deleted.

FDA agrees in part with the comments and has deleted the requirement that the person appointed under this section provide information for improving the quality system. The provision implied that the manufacturer must go beyond the requirements of the regulation. FDA notes, however, that information collected in complying with §§ 820.20(b)(3)(ii) and 820.100 *Corrective and preventive action,* should be used not only for detecting deficiencies and for subsequent correction of the deficiencies but also to improve the device and quality system.

51. Many comments stated that the report required by § 820.20(c), "Management review," should not be subject to FDA review, due to the same liability and self-incrimination concerns related to the internal audit.

FDA agrees in part with the comments. The proposed regulation did not state FDA's intentions with respect to inspectional review of the results of the required management review. After careful consideration of the comments, FDA agrees that it will not request to inspect and copy the reports of reviews required by § 820.20(c) when conducting routine inspections to determine compliance with this part. FDA believes that refraining from routinely reviewing these reports may help ensure that the audits are complete and candid and of maximum use to the manufacturer. However, FDA believes that it is important that the dates and results of quality system reviews be documented, and FDA may require that management with executive responsibility certify in writing that the manufacturer has complied with the requirements of § 820.20(c). FDA will also review the written procedures required by § 820.20(c), as well as all other records required under § 820.20.

52. A few comments stated that the management review should not be dictated by established review procedures because management level employees should be fully capable of reviewing documents without a written procedure.

As noted above, FDA has retained the requirement for establishing procedures to conduct the required management review in § 820.20(c). FDA believes that

R

a manufacturer can establish procedures flexible enough for management to vary the way in which a review is conducted, as appropriate. Procedures should require that the review be conducted at appropriate intervals and should be designed to ensure that all parts of the quality system are adequately reviewed. A manufacturer may, of course, develop procedures that permit review of different areas at different times, so long as such reviews are sufficient to carry out the objectives of this section. If there are known problems, for example, a "sufficient frequency" may be fairly frequent. Further, because FDA will not be reviewing the results of such reviews, FDA must be assured that this function will occur in a consistent manner.

53. A few comments stated that § 820.20(c) should be deleted because it duplicates the quality audit required by § 820.22.

FDA disagrees that § 820.20(c) duplicates the requirements in § 820.22. The purpose of the management reviews required by § 820.20(c) is to determine if the manufacturer's quality policy and quality objectives are being met, and to ensure the continued suitability and effectiveness of the quality system. An evaluation of the findings of internal and supplier audits should be included in the § 820.20(c) evaluation. The management review may include a review of the following: (1) The organizational structure, including the adequacy of staffing and resources; (2) the quality of the finished device in relation to the quality objectives; (3) combined information based on purchaser feedback, internal feedback (such as results of internal audits), process performance, product (including servicing) performance, among other things; and (4) internal audit results and corrective and preventive actions taken. Management reviews should include considerations for updating the quality system in relation to changes brought about by new technologies, quality concepts, market strategies, and other social or environmental conditions. Management should also review periodically the appropriateness of the review frequency, based on the findings of previous reviews. The quality system review process in § 820.20(c), and the reasons for the review, should be understood by the organization.

The requirements under § 820.22 *Quality audit* are for an internal audit and review of the quality system to verify compliance with the quality system regulation. The review and evaluations under § 820.22 are very focused. During the internal quality audit, the manufacturer should review all procedures to ensure adequacy and compliance with the regulation, and determine whether the procedures are being effectively implemented at all times. In contrast, as noted above, the management review under § 820.20(c) is a broader review of the organization as a whole to ensure that the quality policy is implemented and the quality objectives are met. The reviews of the quality policy and objectives (§ 820.20(c)) should be carried out by top management, and the review of supporting activities (§ 820.22) should be carried out by management with executive responsibility for quality and other appropriate members of management, utilizing competent personnel as decided on by the management.

54. Some comments suggested that the requirements in § 820.186(a) and (d) be moved to § 820.20 for clarity and to better align with the structure of ISO 9001:1994 and ISO/CD 13485.

FDA agrees and has moved the specific requirements from § 820.186 and rewritten them into new § 820.20 (d) and (e) for clarity, better organization, and closer harmonization. Therefore, § 820.20(d) is consistent with ISO 9001:1994, section 4.2.3, "Quality planning," and § 820.20(e) is consistent with ISO 9001:1994, sections 4.2.1, "General," and 4.2.2, "Quality-system procedures." Section 820.20(e) discusses "[a]n outline of the structure of the documentation used in the quality system." FDA believes that outlining the structure of the documentation is beneficial and, at times, may be critical to the effective operation of the quality system. FDA recognizes, however, that it may not be necessary to create an outline in all cases. For example, it may not be necessary for smaller manufacturers and manufacturers of less complicated devices. Thus, the outline is only required where appropriate.

ii. Quality Audit (§ 820.22)

55. A few comments suggested that FDA delete the requirement that persons conducting the audit be "appropriately trained" from the second sentence of proposed § 820.22(a), because it is subjective and not consistent with ISO 9001.

FDA has deleted the requirement from § 820.22(a) because § 820.25 *Personnel* requires that such individuals be appropriately trained. Further, FDA has attempted to better harmonize with ISO 9001:1994, which does not explicitly state personnel qualifications in each provision. Similarly, in response to general comments suggesting better harmonization, FDA has added the requirement that the audit "determine the effectiveness of the quality system" as required by ISO 9001:1994. This requirement underscores that the quality audit must not only determine whether the manufacturer's requirements are being carried out, but whether the requirements themselves are adequate.

56. Some comments stated that requiring "individuals who do not have direct responsibility for the matters being audited" to conduct the audits is impractical and burdensome, particularly for small manufacturers.

FDA disagrees with the comments. Both small and large manufacturers have been subject to the identical requirement since 1978 and FDA knows of no hardship, on small or large manufacturers, as a result. Small manufacturers must generally establish independence, even if it means hiring outside auditors, because the failure to have an independent auditor could result in an ineffective audit.

Manufacturers must realize that conducting effective quality audits is crucial. Without the feedback provided by the quality audit and other information sources, such as complaints and service records, manufacturers operate in an open loop system with no assurance that the process used to design and produce devices is operating in a state of control. ISO 9001:1994 has the same requirement for independence from the activity being audited.

57. Several comments claimed that the last sentence in proposed § 820.22(a), which required that followup corrective action be documented in the audit report, made no sense. The comments said that corrective action would be the subject of a followup report.

It was the agency's intent that the provision require that where corrective action was necessary, it would be taken and documented in a reaudit report. The provision has been rewritten to make that clear. New § 824.22 also clarifies that a reaudit is not always required, but where it is indicated, it must be conducted. The report should verify that corrective action was implemented and effective. Because FDA does not review these reports, the date on which the audit and reaudit were performed must be documented and will be subject to FDA review. The revised reaudit provision is consistent with ISO 9001:1994.

58. Many comments were received on proposed § 820.22(b) regarding the reports exempt from FDA review. Most of the comments objected to FDA reviewing evaluations of suppliers. FDA has decided not to review such

evaluations at this time and will revisit this decision after the agency gains sufficient experience with the new requirement to determine its effectiveness. A thorough response to the comments is found with the agency's response to other comments received on § 820.50 *Purchasing controls.* FDA has moved the section regarding which reports the agency will refrain from reviewing from § 820.22(b) to new § 820.180(c), "Exemptions," under the related records requirements. FDA believes this organization is easier to follow.

iii. Personnel (§ 820.25)

59. A few comments stated that the requirement in § 820.25 *Personnel* for the manufacturer to employ "sufficient" personnel should be deleted, because whether there are "sufficient" personnel is a subjective determination, and it is unnecessary to require it since the manufacturer will know how best to staff the organization. A few other comments stated that the provision should not base the personnel requirements on ensuring that the requirements of the regulation are "correctly" performed, because no manufacturer can ensure that all activities are performed correctly. Another comment stated that the term "employ" should be changed because personnel may include qualified temporaries, contractors, and others who may not typically be considered "employees."

FDA disagrees with the suggestions that the terms "sufficient" and "correctly" be deleted. Whether "sufficient" personnel are employed will be determined by the requirements of the quality system, which must be designed to ensure that the requirements of the regulation are properly implemented. In making staffing decisions, a manufacturer must ensure that persons assigned to particular functions are properly equipped and possess the necessary education, background, training, and experience to perform their functions correctly. However, FDA changed "ensure" to "assure" to address the concerns that people do make mistakes and management cannot guarantee that work is correctly performed all of the time. Further, FDA agrees that the manufacturer must determine for itself what constitutes "sufficient" personnel with proper qualification in the first instance. However, if the manufacturer does not employ sufficient personnel, or personnel with the necessary qualifications to carry out their functions, the manufacturer will be in violation of the regulation. FDA has

often found that the failure to comply with this requirement leads to other significant regulatory violations. FDA agrees with the comment that the term "employ" should be deleted so that the requirement covers all personnel who work at a firm.

60. In § 820.25(b), "Training," FDA deleted the requirement that employees be trained "by qualified individuals," because § 820.25(a) requires this. Several comments stated that FDA should add the requirement that the training procedure include the identification of training needs, to be consistent with the requirements in ISO 9001:1994 and ISO/CD 13485. Other comments stated that personnel need not be trained to the extent that they can quote chapter and verse of the regulation as long as they can adequately perform their assigned responsibilities. Several comments suggested deleting the requirements in the last two sentences in favor of a broad, general requirement that personnel be trained. A few comments stated that the last two sentences should be retained because they are crucial and sound requirements but that validation activities should be included with verification activities.

FDA amended the requirement so that the training procedure includes the identification of training needs. FDA deleted the requirement on understanding the CGMP requirements applicable to job functions to avoid the perception that personnel would need to know "chapter and verse of the regulation." FDA notes, however, that a training program to ensure personnel adequately perform their assigned responsibilities should include information about the CGMP requirements and how particular job functions relate to the overall quality system. FDA further believes that it is imperative that training cover the consequences of improper performance so that personnel will be apprised of defects that they should look for, as well as be aware of the effect their actions can have on the safety and effectiveness of the device. In addition, FDA disagrees with comments that suggested that only "personnel affecting quality" should be required to be adequately trained. In order for the full quality system to function as intended, all personnel should be properly trained. Each function in the manufacture of a medical device must be viewed as integral to all other functions. FDA has reorganized the last two sentences, however, to place the requirements under § 820.25(b), "Training," and has added validation activities as suggested by the comments.

61. Many comments objected to the proposed requirements of § 820.25(c), "Consultants," stating that requiring a manufacturer to chose consultants that have sufficient qualifications and to keep records subject to FDA review of all consultants used, along with copies of their resumes and lists of previous jobs, would unreasonably interfere with the manufacturer's business activities and restrict the right of a manufacturer to hire consultants on any basis it chooses. Other comments said that a manufacturer's employment of a consultant has the same potential impact on the safety and effectiveness of medical devices as employment of any other contractor for services, and that consultants should, therefore, be covered by § 820.50 *Purchasing controls.*

FDA agrees in part with these comments. Although employing a consultant is a business decision, when a manufacturer hires consultants who do not have appropriate credentials, and manufacturing decisions are made based on erroneous or ill-conceived advice, the public suffers. Of course, the manufacturer is still ultimately responsible for following the CGMP requirements and will bear the consequences of a failure to comply. FDA notes that the use of unqualified consultants has led to regulatory action for the failure to comply with the CGMP regulation in the past. Thus, because of the significant impact a consultant can have on the safety and effectiveness of a device, FDA believes that some degree of control is required in the regulation.

The requirements are revised somewhat in response to comments, however, to reflect that it is not FDA's goal to dictate whom a manufacturer may use as a consultant, but instead to require that a manufacturer determine what it needs to adequately carry out the requirements of the regulation and to assess whether the consultant can adequately meet those needs. The requirements related to consultants have been added in § 820.50 *Purchasing controls* because a consultant is a supplier of a service.

C. Design Controls (Subpart C)

Since early 1984, FDA has identified lack of design controls as one of the major causes of device recalls. The intrinsic quality of devices, including their safety and effectiveness, is established during the design phase. Thus, FDA believes that unless appropriate design controls are observed during preproduction stages of development, a finished device may be neither safe nor effective for its intended use. The SMDA provided FDA with the

R

authority to add preproduction design controls to the device CGMP regulation. Based on its experience with administering the original CGMP regulation, which did not include preproduction design controls, the agency was concerned that the original regulation provided less than an adequate level of assurance that devices would be safe and effective. Therefore, FDA has added general requirements for design controls to the device CGMP regulation for all class III and II devices and certain class I devices. FDA is not subjecting the majority of class I devices to design controls because FDA does not believe that such controls are necessary to ensure that such devices are safe and effective and otherwise in compliance with the act. However, all devices, including class I devices exempt from design controls, must be properly transferred to production in order to comply with § 820.181, as well as other applicable requirements. For most class I devices, FDA believes that the production and other controls in the new quality system regulation and other general controls of the act will be sufficient, as they have been in the past, to ensure safety and effectiveness.

62. Many comments were submitted in response to the addition of design control requirements in general, many questioning how these new requirements would be implemented and enforced. For instance, several comments stated that the design control requirements do not reflect how medical devices are actually developed, because the concept of a design rarely originates with the manufacturer, who may not become involved until relatively late in the design evolution. Others expressed concern that FDA investigators will second-guess design issues in which they are not educated or trained, and stated that investigators should not debate whether medical device designs are ''safe and effective.''

FDA agrees in part with the comments. The design control requirements are not intended to apply to the development of concepts and feasibility studies. However, once it is decided that a design will be developed, a plan must be established to determine the adequacy of the design requirements and to ensure that the design that will eventually be released to production meets the approved requirements.

Those who design medical devices must be aware of the design control requirements in the regulation and comply with them. Unsafe and ineffective devices are often the result of informal development that does not ensure the proper establishment and assessment of design requirements

which are necessary to develop a medical device that is safe and effective for the intended use of the device and that meets the needs of the user.

However, FDA investigators will not inspect a device under the design control requirements to determine whether the design is appropriate or ''safe and effective.'' Section 520(f)(1)(a) of the act precludes FDA from evaluating the ''safety or effectiveness of a device'' through preproduction design control procedures. FDA investigators will evaluate the process, the methods, and the procedures that a manufacturer has established to implement the requirements for design controls. If, based on any information gained during an inspection, an investigator believes that distributed devices are unsafe or ineffective, the investigator has an obligation to report the observations to the Center for Devices and Radiological Health (CDRH).

63. Several comments expressed concern that the application of design controls would severely restrict the creativity and innovation of the design process and suggested that design controls should not apply too early in the design development process.

FDA disagrees with the comments. It is not the intent of FDA to interfere with creativity and innovation, and it is not the intent of FDA to apply the design control requirements to the research phase. Instead, the regulation requires the establishment of procedures to ensure that whatever design is ultimately transferred to production is, in fact, a design that will translate into a device that properly performs according to its intended use and user needs.

To assist FDA in applying the regulation, manufacturers should document the flow of the design process so that it is clear to the FDA investigator where research is ending and development of the design is beginning.

64. A few comments stated that design controls should not be retroactive and that ongoing design development should be exempted.

FDA agrees in part with the comments. FDA did not intend the design requirements to be retroactive, and § 820.30 *Design controls* will not require the manufacturer to apply such requirements to already distributed devices. When the regulation becomes effective on June 1, 1997, it will apply to designs that are in the design and development phase, and manufacturers will be expected to have the design and development plan established. The manufacturer should identify what stage a design is in for each device and will be expected to comply with the

established design and development plan and the applicable paragraphs of § 820.30 from that point forward to completion. If a manufacturer had a design in the *development stage* before June 1, 1997, and cannot comply with any particular paragraph of § 820.30, the manufacturer must provide a detailed justification as to why such compliance is not possible. However, designs will not have to be recycled through previous phases that have been completed. Manufacturers will be expected to comply in full by June 1, 1998. As stated earlier, FDA wants to emphasize that *it expects manufacturers to be in a reasonable state of compliance with the design control requirements from June 1, 1997, to June 1, 1998, because extra time was given to the industry for implementing design controls before the final regulation became effective.*

When changes are made to new or existing designs, the design controls of § 820.30 must be followed to ensure that the changes are appropriate and that the device will continue to perform as intended. FDA notes that the original CGMP regulation contained requirements for specification controls and controls for specification or design changes under § 820.100(a).

65. One comment asked how the proposed design controls would apply to investigational device exemption (IDE) devices, since devices under approved IDE's have been exempt from the CGMP regulation. Some comments suggested that any changes to the IDE regulation should be done in a separate rulemaking. Other comments stated that any change to the IDE regulation should be worded so that all of § 820.30 applies since the IDE process is supplying information in support of the design validation requirements but that all design requirements need not be completed prior to the start of the IDE because the clinical evaluation process often brings valuable information to the design project which may need to be incorporated into the design before design transfer.

The IDE regulation was published in 1976 and last updated in 1978, and has been in effect since that time. Devices being evaluated under IDE's were exempted from the original CGMP regulation because it was believed that it was not reasonable to expect sponsors of clinical investigations to ensure compliance with CGMP's for devices that may never be approved for commercial distribution. However, sponsors of IDE studies were required to ensure that investigational devices were manufactured under a state of control.

With respect to the new regulation, FDA believes that it is reasonable to expect manufacturers who design medical devices to develop the designs in conformance with design control requirements and that adhering to such requirements is necessary to adequately protect the public from potentially harmful devices. The design control requirements are basic controls needed to ensure that the device being designed will perform as intended when produced for commercial distribution. Clinical evaluation is an important aspect of the design verification and validation process during the design and development of the device. Because some of the device design occurs during the IDE stage, it is logical that manufacturers who intend to commercially produce the device follow design control procedures. Were a manufacturer to wait until all the IDE studies were complete, it would be too late to take advantage of the design control process, and the manufacturer would not be able to fulfill the requirements of the quality system regulation for that device.

Therefore, FDA has concurrently amended the IDE regulation,

812.1   Scope to state:

(a) * * * An IDE approved under § 812.30 or considered approved under § 812.2(b) exempts a device from the requirements of the following sections of the Federal Food, Drug, and Cosmetic Act (the act) and regulations issued thereunder: * * * good manufacturing practice requirements under section 520(f) *except for the requirements found in § 820.30, if applicable* (unless the sponsor states an intention to comply with these requirements under § 812.20(b)(3) or § 812.140(b)(4)(v)) and color additive requirements under section 721. (Emphasis added.)

FDA does not expect any new information in IDE applications as a result of this amendment, nor will FDA inspect design controls during bioresearch monitoring inspections. FDA is simply making a conforming amendment to the IDE regulation to make clear that design controls must be followed when design functions are undertaken by manufacturers, including design activity which occurs under an approved IDE. FDA will evaluate the adequacy of manufacturers' compliance with design control requirements in routine CGMP inspections, including preapproval inspections for premarket approval applications (PMA's).

66. Many written comments and oral comments at the August and September 1995 meetings recommended that, because design controls are a major addition to the regulation, the effective date for design controls should be delayed until 18 months after publication of the final rule.

FDA has addressed these comments by extending the effective date of the regulation until June 1, 1997, and by the inspectional strategy described earlier.

67. A couple of comments suggested that FDA lacked the authority to establish the design control requirements.

FDA disagrees with the comments. The act and its legislative history make clear that FDA has the authority to impose those controls necessary to ensure that devices are safe and effective. The SMDA gave FDA explicit authority to promulgate design controls, including a process to assess the performance of a device (see section 520(f)(1)(A) of the act). The legislative history of the SMDA supports a "*comprehensive* device design validation regulation." H. Rept. 808, 101st Cong., 2d sess. 23 (emphasis added). Congress stated that the amendment to the statute was necessary because almost half of all device recalls over a 5-year period were "related to a problem with product design." Id. There is a thorough discussion on the evolution of and need for the design controls in the preamble to the November 23, 1993 (58 FR 61952), proposal.

68. A few comments objected to FDA requiring design controls for any class I devices in § 820.30(a).

FDA believes that, for the class I devices listed, design controls are necessary and has retained the requirements. Those relatively few devices, while class I, require close control of the design process to ensure that the devices perform as intended, given the serious consequences that could occur if their designs were flawed and the devices were to fail to meet their intended uses. In fact, some of the devices included on the list have experienced failures due to design related problems that have resulted in health hazards, injuries, or death. Further, verification, or even validation, cannot provide the assurance of proper design for some devices, especially those containing extensive software. Thus, all automated devices must be developed under the design control requirements.

69. Several comments stated that FDA has underestimated the complexity of a design project in requiring that the plans identify "persons responsible for each activity" in proposed § 820.30(b). One comment stated that "define responsibility for implementation" and "activities shall be assigned" were basically redundant requirements. A few other comments stated that ISO 9001:1994 does not call for the design plans to be "approved" and that this requirement should be deleted because it would be burdensome.

FDA agrees in part with the comments and has revised § 820.30(b) to require the plan to describe or reference design activities and define responsibility for implementing the activities, rather than requiring that the plan identify each person responsible for carrying out each activity. In making this change, FDA notes that § 820.20(b)(1) requires manufacturers to establish the appropriate responsibility for activities affecting quality, and emphasizes that the assignment of specific responsibility is important to the success of the design control program and to achieving compliance with the regulation. Also, the design and development activities should be assigned to qualified personnel equipped with adequate resources as required under § 820.20(b)(2). The requirements under § 820.30(b) were rewritten to be very similar to the requirements in ISO 9001:1994, sections 4.4.2 and 4.4.3. FDA does not agree that the design plan should not be "approved." ISO 9001:1994, section 4.4.2 requires that the plan be "updated," and section 4.4.3 requires that the plan be "regularly reviewed." Therefore, the approval is consistent with ISO 9001:1994 and would not be unduly burdensome since the FDA does not dictate how or by whom the plan must be approved. The regulation gives the manufacturer the necessary flexibility to have the same person(s) who is responsible for the review also be responsible for the approval of the plan if appropriate.

70. A few comments stated that the proposed requirement to describe "any interaction between or among different organizational and technical groups" in § 820.30(b) for the design and development plan should be deleted because it is overly broad, unnecessary, and burdensome. One comment said that the communication expected between these groups should be clarified.

In response, FDA has amended the requirement as suggested by one comment so that the plan shall identify and describe the interfaces with different groups or activities that provide, or result in, input to the design process. Many organization functions, both inside and outside the design group, may contribute to the design process. For example, interfaces with marketing, purchasing, regulatory affairs, manufacturing, service groups, or information systems may be necessary during the design

R

development phase. To function effectively, the design plan must establish the roles of these groups in the design process and describe the information that should be received and transmitted.

71. One comment stated that the requirement in § 820.30(b) that manufacturers establish a design plan completely ignores the creative and dynamic process of designing by requiring a plan to have complete design and testing criteria established, with specifications, before the design process is started.

FDA disagrees with the comment. Section 820.30(b) does not require manufacturers to complete design and testing criteria before the design process begins. This section has been revised to state that "plans shall be reviewed, updated, and approved as design and development evolves," indicating that changes to the design plan are expected. A design plan typically includes at least proposed quality practices, assessment methodology, recordkeeping and documentation requirements, and resources, as well as a sequence of events related to a particular design or design category. These may be modified and refined as the design evolves. However, the design process can become a lengthy and costly process if the design activity is not properly defined and planned. The more specifically the activities are defined up front, the less need there will be for changes as the design evolves.

72. One comment stated that the language contained in proposed § 820.30(c) should more closely match that of ISO 9001. Many other comments stated that the provision should not require the input requirements to "completely" address the intended use of the device because inputs could never "completely" address the intended use. Several comments stated that the requirement of ISO 9001 that "incomplete, ambiguous or conflicting requirements shall be resolved with those responsible for imposing these requirements" should be added to § 820.30(c), "Design input," because it is important that the regulation identify the method of resolving conflicting information.

FDA agrees with the harmonization comment and has revised the language to incorporate the requirement of section 4.4.4, "Design input," of ISO 9001:1994. FDA does not believe that it is necessary to have identical language to harmonize quality system requirements. ISO 9001:1994, section 4.4.1, "General," requires that the manufacturer "establish and maintain documented procedures to control and verify the design of the product in order to ensure that the specified requirements are met." FDA's regulation, under § 820.30(a), imposes the same requirements.

Regarding the comments that input requirements cannot completely address the intended use of the device, FDA recognizes that the provision could be interpreted to impose a burden that may not always be possible to meet and has deleted the word "completely." FDA did not intend the provision to suggest that a manufacturer must foresee every possible event.

FDA emphasizes, however, that the section requires the manufacturer to ensure that the design input requirements are appropriate so the device will perform to meet its intended use and the needs of the user. In doing this, the manufacturer must define the performance characteristics, safety and reliability requirements, environmental requirements and limitations, physical characteristics, applicable standards and regulatory requirements, and labeling and packaging requirements, among other things, and refine the design requirements as verification and validation results are established. For example, when designing a device, the manufacturer should conduct appropriate human factors studies, analyses, and tests from the early stages of the design process until that point in development at which the interfaces with the medical professional and the patient are fixed. The human interface includes both the hardware and software characteristics that affect device use, and good design is crucial to logical, straightforward, and safe device operation. The human factors methods used (for instance, task/function analyses, user studies, prototype tests, mock-up reviews, etc.) should ensure that the characteristics of the user population and operating environment are considered. In addition, the compatibility of system components should be assessed. Finally, labeling (e.g., instructions for use) should be tested for usability.

FDA agrees with the comments, in that it is important that incomplete, ambiguous, or conflicting requirements be resolved with those responsible for imposing these requirements. Therefore, FDA has added the requirement that the procedures shall include a mechanism for addressing incomplete, ambiguous, or conflicting requirements. FDA notes that this must be done to "ensure that the design requirements are appropriate and address the intended use of the device," as required under § 820.30(c).

73. A few other comments stated that ISO 9001:1994 does not call for the design input to be "approved" and therefore, this requirement should be deleted because it would be burdensome.

FDA does not agree that the "approval" of design input requirements should be deleted, nor that the requirement is inconsistent with ISO. ISO 9001:1994, section 4.4.4, "Design Input," requires that the design input requirements be "reviewed by the supplier for adequacy." Therefore, the approval would not add any additional burden because FDA does not dictate how or by whom the design input requirements must be approved, thus giving the manufacturer the necessary flexibility to have the same person(s) who is responsible for the "review for adequacy" also be responsible for the approval, if appropriate. Further, it is important that the design input be assessed as early as possible in the development process, making this an ideal time in the device's design development to have a design review to "approve" the design input.

74. A few comments stated that the proposed requirement under § 820.30(c) that "design input shall be reviewed and approved by a designated qualified individual" should be deleted as it implies that one person must be designated to review and approve a design, and that there may not be one person who is qualified to assess all of the design input requirements. Addressing the same point, several comments suggested that the provision be revised to allow for more than one person to review and approve the design. One comment said that the FDA's requirement appears to be at odds with the team approach.

FDA agrees with the concern expressed by the comments and has modified the requirement to allow more than one individual to review and approve the design input. FDA endorses the team approach and believes that designs should be reviewed and evaluated by all disciplines necessary to ensure the design input requirements are appropriate.

75. Two comments stated that proposed § 820.30(c) should be reworded to focus on systems for assuring adequate design input, not on the input itself. One additional comment on this section said that the design input requirements should include not only the device's intended use and needs of the user, but the environmental limits of where it will be used.

FDA agrees that procedures for ensuring appropriate design controls are of the utmost importance and has modified the section to clarify that the manufacturer must establish and maintain procedures to ensure that the design requirements are properly addressed. FDA made this change to the other paragraphs as well, but notes that § 820.30(a), "General," requires the manufacturer to establish and maintain procedures to control the design of the device in order to ensure that specified design requirements are met. The sections that follow set forth some of the requirements for which procedures must be established. It should be emphasized that the input itself must also be appropriate; the requirement is for the procedures to be defined, documented, *and implemented.* Thus, if the input requirements related to a device fail to address the intended use of the device, for example, the manufacturer has failed to comply with the provision.

FDA also agrees with the additional comment but believes that identifying and establishing the environmental limits for safe and effective device operation is inherent in the requirements for ensuring that a device is appropriate for its intended use. Some factors that must be considered when establishing inputs include, where applicable, a determination of energy (e.g., electrical, heat, and electromagnetic fields), biological effects (e.g., toxicity and biocompatibility) and environmental effects (e.g., electromagnetic interference and electrostatic discharge).

76. Several comments stated that proposed § 820.30(f), "Design output," should be rewritten or deleted because many of the requirements were already stated in proposed §§ 820.30(d), "Design verification," and 820.30(e), "Design review," and, if retained, should be reordered similar to ISO 9001.

FDA agrees in part with the comments and has rewritten the requirements of design output to be consistent with ISO 9001:1994, section 4.4.5, "Design output," and reordered the sections to be consistent with ISO 9001:1994. FDA retained the provision, however, because it does not agree that the section is redundant with the sections on design verification, design validation, or design review. Design output are the design specifications which should meet design input requirements, as confirmed during design verification and validation and ensured during design review. The output includes the device, its labeling and packaging, associated specifications and drawings, and production and quality assurance specifications and procedures. These documents are the basis for the DMR. The total finished

design output consists of the device, its labeling and packaging, and the DMR.

77. One comment stated that the sentence "Design output procedures shall ensure that design output meets the design input requirements" is redundant with the requirement under design verification. Another comment asked what is meant by "release."

FDA agrees with the first comment and has deleted that sentence in § 820.30(d) but notes that the design output must be documented and expressed *in terms that can be verified* against the design input requirements.

Design output can be "released" or transferred to the next design phase at various stages in the design process, as defined in the design and development plan. The design output is reviewed and approved before release or transfer to the next design phase or production. The design output requirements are intended to apply to all such stages of the design process.

78. One small manufacturer commented that the problems that § 820.30(e), "Design review," is meant to reveal involve coordination, cooperation, or communication difficulties among the members of an organization and that these difficulties do not exist in a small company. Therefore, the comment stated that the design review requirements should not apply to small manufacturers.

The purpose of conducting design reviews during the design phase is to ensure that the design satisfies the design input requirements for the intended use of the device and the needs of the user. Design review includes the review of design verification data to determine whether the design outputs meet functional and operational requirements, the design is compatible with components and other accessories, the safety requirements are achieved, the reliability and maintenance requirements are met, the labeling and other regulatory requirements are met, and the manufacturing, installation, and servicing requirements are compatible with the design specifications. Design reviews should be conducted at major decision points during the design phase.

For a large manufacturer, design review provides an opportunity for all those who may have an impact on the quality of the device to provide input, including manufacturing, quality assurance, purchasing, sales, and servicing divisions. While small manufacturers may not have the broad range of disciplines found in a large company, and the need to coordinate and control technical interfaces may be lessened, the principles of design

review still apply. The requirements under § 820.30(e) allow small manufacturers to tailor a design review that is appropriate to their individual needs.

79. One comment stated that the wording of proposed § 820.30(e) implies that only one design review is expected, and that design review should be conducted at several stages of product development. Several comments stated that to demand that every design review be conducted by individuals who do not have direct responsibility for design development is impractical, especially for small companies.

FDA agrees with the first comment and has rewritten the requirement to make clear that design reviews must be conducted at appropriate stages of design development, which must be defined in the established design and development plan. The number of design reviews will depend on the plan and the complexity of the device. FDA also amended the requirements so that the results of a design review include identification of the design, the date, and the individual(s) performing the review. Thus, multiple reviews can occur and the manufacturer must document what is being reviewed, when, and by whom.

FDA never intended to mandate that an individual without design responsibility conduct the design reviews and, to clarify its position, has rewritten the requirement. The requirement now states that the procedures shall ensure that each design review includes an individual(s) who does not have direct responsibility for the design stage being reviewed. This requirement will provide an "objective view" from someone not working directly on that particular part of the design project, to ensure that the requirements are met. In making this change, FDA also notes that it was not FDA's intention to prohibit those directly responsible for the design from *participating* in the design review.

80. One comment stated that as part of the systematic review of the adequacy of the device design, it is occasionally necessary to produce a prototype device and have it evaluated by a physician who is an expert in the area of the device's intended use. Thus, the comment stated that the regulation should be revised to allow a means for a manufacturer to ship a prototype device to a physician for evaluation. One comment questioned whether design verification and validation can be conducted using prototypes or machine shop models.

FDA regulations do not prohibit the shipment of prototypes for clinical or

R

other studies. Prototypes used in clinical studies involving humans may be shipped in accordance with the IDE provisions in part 812 (21 CFR part 812).

FDA understands that it is not always practical to conduct clinical studies on finished production units and, therefore, the use of prototypes in clinical studies is acceptable. When prototype devices are used on humans they must be verified as safe to the maximum extent feasible. Final design validation, however, cannot be done on prototypes because the actual devices produced and distributed are seldom the same as the research and development prototypes. The final verification and validation, therefore, must include the testing of actual production devices under actual or simulated use conditions.

81. A few comments stated that § 820.30(d), "Design verification," should be rewritten and reordered similar to ISO 9001.

FDA agrees with the comments and has rewritten and reordered this section to be consistent with ISO 9001:1994. The language in revised § 820.30(f) and (g) incorporates the requirement of ISO 9001:1994, sections 4.4.7, "Design verification," and 4.4.8, "Design validation," respectively.

Under the revised provisions, the design must be verified and validated. It is important to note that design validation follows successful design verification. Certain aspects of design validation can be accomplished during the design verification, but design verification is not a substitute for design validation. Design validation should be performed under defined operating conditions and on the initial production units, lots, or batches, or their equivalents to ensure proper overall design control and proper design transfer. When equivalent devices are used in the final design validation, the manufacturer must document in detail how the device was manufactured and how the manufacturing is similar to and possibly different from initial production. Where there are differences, the manufacturer must justify why design validation results are valid for the production units, lots, or batches. Manufacturers should not use prototypes developed in the laboratory or machine shop as test units to meet these requirements. Prototypes may differ from the finished production devices. During research and development, conditions for building prototypes are typically better controlled and personnel more knowledgeable about what needs to be done and how to do it than are regular

production personnel. When going from laboratory to scale-up production, standards, methods, and procedures may not be properly transferred, or additional manufacturing processes may be added. Often, changes not reflected in the prototype are made in the device to facilitate the manufacturing process, and these may adversely affect device functioning and user interface characteristics. Proper testing of devices that are produced using the same methods and procedures as those to be used in routine production will prevent the distribution and subsequent recall of many unacceptable medical devices.

In addition, finished devices must be tested for performance under actual conditions of use or simulated use conditions in the actual or simulated environment in which the device is expected to be used. The simulated use testing provision no longer requires that the testing be performed on the *first three* production runs. However, samples must be taken from units, lots, or batches that were produced using the same specifications, production and quality system methods, procedures, and equipment that will be used for routine production. FDA considers this a critical element of the design validation. The requirement to conduct simulated use testing of finished devices is found in the original CGMP in § 820.160, as part of finished device inspection. This requirement has been moved to § 820.30(g) because FDA believes that simulated use testing at this point is more effective in ensuring that only safe and effective devices are produced. Manufacturers must also conduct such tests when they make changes in the device design or the manufacturing process that could affect safety or effectiveness as required in the original CGMP in § 820.100(a)(2). The extent of testing conducted should be governed by the risk(s) the device will present if it fails. FDA considers these activities essential for ensuring that the manufacturing process does not adversely affect the device.

Design validation may also be necessary in earlier stages, prior to product completion, and multiple validations may need to be performed if there are different intended uses. Proper design validation cannot occur without following all the requirements set forth in the design control section of the regulation.

82. Several comments stated that adequate controls for verification of design output are contained in proposed § 820.30(d), "Design verification," and repeated in proposed § 820.30(f), "Design output." One comment stated that this section will place undue

burden on designers and require additional documentation which will add little value to a device's safety and effectiveness.

FDA disagrees with the comments. Revised § 820.30(f), "Design verification," and § 820.30(g), "Design validation," require verification and validation of the design output. Section 820.30(d), "Design output," requires that the output be documented in a fashion that will allow for verification and validation. These sections thus contain different requirements that are basic to establishing that the design output meets the approved design requirements or inputs, including user needs and intended uses. All the requirements are essential to assuring the safety and effectiveness of devices. FDA does not believe that these requirements place undue burden on designers or require additional documentation with no value added. These basic requirements are necessary to assure the proper device performance, and, therefore, the production of safe and effective devices, and are acknowledged and accepted as such throughout the world.

83. Several comments stated that the term "hazard analysis" should be defined in reference to design verification. A couple of comments stated that the proposed requirement for design verification, to include software validation and hazard analysis, where applicable, was ambiguous, and may lead an FDA investigator to require software validation and hazard analysis for devices in cases where it is not needed. One comment stated that FDA should provide additional guidance regarding software validation and hazard analysis and what investigators will expect to see. Another comment stated that by explicitly mentioning only software validation and hazard analysis, FDA was missing the opportunity to introduce manufacturers to some powerful and beneficial tools for better device designs and problem avoidance.

FDA has deleted the term "hazard analysis" and replaced it with the term "risk analysis." FDA's involvement with the ISO TC 210 made it clear that "risk analysis" is the comprehensive and appropriate term. When conducting a risk analysis, manufacturers are expected to identify possible hazards associated with the design in both normal and fault conditions. The risks associated with the hazards, including those resulting from user error, should then be calculated in both normal and fault conditions. If any risk is judged unacceptable, it should be reduced to acceptable levels by the appropriate means, for example, by redesign or warnings. An important part of risk analysis is ensuring that changes made to eliminate or minimize hazards do not introduce new hazards. Tools for conducting such analyses include Failure Mode Effect Analysis and Fault Tree Analysis, among others.

FDA disagrees with the comments that state the requirement is ambiguous. Software must be validated when it is a part of the finished device. FDA believes that this control is always needed, given the unique nature of software, to assure that software will perform as intended and will not impede safe operation by the user. Risk analysis must be conducted for the majority of devices subject to design controls and is considered to be an essential requirement for medical devices under this regulation, as well as under ISO/CD 13485 and EN 46001. FDA has replaced the phrase "where applicable" with "where appropriate" for consistency with the rest of the regulation.

FDA believes that sufficient domestic and international guidelines are available to provide assistance to manufacturers for the validation of software and risk analysis. For example, "Reviewer Guidance for Computer Controlled Medical Devices Undergoing 510(k) Review," August 1991; "A Technical Report, Software Development Activities," July 1987; and ISO–9000–3 contain computer validation guidance. Further, FDA is preparing a new "CDRH Guidance for the Scientific Review of Pre-Market Medical Device Software Submissions." Regarding guidance on "risk analysis," manufacturers can reference the draft EN (prEN) 1441, "Medical Devices— Risk Analysis" standard and the work resulting from ISO TC 210 working group No. 4 to include ISO/CD 14971, "Medical Devices—Risk Management— Application of Risk Analysis to Medical Devices."

FDA disagrees that it is missing the opportunity to introduce manufacturers to some powerful and beneficial tools for better device designs and problem avoidance because the manufacturer must apply current methods and procedures that are appropriate for the device, to verify and validate the device design under the regulation. Therefore, FDA need not list all known methods for meeting the requirements. A tool that may be required to adequately verify and validate one design may be unnecessary to verify and validate another design.

84. One comment stated that for some design elements it may be more appropriate to reference data from another prior experimentation rather than conduct new testing, and that the requirement to list verification methods should be modified.

FDA agrees in part with the comment. The revised language of § 820.30(f) will permit the use of data from prior experimentation when applicable. When using data from previous experimentation, manufacturers must ensure that it is adequate for the current application.

85. "Design transfer," now § 820.30(h), has been revised in response to the many comments objecting to the requirements in the proposed section on "Design transfer." Specifically, the proposed requirement for testing production units under actual or simulated use conditions was rewritten and moved to current § 820.30(g), "Design validation."

FDA again emphasizes that testing production units under actual or simulated use conditions prior to distribution is crucial for ensuring that only safe and effective devices are distributed and FDA has therefore retained the requirement. ISO 9001:1994 discusses this concept in notes 12 and 13. As noted above, it is not always possible to determine the adequacy of the design by successfully building and testing prototypes or models produced in a laboratory setting.

The requirement for testing from the first three production lots or batches has been deleted. While FDA believes that three production runs during process validation (process validation may be initiated before or during design transfer) is the accepted standard, FDA recognizes that all processes may not be defined in terms of lots or batches. The number three is, however, currently considered to be the acceptable standard. Therefore, although the number requirement is deleted, FDA expects validation to be carried out properly in accordance with accepted standards, and will inspect for compliance accordingly.

Revised § 820.30(h) now contains a general requirement for the establishment of procedures to ensure that the design basis for the device is correctly translated into production methods and procedures. This is the same requirement that is contained in § 820.100(a) of the original CGMP regulation.

86. A few comments stated that the proposed requirements for "Design release" would prohibit the release of components, partial designs, and production methods before the design was final because the requirements mandate a review of all drawings, analysis, and production methods before allowing the product to go into production. Several comments stated that the proposed section on "Design release" was a duplication of requirements in other paragraphs of § 820.30 and should be deleted.

FDA did not intend the requirements for "Design release" to prohibit manufacturers from beginning the production process until all design activities were completed. The intent of the requirement was to ensure that all design specifications released to production have been approved, verified, and validated before they are implemented as part of the production process. This requirement is now explicitly contained in § 820.30(d).

FDA agrees in part with the second set of comments and has moved the requirement that design output be reviewed and approved to current § 820.30(d), "Design output." The remainder of the requirements have been deleted.

87. Several comments on § 820.30(i), "Design changes," stated that it is unnecessary to control all design changes and to do so would inhibit change and innovation.

FDA disagrees with the comments. Manufacturers are not expected to maintain records of all changes proposed during the very early stages of the design process. However, all design changes made after the design review that approves the initial design inputs for incorporation into the design, and those changes made to correct design deficiencies once the design has been released to production, must be documented. The records of these changes create a history of the evolution of the design, which can be invaluable for failure investigation and for facilitating the design of future similar products. Such records can prevent the repetition of errors and the development of unsafe or ineffective designs. The evaluation and documentation should be in direct proportion to the significance of the change. Procedures must ensure that after the design requirements are established and approved, changes to the design, both pre- production and post-production are also reviewed, validated (or verified where appropriate), and approved. Otherwise, a device may be rendered unable to properly perform, and unsafe and ineffective. ISO 9001:1994, section 4.4.9, similarly provides that "all design changes and modifications shall be identified, documented, reviewed, and approved by authorized personnel before their implementation."

Note that when a change is made to a specification, method, or procedure, each manufacturer should evaluate the change in accordance with an established procedure to determine if the submission of a premarket notification (510(k)) under § 807.81(a)(3) (21 CFR 807.81(a)(3)), or the submission of a supplement to a PMA under § 814.39(a) (21 CFR 814.39) is required. Records of this evaluation and its results should be maintained.

88. Several comments recommended that only changes after design validation and design transfer to full-scale production need to be documented.

FDA disagrees with the comments. The safety and effectiveness of devices cannot be proven by final inspection or testing. Product development is inherently an evolutionary process. While change is a healthy and necessary part of product development, quality can be ensured only if change is controlled and documented in the development process, as well as the production process. Again, manufacturers are not expected to maintain records of changes made during the very early stages of product development; only those design changes made after the approval of the design inputs need be documented. Each manufacturer must establish criteria for evaluating changes to ensure that the changes are appropriate for its designs.

89. One comment on proposed § 820.30(i), ''Design changes,'' stated that validation of design changes is not always necessary and the regulation should provide for other methods to be used. FDA agrees with the comments and has amended the requirement to permit verification where appropriate. For example, a change in the sterilization process of a catheter will require validation of the new process, but the addition of more chromium to a stainless steel surgical instrument may only require verification through chemical analysis. Where a design change cannot be verified by subsequent inspection and test, it must be validated.

90. Many comments noted that the acronym for proposed design history record (DHR) was the same as that of ''device history record'' (DHR), and suggested that the name of the ''design history record'' be changed. Several comments stated that the requirements of the ''design history record'' should be deleted because they were redundant with the requirements of the ''device master record.''

FDA agrees with the first set of comments and has changed the name to ''design history file.''

FDA disagrees with the second set of comments. The DMR contains the documentation necessary to produce a device. The final design output from the design phase, which is maintained or referenced in the DHF, will form the basis or starting point for the DMR. Thus, those outputs must be referred to or placed in the DMR. The total finished design output includes the final device, its labeling and packaging, and the DMR that includes device specifications and drawings, as well as all instructions and procedures for production, installation, maintenance, and servicing. The DHF, in contrast, contains or references all the records necessary to establish compliance with the design plan and the regulation, including the design control procedures. The DHF illustrates the history of the design, and is necessary so that manufacturers can exercise control over and be accountable for the design process, thereby maximizing the probability that the finished design conforms to the design specifications.

91. A few comments stated that the proposed requirements in § 820.30(j) for the design history record should allow a single design history record for each device family or group having common design characteristics.

FDA agrees with the comments. The intent of the DHF is to document, or reference the documentation of, the activities carried out to meet the design plan and requirements of § 820.30. A DHF is, therefore, necessary for each type of device developed. The DHF must provide documentation showing the actions taken with regard to each type of device designed, not generically link devices together with different design characteristics and give a general overview of how the output was reached.

92. Some comments stated that the requirement that the DHF contain ''all'' records necessary to demonstrate that the requirements are met should be deleted because not ''all'' efforts need documentation.

FDA received similar comments on almost every section of the regulation that had the word ''all.'' The proposed requirement does not state that *all* records must be contained in the DHF, but that all records necessary to demonstrate that the requirements were met must be contained in the file. FDA has deleted the word ''all'' but cautions manufacturers that the complete history of the design process should be documented in the DHF. Such records are necessary to ensure that the final design conforms to the design specifications. Depending on the design, that may be relatively few records. Manufacturers who do not document all their efforts may lose the information and experience of those efforts, thereby possibly requiring activities to be duplicated.

D. Document Controls (Subpart D)

93. One comment stated that subpart D of part 820 should be titled ''Document Controls,'' instead of the proposed ''Document and Record Controls'' because the ''record'' requirements are addressed in subpart M. One comment stated that removal of obsolete or unneeded documents should be performed to maintain the integrity of the product configuration and the quality system. The comment suggested adding a requirement for a verification step for document distribution and removal to ensure this important element of a quality system is performed correctly. A few comments stated that proposed § 820.40 should be rewritten to be similar to ISO 9001 and to delete the requirement that documents be ''accurate'' because the comments feared that typographical errors would be considered violations.

FDA agrees with the first comment and has changed the title accordingly. FDA agrees in part with the second comment. The verification of document distribution and removal is very important and can directly affect the quality of a product. Section 820.40, which requires that the manufacturer establish and maintain procedures to control all documents, including those that are obsolete and/or to be removed, requires that the removal (or prevention of use) of obsolete documents be verified. FDA agrees in part with the last set of comments and has rewritten the section, following ISO 9001:1994, to be a general requirement for procedures to control documents that are required under the regulation. The procedures established must, among other things, ensure control of the accuracy and usage of current versions of the documents and the removal or prevention from use of obsolete documents, as well as ensure that the documentation developed is adequate to fulfill its intended purpose or requirement. FDA retained the requirement that the procedures ensure that documents meet the requirements of the regulation because that is the purpose of controlling the documents. FDA deleted the term ''accurate'' but notes that a typographical error can change the meaning of a document and have undesirable consequences.

94. Several comments on proposed § 820.40(a), ''Document approval and issue,'' as well as other sections throughout the regulation, suggested that the term ''signature'' be replaced by the term ''identification.'' Such a change would allow for electronic or computerized identification in lieu of formal written signatures. Other comments stated that ''or stamps''

should be added after "signature" since they are legally recognized in some foreign countries.

FDA is aware that many documentation systems are now maintained electronically, and is in the process of developing an agency-wide policy that will be implemented through rulemaking on the use of electronic signatures. The agency identified several important issues related to the use of such signatures, including how to ensure that the identification is in fact the user's "signature." These issues are discussed in FDA's ANPRM on the use of electronic signatures, published in the Federal Register on July 21, 1992 (57 FR 32185), and the proposed regulation published in the Federal Register on August 31, 1994 (59 FR 45160). Therefore, FDA has not revised the regulation to use the term "identification," but notes that the quality system regulation's use of the term "signature" will permit the use of whatever electronic means the agency determines is the equivalent of a handwritten signature. FDA recommends that manufacturers use the two Federal Register documents as guidance until the regulation is finalized. FDA has not added the term "or stamps" to the regulation; however, stamps could be acceptable if the manufacturer has a formal procedure on how stamps are used in place of handwritten signatures. The procedure would have to address many of the same issues addressed in the electronic signature Federal Register documents, most importantly how the stamps would be controlled and how the manufacturer would ensure that the stamp was in fact the user's "signature."

95. Several comments stated that proposed § 820.40(b), "Document distribution," should be rewritten to be consistent with ISO 9001.

In response, FDA has deleted the section. The requirements for making documents available at all appropriate locations (ISO 9001:1994, section 4.5.2(a)) and the requirements for promptly removing obsolete documents (ISO 9001:1994, section 4.5.2(b)) have been moved, in revised form, to § 820.40(a). In response to comments, FDA has added that obsolete documents, in lieu of being promptly removed from points of use, may be "otherwise prevented from unintended use."

96. Several comments suggested major changes to proposed § 820.40(c), "Documentation changes." Some stated that the requirements should be revised to be consistent with ISO 9001. Others stated that the requirements related to validation should be rewritten and

moved to another section under this part, because § 820.40(c) should only address document changes, not device changes. Several comments stated that the reference to determining whether a 510(k) or PMA supplement is required after making changes to a device should be deleted because it is covered under different parts of the act and regulations. One comment stated that the requirement in § 820.40(c) for changes to be "approved by individuals in the same functions/organizations that performed the original review and approval, unless specifically designated otherwise" is unrealistic and does not reflect the way things are done in real life.

FDA agrees with many of the comments and has substantially rewritten § 820.40(c), now designated as § 820.40(b), to relate specifically to changes to a document. The requirements are now very similar to the ISO 9001:1994 requirements in section 4.5.3. FDA has retained the requirement that the approved changes must be communicated in a timely manner to appropriate personnel. FDA has had many experiences where manufacturers made corrections to documents, but the changes were not communicated in a timely manner to the personnel utilizing the documents. The result of these untimely communications was the production of defective devices.

In addition, FDA has moved the requirement for validating production and process changes to § 820.70(b), "Production and process changes," and notes that changes to the design specifications, at any time during the lifetime of the design of the device, must conform to the requirements in § 820.30(i), "Design changes."

FDA has also deleted the sentence referencing 510(k)'s and PMA supplements because FDA believes this is covered elsewhere, but notes that this sentence is in the preamble above for § 820.30(i).

FDA disagrees that the requirement for changes to be "approved by an individual(s) in the same function or organization that performed the original review and approval, unless specifically designated otherwise" should be deleted and notes that this is a requirement of ISO 9001:1994 as well. The intent of the requirement is to ensure that those who originally approved the document have an opportunity to review any changes because these individuals typically have the best insight on the impact of the changes. The requirement is flexible, however, because it permits the manufacturer to specifically designate individuals who did not perform the

original review and approval to review and approve the changes. To designate such individuals, the manufacturer will need to determine who would be best suited to perform the function, thus ensuring adequate control over the changes. In this way, review and approval will not be haphazard.

97. One comment on proposed § 820.40(d), "Documentation change record," stated that this section should be deleted because the other paragraphs of § 820.40 adequately cover the proposed requirements. Two comments suggested replacing the section with the requirements of section 4.5.2 of ISO 9001.

FDA has deleted § 820.40(d) and placed the revised requirements in paragraphs (a) and (b) of this section. The general requirement of § 820.40 now requires the manufacturer to establish adequate procedures to control all documents required by part 820. The procedures must cover the requirements listed in § 820.40 (a) and (b). Thus, the manufacturer must establish a procedure for ensuring that only the current and approved version of a document is used, achieving the objective of the "Master list or equivalent document control procedure," required in ISO 9001:1994, section 4.5.2.

The other requirement in § 820.40(d), "Document change record," was to maintain a record of changes, to include a description of the changes, among other things. FDA has retained this requirement and has moved it into § 820.40(b), "Document changes," because the agency believes this information to be important and useful when investigating and performing corrective or preventive actions.

FDA believes § 820.40 on *Document controls* now adequately harmonizes with ISO 9001:1994, sections 4.5.1, 4.5.2, and 4.5.3.

E. Purchasing Controls (Subpart E)

98. One comment stated that the proposed CGMP regulation omits any discussion of contract reviews, such as that contained in ISO 9001, section 4.3. Rather than leaving these procedures to the interpretations of individual manufacturers and investigators, the comment stated that FDA should explicitly state its general policy regarding contract reviews in the regulation.

FDA agrees with the concepts underlying the contract review requirements of ISO 9001:1994, but believes these principles are already reflected in requirements in the regulation, such as §§ 820.50 *Purchasing controls* and 820.160 *Distribution.*

R

Therefore, the agency has not added a separate section on contract review.

99. One comment stated that the requirements in § 820.50 amount to overregulation. The comment stated that components are purchased by providing a specification sheet. They are then inspected upon receipt, and defective components are returned. According to the comment, under § 820.50, the manufacturer would be required to spend more time on paperwork, and product would still have to be inspected upon receipt. Another comment stated that the cost of the quality assurance documentation program is going to be significantly higher for a company that runs a Just In Time (JIT) program than what FDA estimated.

FDA disagrees with the comments. The failure to implement adequate purchasing controls has resulted in a significant number of recalls due to component failures. Most of these were due to unacceptable components provided by suppliers. Since FDA is not regulating component suppliers, FDA believes that the explicit addition to CGMP requirements of the purchasing controls of ISO 9001:1994 is necessary to provide the additional assurance that only acceptable components are used. To ensure purchased or otherwise received product or services conform to specifications, purchasing must be carried out under adequate controls, including the assessment and selection of suppliers, contractors, and consultants, the clear and unambiguous specification of requirements, and the performance of suitable acceptance activities. Each manufacturer must establish an appropriate mix of assessment and receiving acceptance to ensure products and services are acceptable for their intended uses. The specifications for the finished device cannot be met unless the individual parts of the finished device meet specifications. The most efficient and least costly approach is to ensure that only acceptable products and services are received. This means that only suppliers, contractors, and consultants that meet specifications should be used.

The regulation has been written to allow more flexibility in the way manufacturers may ensure the acceptability of products and services. Under the requirements, manufacturers must clearly define in the procedures the type and extent of control they intend to apply to products and services. Thus, a finished device manufacturer may choose to provide greater in-house controls to ensure that products and services meet requirements, or may require the supplier to adopt measures necessary to ensure acceptability, as appropriate. FDA generally believes that an appropriate mix of supplier and manufacturer quality controls are necessary. However, finished device manufacturers who conduct product quality control solely in-house must also assess the capability of suppliers to provide acceptable product. Where audits are not practical, this may be done through, among other means, reviewing historical data, monitoring and trending, and inspection and testing.

After evaluation of all of the comments on § 820.50, FDA has decided to change the wording of § 820.50(a) and adopt the wording of ISO 9001:1994 to make clear that manufacturers have flexibility in determining the degree of assessment and evaluation necessary for suppliers, contractors, and consultants. Thus the degree of supplier control necessary to establish compliance may vary with the type and significance of the product or service purchased and the impact of that product or service on the quality of the finished device. In addition, the requirement for manufacturers to establish assessment criteria has been deleted but the evaluation still must include a description how the assessment was made (according to what criteria or objective procedure) and the results must be documented. Each manufacturer must now define the type and extent of control it will exercise over suppliers, contractors, and consultants. This is consistent with the 1994 version of ISO 9001.

Thus, FDA believes that the flexibility of the regulation will allow manufacturers to implement JIT procedures without additional cost. In fact, the new regulation is more conducive to JIT practices by permitting the assessment or evaluation of product or services up front, thereby lessening the degree of in-house control that may be necessary.

100. Several comments said that it was unclear what FDA meant by the phrase "or held by other persons under contract conform to specifications" and that this phrase should be deleted.

FDA agrees with the comments and has deleted the phrase. The phrase was intended to mean product and services which were purchased or processed in some manner by other organizations. Section 820.50 now applies to "purchased or otherwise received product and services" to convey this meaning. FDA emphasizes that the requirements apply to all product and service received from outside of the finished device manufacturer, whether payment occurs or not. Thus, a manufacturer must comply with these provisions when it receives product or services from its "sister facility" or some other corporate or financial affiliate. "Otherwise received product" would include "customer supplied product" as in ISO 9001:1994, section 4.7, but would not apply to "returned product" from the customer.

101. One comment stated that "manufacturing materials" should be deleted from the first sentence of the introductory text of the proposed § 820.50, as the assessment of the manufacturers of manufacturing materials would be a monumental task.

FDA disagrees with the comment. The first sentence of the introductory text of § 820.50 is rewritten to be a general requirement that each manufacturer must establish procedures to ensure that received product and services (purchased or otherwise received) conform to specified requirements. All manufacturers are expected to apply controls to manufacturing materials appropriate to the manufacturing material, the intended use, and the effect of the manufacturing materials on safety and effectiveness. For example, the procedures necessary to ensure that a mold release agent conforms to specified requirements may be less involved than the procedures for controlling latex proteins. The provision allows the manufacturer the flexibility of establishing the procedures to meet its needs and to ensure that the product conforms to specified requirements.

102. One comment said that FDA should delete the last sentence of the introductory text of proposed § 820.50 because it is unnecessary for manufacturers to develop specifications for services that are unrelated to product or process quality, and because the terms "service" and "other persons" lack definition. Other comments stated that "all" should be deleted in the general requirement.

FDA disagrees with the comments. First, as used in the regulation, "service" means parts of the manufacturing or quality system that are contracted to others, for example, plating of metals, testing, and sterilizing, among others. Second, FDA believes that all suppliers of such services must be assessed and evaluated, just like a supplier of a product. As always, the degree of control necessary is related to the product or service purchased. FDA has, however, deleted the term "provided by other persons" because it was unnecessary. FDA did not delete the word "all" because, as discussed above, component manufacturers are not subject to this regulation, so it is the finished device manufacturer who is responsible for "all" product and services.

103. One comment stated that many suppliers of components to the medical device industry have their quality systems certified to an ISO 9000 standard by an independent third party auditor, and that such registration of component manufacturers should be considered in vendor assessment plans.

FDA agrees in part with the comment in that certification may play a role in evaluating suppliers, but cautions manufacturers against relying solely on certification by third parties as evidence that suppliers have the capability to provide quality products or services. FDA has found during inspections that some manufacturers who have been certified to the ISO standards have not had acceptable problem identification and corrective action programs. Therefore, the initial assessment or evaluation, depending on the type and potential effect on device quality of the product or service, should be a combination of assessment methods, to possibly include third party or product certification. However, third party certification should not be relied on exclusively in initially evaluating a supplier. If a device manufacturer has established confidence in the supplier's ability to provide acceptable products or services, certification with test data may be acceptable.

104. Some comments stated that consultants should not be included in the regulation at all. Others stated that it was not consistent with ISO 9001.

FDA added "consultants" to § 820.50(a) in response to the comments from § 820.25(c). FDA disagrees that "consultants" should be deleted because over the years FDA has observed that a surprising number of firms hire consultants who have no particular expertise in the area in which the firm is seeking assistance. Section 820.50 addresses this problem by ensuring that a consultant's capability for the specific tasks for which he or she is retained be assessed and documented. Further, FDA does not believe this requirement is inconsistent with ISO 9001:1994 because ISO uses the term "subcontractor." The term "subcontractor" includes consultants.

105. One comment said that requiring evaluation of potential suppliers, contractors, and consultants "on the basis of their ability to meet requirements" is vague and should be clearly defined.

FDA disagrees that the phrase is vague. Suppliers, contractors, and consultants selected by manufacturers of medical devices should have a demonstrated capability of providing products and services that meet the requirements established by the finished device manufacturer. The capability of the product or service suppliers should be reviewed at intervals consistent with the significance of the product or service provided and the review should demonstrate conformance to specified requirements.

106. One comment questioned the usefulness of § 820.50, given that the requirements under § 820.80 *Receiving, in-process, and finished device acceptance,* require manufacturers to establish and maintain procedures for acceptance of incoming components.

The intent of § 820.50 is to ensure that device manufacturers select only those suppliers, contractors, and consultants who have the capability to provide quality product and services. As with finished devices, quality cannot be inspected or tested into products or services. Rather, the quality of a product or service is established during the design of that product or service, and achieved through proper control of the manufacture of that product or the performance of that service. Section 820.50 thus mandates that products be manufactured and services be performed under appropriate quality assurance procedures. Finished device manufacturers are required under § 820.50 to establish the requirements for, and document the capability of, suppliers, contractors, and consultants to provide quality products and services.

Section 820.80 is specific to a device manufacturer's acceptance program. While finished device manufacturers are required to assess the capability of suppliers, contractors, and consultants to provide quality products and services, inspections and tests, and other verification tools, are also an important part of ensuring that components and finished devices conform to approved specifications. The extent of incoming acceptance activities can be based, in part, on the degree to which the supplier has demonstrated a capability to provide quality products or services. An appropriate product and services quality assurance program includes a combination of assessment techniques, including inspection and test.

107. Several comments stated that it was not clear how a manufacturer could evaluate an off-the-shelf component that is purchased from a distributor rather than directly from its manufacturer, and stated that it would not be helpful to audit the distributor.

FDA agrees that auditing a distributor would not meet the intent of § 820.50.

Manufacturers should remember that the purpose of assessing the capability of suppliers is to provide quality products and to provide a greater degree of assurance, beyond that provided by receiving inspection and test, that the products received meet the finished device manufacturer's requirements. The agency recognizes that finished device manufacturers may not always be able to audit the supplier of a product. In such cases, the manufacturer must apply other effective means to assure that products are acceptable for use.

108. Many comments from both domestic and foreign firms in response to proposed § 820.22(b) said that making supplier audit reports subject to FDA review would have a major adverse impact on the relationships between the finished device manufacturers and their suppliers and service providers. Some stated that the requirement would cause suppliers to refuse to sell components to medical device manufacturers, especially suppliers who provide only a small part of their production to device manufacturers. Others said that this policy is not consistent with FDA's policy for internal audits.

FDA recognizes that quality audits of suppliers have a significant and demonstrated value as a management tool for corrective action, quality improvement, and overall assurance of component and service quality, and does not seek to undermine their value. Therefore, based on the concerns raised by the comments, FDA will not review supplier audit reports during a routine FDA inspection for compliance with part 820, as noted in § 820.180(c), "Exceptions." The audit procedures, the evaluation procedures, and documents other than the supplier audit reports themselves that demonstrate conformance with § 820.50 will be subject to review by an FDA investigator.

109. One comment stated that it was unclear what is meant by the requirement to specify "quality requirements" that must be met by suppliers, contractors, and consultants, as stated in § 820.50(a).

The term "quality requirements" means the quality control and quality assurance procedures, standards, and other requirements necessary to assure that the product or service is adequate for its intended use. FDA does not believe the term is unclear.

110. Several comments on proposed § 820.50(b), "Purchasing forms," suggested that the term "forms" be replaced by "data." Other comments stated that use of the term would not allow electronic data exchange. One comment stated that the use of an

R

exclusive form for purchasing is unnecessary and redundant, and that it is unduly burdensome to require detailed documentation on those commonly available items such as fasteners. The comment stated that it is common practice to use prints or drawings to fulfill the purpose of the form.

FDA agrees in part with the comments, but does not believe that § 820.50(b) prohibits the use of drawings or prints, assuming that the documents contain data clearly describing the product or service ordered, and that the specified requirements are met. However, § 820.50(b) has been rewritten and now requires manufacturers to establish purchasing "data." This provides manufacturers with the flexibility to use both written and electronic means to establish purchasing information.

111. One comment stated that the inclusion of an additional provision mandating that suppliers notify manufacturers of any change in their product or service places an undue burden on suppliers and inhibits their ability to make minor adjustments within the parameters of agreed upon specifications and quality requirements. Many other comments stated that the requirement in § 820.50(b) is feasible only for components that are custom made for the manufacturer, and is meaningless for off-the-shelf components purchased from distributors. Other comments stated that the requirement is part of the original CGMP regulation and experience has shown that suppliers are not willing to supply device manufacturers with such information. A few other comments stated that "any" should be deleted because the term is too broad and could result in burdensome reporting of variables which are irrelevant to the continued performance or specifications of the product or service.

FDA agrees in part with the comments and has amended the requirement to state that such agreement should be obtained "where possible." FDA still believes that this change information is very important to the manufacturer, and that the manufacturer should obtain information on changes to the product or service. Where a supplier refuses to agree to provide such notification, depending on the product or service being purchased, it may render him an unacceptable supplier. However, where the product is in short supply and must be purchased, the manufacturer will need to heighten control in other ways.

FDA has also deleted the term "any" to give manufacturers the flexibility to

define in the agreement the types of changes that would require notification.

112. One comment stated that § 820.50(b) should incorporate a provision that would allow manufacturers to cite published standards in purchasing forms as one suitable method for specifying purchased item quality requirements.

FDA believes the addition is unnecessary, because the regulation permits manufacturers to clearly describe or reference requirements. A reference could be to a standard.

113. One comment stated that it is unclear whether the requirement for a signature to approve purchasing documents pertains to approval of the form used for purchasing or approval of the individual purchasing transaction. The comment also stated that a signature approval by transaction is not practical for firms using electronic document transmittals.

FDA has rewritten the requirement to be more clear. The requirement is for approval of purchasing data or information on the purchasing document used to purchase a product or service. Thus, each manufacturer must review and approve the purchasing data before release of the data. Approval of each purchasing transaction is not required. FDA addressed the use of electronic signatures in response to another comment, and notes that FDA is in the process of developing an agency-wide policy on the use of electronic signatures.

114. One comment stated that purchasing is carried out verbally in many small firms, without the use of component-specific purchasing forms, and that the regulation should be revised to allow such verbal purchasing to continue.

FDA disagrees with the comment. About 15 percent of the recalls each year are due to unacceptable purchased products. Many of these products are unacceptable because the finished device manufacturer did not properly describe the product. The requirements for purchased products and services must be documented to ensure that the supplier, contractor, and consultant provide a product or service which conforms to specified requirements. This requirement, and the goal it seeks to achieve, are applicable to both small and large companies.

115. One comment stated that the requirement that purchasing forms spell out the specifications for manufacturing materials in all cases is excessive, and that the need for specifications should be based on the criticality of and risk associated with the use of the specific manufacturing material.

FDA agrees that the specifications for many manufacturing materials may be so well established that the trade name of the product may be sufficient to describe the material needed. For other materials, specific written specifications may be necessary to ensure that the desired materials are received. The extent of the specification detail necessary to ensure that the product or service purchased meets requirements will be related to the nature of the product or service purchased, taking into account the effect the product or service may have on the safety or effectiveness of the finished device, among other factors. The term "specification" has been replaced with the term "specified requirements" to better reflect the intent of the requirement.

116. FDA has deleted the last two sentences of § 820.50(b) in the Working Draft and has replaced them with a reference to § 820.40, the general document control provision. This does not change the requirement but simply eliminates any confusion about the reviews and approvals being duplicative.

F. Identification and Traceability (Subpart F)

i. Identification (§ 820.60)

117. A few comments on proposed §§ 820.60 *Identification and traceability* and 820.65 *Critical device, traceability* stated that the two sections should be rewritten to delete the distinction between critical and noncritical devices. Some stated they should be consistent with ISO.

FDA agrees in part with the comments and has rewritten § 820.60 to be consistent with ISO 9001:1994 and broad enough to allow the manufacturer the flexibility needed to identify product by whatever means described by the required procedure. The term "critical device" has also been deleted, and traceability is addressed solely in § 820.65.

118. One comment stated that manufacturing materials should be deleted from § 820.60, as the requirements are excessive and not economically justifiable with regard to such materials.

FDA disagrees with the comment. The purpose of § 820.60 is to ensure that all products, including manufacturing materials used in the manufacture of a finished device, are properly identified. This requirement is intended to help prevent inadvertent use or release of unacceptable product into manufacturing. It is as important that the proper manufacturing materials be used as it is that the proper component be used.

119. A few comments thought that § 820.60 *Identification* in the Working Draft was redundant with § 820.86 *Acceptance status.*

FDA disagrees with the comments. Section 820.60 only requires that product be identified but says nothing about the acceptance status of that product. Section 820.86 requires that the acceptance status be identified so that inadvertent use of product does not occur. The manufacturer may choose to set up a system by which the identification required by § 820.60 can also show the acceptance status required by § 820.86, but this is up to the manufacturer.

ii. Traceability (§ 820.65)

120. A few comments stated that proposed § 820.65 *Critical devices, traceability* implies that traceability requirements exist for all devices. Several other written comments and oral testimony at the August and September 1995 meetings stated that the wording of the Working Draft was too broad, vague, and ambiguous, and in effect would require that all devices be traced.

As noted above, FDA has deleted the critical device terminology. Section 820.65 is now entitled *Traceability* and uses the definition from the original CGMP of a critical device to provide the necessary clarity and delineation for this requirement. Thus, traceability is required for the critical devices listed in the Federal Register notice of March 17, 1988 (53 FR 8854). However, FDA is using the definition of critical device in the requirement of § 820.65, rather than a reference to the 1988 list of critical devices, because that list has not been updated since 1988 and there are no plans to revise that list. Therefore, it is imperative that manufacturers use the definition within the requirement of § 820.65 to determine if a particular device needs to be traced; it may not be sufficient to rely solely on the 1988 list. Manufacturers may find it advantageous to provide unit, lot, or batch traceability for devices for which traceability is not a requirement to facilitate control and limit the number of devices that may need to be recalled due to defects or violations of the act.

It is important that the traceability requirements in part 820 are not confused with the Medical Device Tracking regulation in part 821 (21 CFR part 821). The *tracking regulation* is intended to ensure that tracked devices can be traced from the device manufacturing facility to the person for whom the device is indicated, that is,

the patient. Effective tracking of devices from the manufacturing facility, through the distribution network (including distributors, retailers, rental firms and other commercial enterprises, device user facilities, and licensed practitioners) and, ultimately, to any person for whom the device is intended is necessary for the effectiveness of remedies prescribed by the act, such as patient notification (section 518(a) of the act (21 U.S.C. 360h(a)) or device recall (section 518(e).) In contrast, the *traceability provision* requires that a device that meets the definition of a "critical device" can be traced from the manufacturing facility only to the "initial consignee" as discussed in § 820.160 *Distribution.*

121. Another comment on proposed § 820.65 stated that critical device component traceability could be interpreted to be required for almost all electronic components and other components in a critical device. The comment stated that the extent of component traceability should be left to the manufacturer's discretion, since it is an economic risk decision. Several comments stated that component traceability should only be required "where appropriate," that all "critical device" components do not require traceability to comply with the act.

FDA disagrees that the traceability determination should be based solely on economic risk. As noted in the preamble to the November 23, 1993, proposal (58 FR 61964), where traceability is important to prevent the distribution of devices that could seriously injure the user, traceability of components must be maintained so that potential and actual problem components can be traced back to the supplier. The revised requirement mandates traceability of components "where appropriate" as recommended by the GMP Advisory Committee and limited by the discussion in the scope, § 820.1(a)(3). The critical component definition in the original CGMP regulation may be used as guidance. However, to carry out the requirement of the revised provision, the manufacturer should perform risk analysis first on the finished device, and subsequently on the components of such device, to determine the need for traceability. FDA believes that the extent of traceability for both active and inactive implantable devices should include *all* components and materials used when such products could cause the medical device not to satisfy its specified requirements. ISO/CD 13485 also requires that the manufacturer's agents or distributors maintain records of distribution of medical devices with regard to traceability and that such

records be available for inspection. This requirement is found in § 820.160 *Distribution* of this regulation and is consistent with the requirements in § 820.151 of the original CGMP.

While FDA understands that traceability entails additional cost, the agency notes that, if a product recall is necessary, more devices would be subject to recall if units, lots, or batches of specific devices are not traceable, with associated higher recall costs to the manufacturer.

G. Production and Process Controls (Subpart G)

i. Production and Process Controls (§ 820.70)

122. A few comments stated that the requirements in proposed § 820.70(a) *General* are similar to those in ISO 9001, but that ISO 9001 makes clear that the requirements apply only "where applicable" and where deviations from device specifications would "directly affect quality." The comments suggested that FDA similarly employ such language to avoid being too restrictive and overly burdensome.

The requirements in § 820.70(a) are intended to ensure that each manufacturer produces devices that conform to their specifications. Thus, where any deviations from specifications could occur during manufacturing, the process control procedures must describe those controls necessary to ensure conformance. Those controls listed in the regulation may not always be relevant; similarly others may be necessary. For example, where deviations from device specifications could occur as a result of the absence of written production methods, procedures, and workmanship criteria, such production controls are required. Thus, FDA has retained the provision, but revised it slightly to conform with the original CGMP requirements in § 820.100(b)(1).

As noted, the process control requirements apply when any deviation from specifications could occur. FDA believes that such deviations must be controlled, and that linking the requirements to deviations that directly affect quality is inappropriate and subjective, and that it could lead to the manufacture of potentially dangerous devices through the lack of control of processes known to directly affect a device's specifications. Therefore, the provision has not been restricted in this manner. FDA has, however, revised the requirements to state "Where process controls are needed they shall include:" to make it clear that a manufacturer only has to comply with the requirements

R

stated in § 820.70 (a)(1) through (a)(5) if the general criteria described in § 820.70(a) have been met.

123. One comment stated that the second sentence of proposed § 820.70(a) was too restrictive, in that some processes can be accomplished by adequately trained personnel without the use of procedures.

FDA disagrees with the comment because the establishment of procedures is necessary to ensure consistency in manufacture. The procedures may be tailored under the requirement to cover only those controls necessary to ensure that a device meets its specifications. FDA notes that the deletion of the word "all" does not alter the requirements. The first sentence in the general requirement also serves to tie the production and process controls to the design and development phase where many of these controls are originally established in order for the device to conform to its design specifications.

In addition to these changes, FDA has added the requirement that production processes be "monitored" because a manufacturer must monitor a controlled process to ensure that the process remains in control.

124. FDA deleted the requirement for process controls related to "installation and servicing" from proposed § 820.70 (a)(1) and (a)(2) in response to comments. Such control is adequately assured by the requirements in §§ 820.170 *Installation* and 820.200 *Servicing*. FDA amended § 820.70(a)(3) in response to some comments that were confused about compliance with "applied reference standards." The term "applied" was replaced with "specified" to make it clear that the manufacturer must comply with reference standards or codes which he or she has specified in the DMR. FDA has also deleted "and process control procedures" because that requirement is inherent in § 820.70(a), "General." FDA amended § 820.70(a)(5) by adding "identified and approved" in response to comments and to clarify that the "representative samples" have to be identified and deemed appropriate before they are used as reference standards.

125. One comment believed that there is no longer a requirement that process changes be validated. Other comments on the Working Draft § 820.70(b) stated the requirement was still confusing with respect to "unless inspection and test fully verifies," and when the "approval" was to occur.

Revised § 820.70(b), "Production and process changes," addresses the requirement for production and process changes to be "verified or where appropriate validated according to § 820.75." This requirement for validation was moved from § 820.40(c), in revised form, to § 820.70. Verification was added to give the manufacturer the flexibility to verify changes that can be tested and inspected because FDA believes that validation is not always necessary. FDA has provided guidance on when changes should be validated in its "Guideline on General Principles of Process Validation." The agency notes that wherever changes may influence a validated process, the process must be revalidated as described in § 820.75. A few examples of processes that must be validated include sterilization, molding, and welding.

FDA has deleted the last part in § 820.70(b) of the Working Draft about approving changes and has replaced it with "Changes shall be approved in accordance with § 820.40." This does not change the requirement but simply refers back to § 820.40 because this requires the same review and approval. This was done to eliminate any confusion about the reviews and approvals being duplicative.

126. The EU Commission and others stated that environmental conditions only affect the quality of certain devices and that the requirements should, therefore, be limited in their application. Other comments stated that the requirements in proposed § 820.70(b), "Environmental control," were not consistent with the requirements in the original CGMP, § 820.46. Another comment requested that FDA delete the reference to "facilities" inspection and limit the requirement to review of the control system, as contained in the original CGMP regulation.

FDA has amended the requirements now in § 820.70(c) to apply only where environmental conditions could "reasonably be expected to have an adverse effect on product quality." The requirements for procedures to ensure control of conditions, periodic inspection of control systems, and documentation and review of results are similar to the original CGMP requirements. However, the specific list of conditions to be considered for control, which was carried over from the original CGMP regulation to the proposal, was deleted in response to a comment from the GHTF that the list would be better suited for a guidance document. FDA agrees that it is not necessary to give examples of conditions that may need controlling in a regulation, and notes that lighting, ventilation, temperature, humidity, air pressure, filtration, airborne contamination, and static electricity are among many conditions that should be considered for control.

FDA reworded the requirement to make it clear that the inspection must be of the control system. FDA also added that the inspection of the control system(s) shall include "any necessary equipment," e.g., pumps, filters, measurement equipment, etc. The sufficiency of facilities is covered in a new § 820.70(f), "Buildings," that requires that buildings be of suitable design and contain sufficient space to allow for the proper manufacture of devices. Section 820.70(f) is worded similarly to the original CGMP regulation § 820.40, and is intended to achieve the same objectives as that section.

127. One comment stated that the last sentence of proposed § 820.70(b), "Environmental control," should be deleted because it is redundant with the audits required in § 820.22(a). Another comment said that environmental conditions are currently reviewed via internal audit, which an FDA investigator cannot review.

FDA disagrees with the comments. The inspection and review of environmental control systems are routine quality assurance functions that are part of the production quality assurance program. The audits required by § 820.22(a) are audits of the quality system, conducted to ensure the adequacy of and conformance with the quality system requirements. The requirement to conduct a quality audit is in addition to other provisions in the regulation which require that a manufacturer review its specific controls to ensure the requirements are met. FDA may review the activities and results of environmental control system inspections.

128. The GHTF commented that the requirements of proposed § 820.70(c), "Cleaning and sanitation," should be placed in guidance.

After careful consideration, FDA agrees that a separate section on cleaning and sanitation is unnecessary. The objective of proposed § 820.70(c) is adequately met through the requirement of § 820.70(e), "Contamination control," and § 820.70(a), the general process control procedure requirement. Contamination control must include establishing and maintaining adequate cleaning procedures and schedules, if such control is necessary to meet manufacturing process specifications. In addition, § 820.25 *Personnel* requires that employees have a thorough understanding of their job functions, which would include a requirement that the appropriate employees comprehend the cleanliness and sanitation procedures.

129. The GHTF and others commented that the requirements of proposed § 820.70 (d)(1) through (d)(3) should be deleted and placed in guidance because they are redundant with the first sentence in proposed § 820.70(d), "Personnel health and cleanliness."

FDA agrees with the comments and has deleted § 820.70 (d)(1) through (d)(3). FDA has also rewritten the section, now entitled "Personnel," to require procedures to achieve the desired result, rather than dictate the means to achieve the result. The section as rewritten provides the manufacturer with more flexibility and is consistent with ISO/CD 13485. Under this section, a manufacturer's requirements must not permit unclean or inappropriately clothed employees, or employees with medical conditions, to work with devices where such conditions could reasonably be expected to have an adverse effect on product quality. The procedures must also address acceptable clothing, hygiene, and personal practices, if contact between personnel and product or environment could reasonably be expected to have an adverse effect on product quality.

FDA also added the requirement, from ISO/CD 13485, that personnel who are working temporarily (such as maintenance and cleaning personnel) under special environmental conditions (such as a clean room) be appropriately trained or supervised by someone trained to work in such an environment.

130. One comment stated that the requirements of § 820.70(e), "Contamination control," should be deleted and placed in guidance. Another comment stated that the reference to manufacturing materials should be deleted because it is redundant with § 820.70(g), "Equipment."

FDA has rewritten the section to delete the specific references to contaminants that probably gave rise to the suggestion that the section would be more appropriate as guidance. The section now contains a broad requirement for the establishment of procedures to prevent contamination of equipment or product by any substance that could reasonably be expected to have an adverse effect on product quality. Again, this revision adds flexibility.

FDA disagrees with the comment that manufacturing materials should be deleted from this section. Section 820.70(e) requires procedures to ensure that manufacturing materials do not become contaminated. Section

820.70(g), in contrast, establishes requirements related solely to the equipment used in the manufacturing process, and § 820.70(h), "Manufacturing material," addresses requirements for the removal or limitation of manufacturing materials. Thus, § 820.70 (g) and (h) are distinct and are intended to achieve different objectives.

131. The only two comments received on proposed § 820.70(f), "Sewage and refuse disposal," recommended that it be deleted because it was unnecessary and/or covered by other Federal regulations.

Section 820.70(f) has been deleted because the requirements are adequately covered in the current requirements under § 820.70(e), "Contamination control," and § 820.70(c), "Environmental control." Under these sections, sewage, trash, byproducts, chemical effluvium, and other refuse that could affect a device's safety, effectiveness, or fitness-for-use must be adequately controlled.

132. Two comments stated that the requirement related to equipment in § 820.70(g) should ensure that equipment meets "specified requirements," not be "adequate for its intended use," because intended use is determined during the design phase, and because it is easier to assess whether equipment meets specified requirements.

From these comments, FDA can see that the requirement should be revised because it may have been misinterpreted. The requirement is reworded as suggested. Under the requirement, the equipment must be appropriately designed to facilitate maintenance, adjustment, cleaning, and use. It must also meet the requirements that are necessary to ensure its proper functioning for the manufacture of the device.

133. A few comments stated that not all equipment requires maintenance, and the requirement for a maintenance schedule in § 820.70(g)(1) should be revised to make that clear. The GHTF recommended that the second sentence of proposed § 820.70(g)(1), which required that the maintenance schedule be posted or readily available, be deleted and placed in guidance.

FDA agrees that not all equipment may require maintenance and notes that the general requirement of § 820.70(a) requires process control procedures that describe only those controls which are necessary. Therefore, FDA did not revise the requirement.

FDA has deleted the requirement that the maintenance schedule be posted or readily available. Section 820.70(g),

which directs a manufacturer to ensure that equipment meets specified requirements, requires that the manufacturer ensure that maintenance is carried out on schedule to comply with the requirement. To satisfactorily meet this requirement, FDA expects that the schedule will be posted on or near the equipment to be maintained, or otherwise made readily available to appropriate personnel. Deletion of the requirement, however, permits the manufacturer added flexibility in complying with this section.

134. Several comments stated that § 820.70(g)(2), "Inspection," and (g)(3), "Adjustment," should be deleted and placed in guidance because the requirements are adequately covered in § 820.70(g)(1). Another comment stated that the requirement for limitations or tolerances to be "visibly posted on or near equipment" should be deleted.

FDA believes that to adequately ensure that equipment continues to meet its specifications, and to ensure that inherent limitations and allowable tolerances are known, these requirements are imperative. FDA notes inherent limitations and allowable tolerances must be visibly posted on or near equipment *or* made readily available to personnel to allow the manufacturer the flexibility to utilize any system to make sure that the limitations or tolerances are readily available to the personnel that need them. Both § 820.70(g)(2) and (g)(3) are requirements in the original CGMP regulation and the agency has found them to be useful and necessary.

135. One comment stated that requiring the removal of manufacturing material to be documented in proposed § 820.70(g)(4), "Manufacturing material," would result in impossible requirements, such as the requirement to document how much cutting oil is lost during a metal removing operation, such as drilling. Others commented that the requirement needs to be amended to clarify that only manufacturing materials that have an adverse effect or that are unwanted need to be removed or limited.

FDA disagrees with the first comment because § 820.70(g)(4) (now § 820.70(h)) only requires that the fact that manufacturing material was removed or reduced be documented, not how much was removed or how much was lost due to processing. This requirement is carried over from the original CGMP regulation, § 820.60(d). FDA has amended the section, however, to clarify that this requirement is necessary "Where a manufacturing material could reasonably be expected to have an adverse effect on product quality." FDA

R

purposefully qualifies the general requirement by that which adversely affects "*product quality*" (product as defined in § 820.3(r)) and limits the requirement for removal or reduction to "an amount that does not adversely affect the *device's quality*."

136. One comment on § 820.70(h), "Automated processes," (now § 820.70(i)), stated that the section should be revised to reflect that software used in such systems must be validated for "its intended use," not simply validated. Another comment stated that most companies buy software currently available on the market and do not make changes to the software. It was recommended that § 820.70(h) allow for use of outside personnel for validation runs and not necessarily require the development of a software validation procedure. One comment suggested that the section should allow verification rather than validation of off-the-shelf software. Several comments on "automated processes" stated that the term "data processing systems" was unclear and its inclusion rendered the requirement too broad. Others asked for clarification of "automated data processing systems."

FDA has modified the requirement to mandate validation for the intended use of the software. In addition, the requirement that the software be validated by individuals designated by the manufacturer has also been deleted to make clear that validation may be performed by those other than the manufacturer. However, whether the manufacturer designates its own personnel or relies on outside assistance to validate software, there must be an established procedure to ensure validation is carried out properly.

FDA has maintained the requirement for validation because the agency believes that it is necessary that software be validated to the extent possible to adequately ensure performance. Where source code and design specifications cannot be obtained, "black box testing" must be performed to confirm that the software meets the user's needs and its intended uses.

FDA emphasizes that manufacturers are responsible for the adequacy of the software used in their devices, and activities used to produce devices. When manufacturers purchase "off-the-shelf" software, they must ensure that it will perform as intended in its chosen application.

FDA has amended the requirement to state "When computers or automated data processing systems are used as part of production or the quality system," for clarification. Software used in

production or the quality system, whether it be in the designing, manufacturing, distributing, or tracing, must be validated.

ii. Inspection, Measuring, and Test Equipment (§ 820.72)

137. A few comments stated that it is unclear what is meant by the requirement in proposed § 820.84 *Inspection, measuring, and test equipment* that equipment be capable of producing "valid results." The comments stated that such equipment may be "suitable for its intended purpose" and still not always "produce valid results."

FDA believes that the term "valid results" is commonly understood and notes that it has been in the original CGMP regulation under § 820.61 for 18 years. The requirement is for the equipment to work properly, thereby providing "valid results."

FDA renumbered § 820.84 as § 820.72 in response to comments that stated these requirements were more appropriate under subpart G Production and Process Controls. FDA revised the requirement in new § 820.72(a), "Control of inspection, measuring, and test equipment," to make clear that the procedures must also ensure that the equipment is maintained and moved the requirement that the procedure include provisions for handling, preservation and storage of equipment from § 820.84(d) in the Working Draft to § 820.72(a). FDA deleted the term "test software" that was in § 820.84(e) because FDA believes that "test software" is now covered under "electronic inspection and test equipment" in § 820.72(a).

138. A few comments stated that the last sentence in proposed § 820.84(a), "Calibration," is unnecessary because the requirement for trained personnel is redundant with § 820.25(a) *Personnel*. A few comments stated that FDA should identify what must be remedied in proposed § 820.84(a).

FDA agrees that the requirement for trained personnel is redundant and has deleted this sentence from § 820.72(b), "Calibration." FDA has also added to this section the requirement that the calibration procedure include provisions for remedial action to "reestablish the limits and to evaluate whether there was any adverse effect on the device's quality" to clarify this remedial action requirement and its relationship to the requirements in § 820.100 *Corrective and preventive action.*

139. Several comments stated that § 820.84(b), "Calibration standards,"

should allow for the use of international standards.

FDA agrees and has rewritten the section, now § 820.72(b)(1), "Calibration standards," to allow the use of international standards. The standards used must be generally accepted by qualified experts as the prevailing standards.

140. FDA has deleted the requirement in proposed § 820.84(c), now § 820.72(b)(2), "Calibration records," that calibration records be "maintained by individuals designated by the manufacturer" because, on further reflection, the agency believes such a requirement is unnecessary. As long as the required procedures and records are maintained and displayed or readily available as required, the objective of the section, ensuring that calibration is performed and acceptable, will be met. FDA did add "equipment identification" to the list of items that had to be documented in response to a comment that requested clarification in this regard, so that equipment is clearly identified in the calibration records even if the records are not displayed on or near the particular piece of equipment.

141. Two comments suggested deleting proposed § 820.84(d) because they believed it was unnecessary to establish procedures to maintain equipment, because most manufacturers simply store equipment in protective covers.

As already noted, FDA has moved the requirement for establishing maintenance procedures into the general requirement in § 820.72. FDA has retained the requirement because some equipment requires special handling, preservation, and storage. For example, the temperature and humidity of a room may affect the equipment and procedures would need to be established taking those factors into account.

142. Several comments stated that proposed § 820.84(e), "Facilities," should be deleted because it is redundant with the requirements under § 820.70(g) and the general requirements of proposed § 820.84(a).

FDA agrees that revised § 820.84(a), which is now § 820.72(a), would require procedures to ensure that equipment is protected from adjustments that could invalidate the calibration, in that the section requires procedures to ensure that equipment is properly maintained. The procedures that require equipment to be routinely calibrated, inspected, and checked, will also ensure that improperly calibrated equipment is not used. Therefore, FDA has deleted proposed § 820.84(e).

iii. Process Validation (§ 820.75)

143. A few comments on proposed § 820.75 *Special processes* stated that the meaning of the term "special processes" was unclear. Other comments stated that FDA should provide examples of processes that would be considered "special processes." Several comments stated the term "fully verified" was unclear and should be deleted.

In response to the comments, the term "special processes" has been dropped from the regulation and the term "process validation" is defined in § 820.3(z)(1). The section now requires that when a process "cannot be fully verified by subsequent inspection and test, the process shall be validated with a high degree of assurance. * * *" Examples of such processes include sterilization, aseptic processing, injection molding, and welding, among others. The validation method must ensure that predetermined specifications are consistently met. The new § 820.75, entitled "Process validation," is consistent with ISO 9001:1994, section 4.9, including the terminology "fully verified." FDA does not believe this terminology is unclear since it has been used in ISO 9001:1987 and 1994 and explained in several guidance documents.

FDA amended this section by removing the requirement for the signature of the individual(s) performing the process and placing the signature requirement on the approval of the validation where FDA believes it is more important and appropriate. FDA also added that "where appropriate, the major equipment validated" must be documented. Depending on the process that is validated, it may be necessary to document the person performing the process or the equipment or both in order to have adequate controls on the process.

144. Several comments were received on proposed § 820.75(a)(1) through (a)(4) that stated that the requirements were redundant with other parts of the regulation and should be modified or deleted.

FDA disagrees with the comments and believes that, due to the importance of process validation and correct performance of the validated process, the requirements are necessary. The requirements have been rearranged in the revised section.

145. Comments on the first sentence of proposed § 820.75(b) stated that it was unclear and unrealistic. Other comments stated that the requirement for continuous monitoring is not practical or necessary.

In response to the comments, FDA has revised the requirements. Section 820.75(b) applies to the performance of a process *after* the process has been validated. In contrast, § 820.75(a) relates to the initial validation of the process. FDA deleted the term "continuous" because the agency concurs that monitoring can be accomplished at a determined interval and frequency depending on the type of validated process being monitored and controlled. FDA notes that the interval and frequency should be periodically evaluated for adequacy, especially during any evaluation or revalidation that occurs in accordance with the requirements in new § 820.75(c).

New § 820.75(b)(1), which was proposed § 820.75(c) of the Working Draft, requires that validated processes be performed by a qualified individual(s). FDA notes that § 820.75(b)(1) is similar to the requirements under § 820.25 *Personnel* but emphasizes that validated processes must not only be performed by personnel with the necessary education, background, training, and experience for their general jobs but must be performed by personnel qualified for those particular functions. Revised § 820.75(b)(2), which was proposed § 820.75(d) of the Working Draft, contains the amended documentation requirements for validated processes, to include the monitoring and control methods and data. FDA notes that it is always "appropriate" to document the equipment used in the process where the manufacturer uses different equipment on different manufacturing lines. To investigate a problem with the device, the manufacturer will need to know which equipment was used, since the problem could be with the equipment itself. The same holds true for the individual(s) performing the process.

Section 820.75(c) contains requirements on process revalidation in response to several comments and concerns on when revalidation activities were necessary. FDA believes that the new arrangement of § 820.75 should clarify the requirement.

H. Acceptance Activities (Subpart H)

i. Receiving, In-Process, and Finished Device Acceptance (§ 820.80)

146. One comment stated that the emphasis on testing and inspection in proposed § 820.80 completely ignores the quality goals, the benefit of requiring purchasing controls, and statements made in the preamble of the proposal reflecting FDA's negative opinion about manufacturers relying solely on testing

and inspection. A few comments on the Working Draft stated that "acceptance activities" should be defined as inspections, tests, or other verification activities so that the regulation does not require all of these activities but gives the manufacturer the flexibility to choose the appropriate method.

FDA agrees with the comments and has replaced the term "inspection and test" with "acceptance activities" in § 820.80. Further, FDA now defines "acceptance activities" to include inspections, test, or other verification activities, such as supplier audits.

147. One comment stated that recordkeeping is a significant cost factor in the operation of a total quality system, and that the revised CGMP regulation should not add cost through duplication of documentation. The comment said recording all quantitative data is inappropriate and of little value.

FDA agrees that unnecessary duplication of documentation should be avoided. FDA believes that the quality system regulation requires the minimum documentation necessary to ensure that safe and effective devices are designed and produced. FDA similarly believes that maintaining records of results of acceptance activities is imperative to ensure that nonconforming product is not inadvertently used or distributed. FDA has, however, deleted from § 820.80(a) the requirement for recording the results of inspections and testing because § 820.80(e) requires that the results of acceptance activities be recorded. The requirement in § 820.80(a) was therefore unnecessary. Further, the regulation does not specify quantitative data but simply requires that the results be recorded. FDA believes that it is essential for the manufacturer to maintain records which provide evidence that the product has gone through the defined acceptance activities. These records must clearly show whether the product has passed or failed the acceptance activities according to the defined acceptance criteria. Where product fails to pass acceptance activities, the procedures for control of nonconforming product must be implemented, to include investigations where defined. If the acceptance records are not clear about how the product failed, then the manufacturer may end up duplicating the acceptance activities in order to perform appropriate investigations.

148. Several comments stated that proposed § 820.80(b), "Receiving inspection and testing," did not allow for urgent use of incoming items. The comments said that urgent use should be permitted if forward traceability is maintained so that recall and

R

replacement is possible if the material is subsequently found to be nonconforming. One comment stated that the requirements in proposed § 820.80(b) were too specific and did not allow flexibility.

FDA agrees in part with the comments. FDA has permitted manufacturers to use incoming items that had not yet been proven acceptable for use, provided that the manufacturer maintained control of the unapproved items and could retrieve the product that contained the unapproved items *before* distribution. Therefore, the requirement that product "shall not be used or processed until * * * verified" has been deleted from § 820.80(b), now entitled "Receiving acceptance activities." However, FDA emphasizes that while the product can be used in production prior to verification, it *cannot* be distributed prior to verification. FDA does not permit the distribution of unapproved product through an urgent use provision, because all finished devices must comply with § 820.80(d), "Final acceptance activities," before they are released for distribution.

In addition to the changes noted above, FDA has deleted the requirement that "individual(s) designated by the manufacturer shall accept or reject incoming" product. FDA does not believe this requirement is necessary in § 820.80(b) because § 820.80(e) requires that the identification of the individual(s) conducting the acceptance activities be recorded.

149. Several comments stated that an absolute requirement under proposed § 820.80(c), "In-process inspection and testing," for in-process testing was inconsistent with the preamble, which stated that an appropriate mix of controls should be established. Other comments stated that in-process inspection and testing is unnecessary if the process is validated and the devices are subject to final inspection. A few comments on the Working Draft stated that the term "held" was too restrictive and was not consistent with the requirements and the preamble discussion for § 820.80(b).

FDA agrees with the comments in part, but believes that § 820.80 as now written, with the inclusion of "where appropriate," does not mandate in-process inspection and testing. FDA acknowledges that in-process acceptance activities may not be necessary or possible for every device, for example, medical socks. Further, the requirement states that in-process product must be *controlled* until the required inspection and test, or other verification activities, have been

performed. This will permit manufacturers to use, under defined conditions and procedures, product that has not *completed* the acceptance activities described in § 820.80(b) and (c). This does not means that manufacturers can ignore the requirements in § 820.80(b) and (c) because these requirements must be completed in order to comply with § 820.80(d), which must be satisfied before devices are released for distribution.

150. FDA received a similar comment on proposed § 820.80(d), "Final inspection and test," which said that the provision requires finished device inspection for all devices, without defining what inspection is expected. The comment suggested that § 820.80(d) could be interpreted to require actual product inspection, which has been shown to be ineffective as a means of controlling product quality. One comment stated that signatures should not be the only approved method for identification of the individual(s) responsible for release. The comment stated that use of inspection stamps and initials should be allowed.

FDA has rewritten § 820.80(d) to require that manufacturers establish and maintain procedures for finished device acceptance to ensure that each production run, lot, or batch of finished devices meets specified requirements. Manufacturers have the flexibility to choose a combination of methods, including finished device inspection and test, provided such methods will accomplish the required result.

FDA believes that it is important for the person responsible for release to have personally documented and dated that release. This can be accomplished through use of an inspection stamp, if the stamp is controlled as discussed above under § 820.40 *Document controls.* Therefore, FDA has retained the requirement for a signature.

151. Several comments on proposed § 820.80(e), "Inspection and test records," stated that manufacturers should not be required to record the use of general equipment in inspection and test records, because this requirement would be burdensome to large manufacturers who use many common pieces of equipment. A few comments stated that the record requirements under § 820.80(e) are overly prescriptive and go well beyond ISO 9001's comparable requirements. The comments stated that recordkeeping should be specified by the manufacturer in the spirit of ISO 9001, and should include only the minimum records necessary to show that finished device

inspections are performed in accordance with established procedures.

FDA agrees that it may not be necessary to document every piece of equipment used in acceptance activities. The requirement, renamed "Acceptance records," now provides that equipment used shall be documented "where appropriate." For some critical operations and testing, identification of the equipment used will be imperative for proper investigations into nonconforming product.

The requirements, as revised, are similar to those in ISO 9001:1994. As discussed above, certain information must be captured on acceptance records for the records to be useful in evaluating nonconformance. Through many years of experience, FDA has determined what it believes to be a minimum requirement for these records. Section 820.80(e) reflects that determination.

ii. Acceptance Status (§ 820.86)

152. Several comments on proposed § 820.86, "Inspection and test status," stated that the section was not flexible enough to allow identification of the inspection and test status of product by various means, because the requirement was for the status to be "visible." One comment questioned why "component acceptance" was addressed separately.

FDA agrees that the inspection and test status may be identified by any method that will achieve the result, which might include acceptable computerized identification, markings, etc. The section has been rewritten to reflect this intent, has been renamed "Acceptance status," and is now consistent with ISO 9001:1994. FDA also agrees that "component acceptance" is covered by "manufacturing" and has deleted the term.

153. FDA has deleted proposed § 820.86(b) which required that records identify those responsible for release of the product, because the agency believes that the records required by § 820.80(e) will identify those responsible for release of product.

I. Nonconforming Product (Subpart I)

154. FDA has rewritten § 820.90 *Nonconforming product* to utilize the term "product" throughout, as defined in § 820.3(r), for both shorthand purposes and consistency with ISO 9001:1994.

155. One comment suggested deleting the term "inadvertently" and adding the word "distributed" before "installed" in § 820.90(a). Several written comments and persons who testified at the August and September 1995 meetings stated that § 820.90(a) should be written so

that it is not interpreted to require investigations for every nonconformance. A few comments stated that the term "provide for" was too broad and unclear. Other comments stated that the requirement to "ensure" nonconforming product was "not used or distributed" was inconsistent with the provisions in § 820.90(b) which allowed for concessions under certain circumstances. One comment stated that the requirement that persons responsible for nonconforming product be "notified" should be deleted because it is overly burdensome and not needed in all cases.

FDA has reworded the general requirement for procedures to control nonconforming product and has deleted the term "inadvertently." FDA has also added the requirement that the procedures provide for the "evaluation" of nonconforming product because evaluation is key to protecting against recurring nonconformance. The addition is consistent with ISO 9001:1994.

FDA has further revised § 820.90 in response to the comments on the Working Draft. First, the manufacturer must establish procedures to "control" nonconforming product. Second, the procedures shall "*address* the identification, documentation, evaluation, segregation, and disposition of nonconforming product," which gives the manufacturers the flexibility to define how they are going to "control" products that are nonconforming. Third, the evaluation process addressed in the procedure "shall include a determination of the need for an investigation." Therefore, the procedures will need to set forth the manufacturer's SOP on when investigations will take place and provisions for trending and/or monitoring the situation in the future. Fourth, FDA added "The evaluation and any investigation shall be documented," which would include the explanations for not performing investigations and how nonconformances will be trended and/or monitored. Further, the phrase "is not used or distributed" has been deleted to be consistent with § 820.90(b).

FDA disagrees that the notification requirement should be deleted. Where some person or organization is responsible for nonconformances, they must be notified to ensure that future nonconformances are prevented. This requirement is also in ISO 9001:1994, section 4.13.1.

156. FDA has rewritten § 820.90(b)(1), "Nonconformity review and disposition," to make clear that the section requires procedures that define

the responsibility for review and authority for disposition of nonconforming product and that set forth the review and disposition process. FDA believes that proper disposition of nonconforming product is essential for ensuring the safety and effectiveness of devices. Manufacturers have made determinations that nonconforming product may be used which have resulted in defective devices being distributed. Thus, although it may be appropriate at times to use nonconforming products, the disposition process must be adequately controlled.

The revision requires that disposition and justification for concessions be documented. FDA believes that the justification should be based on scientific evidence, which a manufacturer should be prepared to provide upon request. Concessions should be closely monitored and not become accepted practice. This section is consistent with ISO 9001:1994, section 4.13.2.

Several comments on the Working Draft stated that the term "concession" should be deleted because it is confusing. FDA has rewritten the sentence to ensure the meaning of this requirement is clear. The sentence now reads, "Documentation shall include the justification for the use of nonconforming product and the signature of the individual(s) authorizing the use."

157. Several comments were received on proposed § 820.90(b)(2). One comment stated that the requirement should allow for other types of disposition besides reprocessing. One comment suggested replacing the term "reinspection" with "evaluation," to allow for greater flexibility in verification methods. Many comments suggested that the requirement for identification of reprocessed product should be deleted because they believed it would cause the consumer to forego purchasing the product. Several comments requested that the term "rework" be used instead of "reprocessing" to harmonize terminology with ISO standards.

FDA agrees in part with the comments. FDA, as noted in the definition section, has substituted the term "rework" and the ISO 8402:1994 definition for the term "reprocessing" in response to the comments. FDA believes that the revised § 820.90(b)(1) clearly allows for other methods of disposition besides rework. Section 820.90(b)(2), which governs rework when it is chosen as a method of disposition, has been revised as requested by replacing the term "reinspection" with

"reevaluation." The change will allow manufacturers the flexibility to inspect or use other verification activities.

FDA has also deleted the requirement for identification of reworked product from this section because FDA believes that it is adequately covered in §§ 820.60 *Identification* and 820.86 *Acceptance status*.

Other minor changes made to the section include requiring that a determination of any adverse effect of the rework upon the product be made, whether there is "repeated" rework or not. FDA's intent is that such a determination be made with any rework, given the potential harmful effect rework could have on the product. The change harmonizes § 820.90 with ISO/CD 13485. In addition, the sentence requiring a "complete reinspection" for reworked product was deleted because the section already requires retesting and reevaluation of reworked product. FDA has also substituted "current" for "original or subsequently modified" approved specifications for clarity. The requirements as written are consistent with the original CGMP requirements in §§ 820.115 and 820.116.

J. Corrective and Preventive Action (Subpart J)

158. A few comments suggested revising proposed § 820.100 *Corrective and preventive action* to require procedures for implementing corrective and preventive action, consistent with ISO 9001. One comment stated that the procedures should provide for an initial halt of distribution of suspect products or tight control and action concerning products already distributed before taking the long term action listed in this section.

FDA agrees that it is essential that the manufacturer establish procedures for implementing corrective and preventive action and has revised § 820.100(a) accordingly. The procedures must include provisions for the remaining requirements in the section. These procedures must provide for control and action to be taken on devices distributed, and those not yet distributed, that are suspected of having potential nonconformities.

159. Other comments stated that the degree of remedial action should be commensurate with the risk associated with a product failure.

FDA agrees that the degree of corrective and preventive action taken to eliminate or minimize actual or potential nonconformities must be appropriate to the magnitude of the problem and commensurate with the risks encountered. FDA cannot dictate in a regulation the degree of action that

R

should be taken because each circumstance will be different, but FDA does expect the manufacturer to develop procedures for assessing the risk, the actions that need to be taken for different levels of risk, and how to correct or prevent the problem from recurring, depending on that risk assessment.

FDA emphasizes that any death, even if the manufacturer attributes it to user error, will be considered relevant by FDA and will have a high risk potentially associated with it. User error is still considered to be a nonconformity because human factors and other similar tools should have been considered during the design phase of the device. FDA acknowledges that a manufacturer cannot possibly foresee every single potential misuse during the design of a device, but when the manufacturer becomes aware of misuse, the corrective and preventive action requirements should be implemented to determine if redesign of the device or labeling changes may be necessary.

160. Several comments on proposed § 820.100(a)(1) stated that requiring a manufacturer to analyze "all" processes, work operations, and other factors listed, is excessive and unrealistic. Some comments stated that there should not be a requirement to conduct an analysis for "potential causes" of nonconformances. A few comments stated that including "quality audits" in the list was inconsistent with the FDA policy of not reviewing internal audits. A few comments stated that the requirement that the analysis include "trend analysis" should be modified because it places unnecessary emphasis on only one statistical method or tool. Other comments stated that statistical tools are not always necessary and that the requirement should be modified.

FDA agrees in part with the comments. It was not FDA's intent to require that processes unrelated to an existing nonconformity be analyzed. Instead, § 820.100(a)(1) requires an analysis of those items listed that could be related to the problem. To prevent confusion, the word "all" has been deleted. The requirement is similar to that of ISO 9001:1994, section 4.14.3(a).

The inclusion of "quality audits" as a valuable feedback mechanism for the manufacturer does not conflict with FDA's policy of not reviewing internal quality audits. Internal audits are valuable and necessary tools for the manufacturer to evaluate the quality system. The audit reports should be used to analyze the entire quality system and provide feedback into the system to close the feedback loop, so that corrective or preventive actions can

be taken where necessary. FDA will review the corrective and preventive action procedures and activities performed in conformance with those procedures without reviewing the internal audit reports. FDA wants to make it clear that corrective and preventive actions, to include the documentation of these activities, which result from internal audits and management reviews are not covered under § 820.180(c).

FDA has further revised the requirement to delete the reference to trend analysis in response to the comments. The provision now requires that "appropriate statistical methodology" be employed where necessary to detect recurring quality problems. This revision is made because there may be other statistical tools available beyond "trend analysis." FDA emphasizes that the *appropriate* statistical tools must be employed when it is necessary to utilize statistical methodology. FDA has seen far too often the misuse of statistics by manufacturers in an effort to minimize instead of address the problem. Such misuse of statistics would be a violation of this section.

FDA has retained the requirement for analysis to identify "potential causes of nonconforming product," however, because FDA believes this is an important aspect of preventive action. FDA notes that ISO 9001:1994, section 4.14.1, specifically acknowledges that corrective and preventive actions are associated with actual and *potential* nonconformities.

161. Several comments stated that proposed § 820.100(a)(2) was redundant with requirements in § 820.198 *Complaints*.

FDA agrees in part with the comments and has written the section to require investigation of the cause of nonconformities relating to process, product, and the quality system, consistent with ISO 9001:1994, section 4.14.2(b). The requirement in this section is broader than the requirement for investigations under § 820.198, because it requires that nonconforming product discovered before or after distribution be investigated to the degree commensurate with the significance and risk of the nonconformity. At times a very indepth investigation will be necessary, while at other times a simple investigation, followed by trend analysis or other appropriate tools will be acceptable. In addition, in contrast to § 820.198, the requirement in this section applies to process and quality system nonconformities, as well as product nonconformities. For example, if a

molding process with its known capabilities has a normal 5 percent rejection rate and that rate rises to 10 percent, an investigation into the nonconformance of the process must be performed.

162. One comment stated that proposed § 820.100(a)(3) should not require identification of action necessary to correct "other quality problems." Another stated that the section should be harmonized with ISO. One comment thought that the requirement should be to identify action to correct problems identified by "trend analysis."

FDA agrees that harmonization is important and has harmonized the terminology (and intent) of the section with ISO 9001:1994, sections 4.14.2(c) and 4.14.3(b). However, FDA disagrees that the section should not require identification of action necessary to correct "other quality problems" because the objective of § 820.100 is to correct and prevent poor practices, not simply bad product. Correction and prevention of unacceptable quality system practices should result in fewer nonconformities related to product. Therefore, this section addresses problems within the quality system itself. For example, it should identify and correct improper personnel training, the failure to follow procedures, and inadequate procedures, among other things.

FDA also disagrees with the suggestion to link the requirement in § 820.100(a)(3) to trend analysis and has deleted the reference to trend analysis in § 820.100(a)(1) to give the manufacturer the flexibility to use whatever method of analysis is appropriate.

163. FDA has revised § 820.100(a)(4) to reflect that preventive, as well as corrective, action must be verified or validated. The section is now consistent with ISO 9001:1994, sections 4.14.2(d) and 4.14.3(c). Two comments stated that the definitions of validation and verification cause confusion here, but FDA believes that these concerns should be resolved with the amended definitions under § 820.3 (z) and (aa).

164. FDA has also revised § 820.100(a)(5) in the same manner, to relate the requirements to preventive action. This section is consistent with ISO 9001:1994, section 4.14.1, third paragraph.

165. One comment suggested that proposed § 820.100(a)(6) be revised to reflect that minor quality problems may not need to be disseminated to those directly responsible for ensuring quality and to be reviewed by management.

FDA agrees in part with this comment. The revised § 820.100 (a)(6) and (a)(7) require that procedures ensure that information is disseminated to those directly responsible for assuring quality or the prevention of such problems, and provide for submitting relevant information on identified quality problems, as well as corrective and preventive actions, for management review. This revision should address the concern raised by the comment because only certain information need be directed to management. The manufacturer's procedures should clearly define the criteria to be followed to determine what information will be considered "relevant" to the action taken and why. FDA emphasizes that it is always management's responsibility to ensure that all nonconformity issues are handled appropriately. This section is now consistent with ISO 9001:1994, section 4.14.3(d).

166. Two comments stated that the records required under § 820.100(b) should be treated as part of the internal audit.

FDA disagrees with these comments because this information is directly relevant to the safety and effectiveness of finished medical devices. FDA has the authority to review such records and the obligation to do so to protect the public health. Comparable information and documentation is reviewed by the FDA under the requirements of the original CGMP, §§ 820.20 (a)(3) and (a)(4) and 820.162. Manufacturers will be required to make this information readily available to an FDA investigator, so that the investigator may properly assess the manufacturer's compliance with these quality system requirements.

K. Labeling and Packaging Control (Subpart K)

i. Device Labeling (§ 820.120)

167. Several comments on proposed § 820.162 *Device labeling* stated that the section should be deleted and placed in guidance because it is unnecessary and redundant with requirements under §§ 820.80 and 820.86. A few comments stated that the section should be changed to be the same as that in the original CGMP regulation, under §§ 820.120 and 820.121. Another comment stated that labeling and packaging requirements should be in subpart K of part 820 and handling, storage, distribution, and installation requirements should be in subpart L of part 820 because labeling and packaging functionally occur before distribution and installation.

FDA believes that the section, as written, is consistent with the

requirements in the original CGMP. Section 820.120 relates specifically to labeling and its requirements are in addition to those in both §§ 820.80 and 820.86. Further, FDA believes that the degree of detail in this section is necessary because these same requirements have been in place for 18 years, yet numerous recalls every year are the result of labeling errors or mixups. FDA therefore believes that more, not less, control is necessary.

FDA has reordered the subparts but notes that the handling and storage requirements apply throughout the production process.

168. One comment stated that "to maintain labeling integrity and to prevent labeling mixups" should be deleted from the general requirement because the requirements are detailed in the following sections. Other comments stated that all labels need not be affixed to the device and others stated that "legible and affixed" may not be appropriate for all implantable devices.

FDA agrees with the comments and has revised the requirements accordingly.

169. A few comments stated that what is now § 820.120(b), "Labeling inspections," should allow automated readers to be used in place of a "designated individual(s)" to examine the labeling.

FDA disagrees with the comments because several recalls on labeling have been attributed to automated readers not catching errors. The requirement does not preclude manufacturers from using automated readers where that process is followed by human oversight. A "designated individual" must examine, at a minimum, a representative sampling of all labels that have been checked by the automated readers. Further, automated readers are often programmed with only the base label and do not check specifics, such as control numbers and expiration dates, among other things, that are distinct for each label. The regulation requires that labeling be inspected for these items prior to release.

170. FDA has amended § 820.120(b) to add "any" to additional processing instructions in response to a comment for clarity. FDA has amended § 820.120(d) to include "The label and labeling used for each production unit, lot, or batch shall be documented in the DHR" in response to comments questioning whether the labeling used should be recorded in the DMR or the DHR. FDA also amended § 820.120(e) by adding "or shall accompany the device through distribution" and deleting "itself or its label" for clarity.

171. A few comments on proposed § 820.165 *Critical devices, labeling* stated that this section should be deleted to eliminate any distinction between critical and noncritical devices.

FDA agrees in part and has deleted § 820.165, but has added the requirement on control numbers to § 820.120(e).

ii. Device Packaging (§ 820.130)

172. Two comments on proposed § 820.160 *Device packaging* stated that the section should be changed to allow manufacturers to use third parties, if desired, for packaging. Another comment stated that it is very difficult if not impossible to protect from intentional damage, such as tampering.

FDA agrees with the comments and has changed the requirement, now in § 820.130, accordingly. FDA believes, however, that any intentional tampering would not be covered because the requirement states "during customary conditions."

L. Handling, Storage, Distribution, and Installation (Subpart L)

i. Handling (§ 820.140)

173. One comment on proposed § 820.120 *Handling* suggested that the procedures be "designed to prevent," rather than be established to "ensure that," problems delineated in the section do not occur. The comment stated that the word "prevent" would add clarity, without compromising the meaning of the sentence. Another comment stated that the handling procedures should apply "prior to distribution," not during "any stage of handling." One comment stated that the requirement does not cover the need for special precautions in handling used devices which may be contaminated, and that this is an important issue covered by ISO/CD 13485.

FDA does not believe that § 820.120, now § 820.140, as written is unclear. The procedures are expected to ensure that mixups, damage, deterioration, contamination, or other adverse effects do not occur. FDA amended the requirement, however, to remove "any stage of" so it reads "during handling." The requirement continues to apply to all stages of handling in which a manufacturer is involved, which may in some cases go beyond initial distribution.

The comparable provision in ISO/CD 13485 states, "If appropriate, special provisions shall be established, documented and maintained for the handling of used product in order to prevent contamination of other product, the manufacturing environment and personnel." FDA agrees with this requirement and has therefore added the term "contamination" to §§ 820.140 *Handling* and 820.150 *Storage*.

ii. Storage (§ 820.150)

174. Two comments stated that proposed § 820.122 *Storage* should be amended to be similar to ISO 9001, and that the rest of the requirements should be deleted and included in a guidance document. One comment stated that the term "obsolete" should be deleted because, although a device may no longer be sold, thereby making it obsolete, the components for that device may still be stored for customer support of the existing devices.

FDA agrees that § 820.122, now § 820.150, could be more consistent with ISO 9001 and has revised the section to harmonize with ISO 9001:1994. FDA has not deleted the term "obsolete." FDA understands that a device may no longer be sold, but that parts and subassemblies may still be required for customer support; therefore, those components or subassemblies are not "obsolete." FDA's intent in this requirement is to ensure that only the appropriate product be used or distributed.

FDA has deleted the requirement that control numbers or identifications be legible and visible because it believes the requirement is inherent in § 820.150(a), which requires the manufacturer to establish procedures to prevent mixups. To do this, a manufacturer must ensure that product can be properly identified.

175. A comment stated that restricting access to designated areas through the use of keys, bar code readers, or other means, should be sufficient to meet the intent of the requirement in proposed § 820.122(b), without the need for written procedures for authorizing receipt.

FDA has not deleted the requirement for procedures, now in § 820.150(b), to authorize receipt of product because the agency believes that strict control over product in storage areas and stock rooms results in decreased distribution of nonconforming product. Thus, even where locked storage rooms are utilized, the procedures should detail, among other things, who is permitted access and what steps should be followed prior to removal.

iii. Distribution (§ 820.160)

176. A few comments on proposed § 820.124 *Distribution* stated that there are times when "first in, first out" inventory procedures may not be in the best interest of the customer. The comments said that especially when

expiration dating is defined and labeled, a "first in, first out" system should not be required. The GHTF and other EU comments stated that if a new section "Contract review," similar to ISO 9001:1994, section 4.3 was not added to the regulation, the requirement that "purchase orders are reviewed to ensure that ambiguities and errors are resolved before devices are released for distribution" should be added to this section.

FDA agrees with the comments. FDA has amended the requirement in § 820.160 to state that the procedures must ensure that "expired devices or devices deteriorated beyond acceptable fitness for use" are not distributed. FDA has also added the sentence on reviewing purchase orders.

177. A few comments on proposed § 820.124(b) stated that class I devices should be exempt, or that the requirement should apply only to critical devices, because all devices do not require control numbers. Other comments stated that the term "consignee" should be defined, or the word "primary" should be added before "consignee" for clarity.

FDA agrees in part with the comments and in § 820.160(b) has added the term "initial" before "consignee" to make clear that the requirement for maintaining distribution records extends to the first consignee. FDA has retained the word "consignee" and notes that it is a person to whom the goods are delivered. FDA has also clarified § 820.160(b)(4) by requiring "Any control number(s) used." Therefore, if the manufacturer is required by § 820.65 to have control numbers, these must be recorded along with any control numbers voluntarily used. Logically, control numbers are used for traceability so they should be recorded in the DHR distribution records. FDA disagrees, however, that the requirement to maintain distribution records should not apply to class I devices. The information required by this section is basic information needed for any class of product in order to conduct recalls or other corrective actions when necessary.

iv. Installation (§ 820.170)

178. Several comments received on proposed § 820.126, *Installation* stated that not all devices require installation. Several comments on the Working Draft asked that, "The results of the installation inspection shall be made available to FDA upon request" be deleted because this was redundant with FDA's access to these documents under § 820.180.

FDA agrees with the first set of comments. As discussed in § 820.1, the installation requirements only apply to devices that are capable of being installed. However, to further clarify the requirements in § 820.170, FDA has made clear that the requirement applies to "devices requiring installation." FDA also agrees that the sentence on document availability is redundant with § 820.180 for all records and has deleted the sentence.

179. Several comments raised the issue of applying the regulation requirements to third party installers.

FDA has rewritten § 820.170. Persons who install medical devices have been regulated under the original CGMP under § 820.3(k) which describes a manufacturer as one who "assembles or processes a finished medical device," and continue to be regulated under this quality system regulation under § 820.3(o). Section 820.152 *Installation* of the original CGMP discussed the manufacturer or its authorized representative and persons other than the manufacturer's representative. This regulation eliminates that terminology. Under the revised requirement in § 820.170(a), the manufacturer establishes installation and inspection instructions, and where appropriate test procedures. The manufacturer distributes the instructions and procedures with the device or makes them available to person(s) installing the device. Section 820.170(b) requires that the person(s) installing the device follow the instructions and procedures described in § 820.170(a) and document the activities described in the procedures and instructions to demonstrate proper installation.

The revised provisions in § 820.170(b) explicitly require that the installation be performed according to the manufacturer's instructions, regardless of whether the installer is employed by or otherwise affiliated with the manufacturer. Section 820.170(b) requires records to be kept by whomever performs the installation to establish that the installation was performed according to the procedures. Such records will be available for FDA inspection. FDA does not expect the manufacturer of the finished device to maintain records of installation performed by those installers not affiliated with the manufacturer, but does expect the third party installer or the user of the device to maintain such records.

FDA believes that making these requirements explicit in the regulation is necessary to ensure that devices are safe and effective, and that they perform as intended after installation. FDA notes again that installers are considered to be manufacturers under the original CGMP regulation and that their records are, and will continue to be, subject to FDA inspections when the agency deems it necessary to review such records.

M. Records (Subpart M)

i. General Requirements (§ 820.180)

180. Several comments under § 820.180 *General requirements* suggested that FDA delete the requirement that records be stored to allow "rapid retrieval" because a reasonable time frame should be allowed. One comment stated that the wording of the section needed to be amended to allow records to be located in different places, especially for foreign manufacturers and distributors. Two comments stated that the requirement should be qualified by "subject to conflicting legal requirements in other countries" because some countries have "blocking statutes" that would prohibit the release of some information. One comment stated that wherever the word "all" appeared in the requirements, FDA should remove it.

FDA has rearranged this section, and notes that records must be kept in a location that is "reasonably accessible" to both the manufacturer and FDA investigators, and that records must be made "readily available." FDA expects that such records will be made available during the course of an inspection. If the foreign manufacturer maintains records at remote locations, such records would be expected to be produced by the next working day or 2, at the latest. FDA has clarified that records can be kept at other than the inspected establishment, provided that they are made "readily available" for review and copying. This should provide foreign manufacturers and initial distributors the necessary flexibility.

FDA has not qualified § 820.180 in response to the comments on the "blocking statues" because if manufacturers want to import medical devices into the United States, then they must comply with applicable statutory and regulatory requirements, including part 820. The records section of this regulation is essentially the same as that of the original CGMP and FDA has not found these "blocking statutes" to present a problem. Further, countries increasingly realize the importance of a global market, thus FDA does not anticipate this issue to be a problem in the future.

In response to the comment on the term "all", FDA notes that where a requirement exists for ensuring that records are maintained in a certain

fashion, a manufacturer must keep *all* records subject to the regulation in that manner. The revised section makes clear that it is "all records required" by the regulation to which the section's requirements pertain.

181. A few comments on § 820.180(b), "Record retention period," stated that the section should be amended because all quality records may not be tied to a specific device; therefore, such quality records may not need to be maintained over the lifetime of a device. A few comments stated that the retention period requirement is unclear and burdensome, while others stated that the period should be left to the manufacturer to define. One comment suggested the deletion of the requirements related to photocopying records in proposed § 820.180(b) because it is technology that is not necessarily being used.

FDA believes that all records should be retained for a period equivalent to the design and expected life of the device, but in no case less than 2 years, whether the records specifically pertain to a particular device or not. The requirement has been amended to make clear that all records, including quality records, are subject to the requirement. FDA believes this is necessary because manufacturers need all such records when performing any type of investigation. For example, it may be very important to access the wording of a complaint handling procedure at the time a particular complaint came in when investigating a trend or a problem that extends to several products or over an extended period of time. Further, FDA does not believe that allowing the manufacturer to define the retention period will serve the public's best interest with regard to safety concerns and hazard analysis.

In response to the comment on photocopying, FDA has deleted the last two sentences. The agency believes that this requirement is outdated and does not necessarily reflect the technology being utilized today. Section 820.180 requires that records be readily available for inspection and copying by FDA, and FDA will interpret "copying" to include the printing of computerized records, as well as photocopying.

182. One comment on proposed § 820.180(c) stated that all quality audit reports should be subject to FDA review and public disclosure. A few other comments stated that for a management representative to certify that "corrective action has been taken" would be difficult because some corrective actions are long term and may not be completed at the time of certification.

FDA disagrees with the comment that quality audit reports should be subject to FDA review for the reasons given in the preamble of the original CGMP regulation, published in the Federal Register on July 21, 1978 (43 FR 31508), and believes that the disclosure of the audit reports themselves would be counterproductive to the intent of the quality system. FDA has added § 820.180(c), "Exceptions," to address which records FDA, as a matter of policy, will not request to review or copy during a routine inspection; such records include quality audit reports. FDA may request an employee in management with executive responsibility to certify in writing that the management reviews, quality audits, and supplier audits (where conducted) have been performed, among other things. FDA may also seek production of these reports in litigation under applicable procedural rules or by inspection warrant where access to the records is authorized by statute. Again, FDA emphasizes that its policy of refraining from reviewing these reports extends only to the specific reports, not to the procedures required by the sections or to any other quality assurance records, which will be subject to review and copying.

FDA agrees with the comments on the timing of corrective actions and has amended the certification requirement to state "corrective action has been undertaken."

ii. Device Master Record (DMR) (§ 820.181)

183. A few comments on proposed § 820.181 *Device master record* stated that the requirement for a "qualified" individual to prepare the DMR should be deleted because it is unclear or redundant with the requirements in § 820.25.

FDA has not deleted the requirement for the DMR to be prepared, dated, and approved by a qualified individual because the agency believes this is necessary to assure consistency and continuity within the DMR. The section is consistent with the original CGMP, § 820.181. FDA has, however, substituted the phrase "prepared and approved in accordance with § 820.40" to be consistent with the requirements already in § 820.40 and to eliminate any redundancy.

184. Two comments on § 820.181(a) stated that "software design specifications" should not be included in the DMR because these documents will be located in the DHF. Another comment requested that the requirement that the DMR contain "software source code" information be amended because

R

source codes for commercialized software will not be available to the device manufacturers. Another comment stated that the source code should not be in the DMR because it will already be in the DHF.

FDA deleted the reference to "software source code" because this is already covered with the requirement for "software specifications." The final software specifications should be transferred into production. Therefore, the final software specification for the particular device or type of device should be located or referenced in the DMR, while any earlier version should be located or referenced in the DHF. FDA believes that it is more important for manufacturers to construct a document structure that is workable and traceable, than to worry about whether something is contained in one file as compared to another. The DMR is set up to contain or reference the procedures and specifications that are current on the manufacturing floor. The DHF is meant to be more of a historical file for utilization during investigations and continued design efforts.

185. One comment on § 820.181(c) stated that the DMR should not contain quality system documents, but rather the quality control documents related to the specific device. Three comments stated that validation and verification information belongs in the DHF, not the DMR.

FDA agrees in part with the comments and has revised the section to clarify that the quality records required in the DMR relate to the specific current design, not the more general requirements of the quality system, which are addressed under new § 820.186. However, the comments are incorrect that all validation and verification information is related solely to design. There are requirements for validation and verification pertaining to device processing that may be better kept in the DMR instead of the DHF. The documentation of such verification and validation activities relating to processes that are performed for several different devices or types of devices can be placed or referenced in the location that best suits the manufacturer. Again, it is more important that the manufacturer store and retrieve information in a workable manner, than keep such information in particular files.

186. FDA notes that the regulation contains a few requirements which apply "where appropriate" or "at appropriate stages." FDA emphasizes that the procedures that the manufacturer places in the DMR must clearly define the requirements the manufacturer is following and when particular activities are appropriate. The manufacturer will have failed to comply with the requirements of the section if the procedures simply state that the review or activity occurs at "appropriate stages."

The same principle applies for every section of this regulation, which is written to be flexible enough to cover the manufacture of all types of devices. Manufacturers must adopt quality systems appropriate for their specific products and processes. In establishing these procedures, FDA will expect manufacturers to be able to provide justifications for the decisions reached.

iii. Device History Record (§ 820.184)

187. One comment on § 820.184 stated that labeling should not be required in the DHR because it is already required in the DMR. Another comment stated that some devices have 25 or more labels and that only the primary identification labels are necessary in the DHR. One comment stated the requirement should be amended because it explicitly requires that dates and quantities for each batch be in the DHR, while only implying through the general requirement that the DHR must also contain the batch test data.

FDA agrees that it may not be necessary to include all labeling used in the DHR. However, FDA continues to believe, as it explained in the preamble to proposed regulation published in the Federal Register on November 23, 1993 (58 FR 61952 at 61968), that increased control over labeling is necessary due to the many labeling errors resulting in recalls. Therefore, FDA has retained a requirement related to labeling in the DHR, but revised it to make it less burdensome. The requirement was amended to "the primary identification label and labeling" which is consistent with that contained in the original CGMP regulation, § 820.185. FDA believes that the requirement that the DHR contain the primary label and labeling used for each production unit, coupled with the labeling controls in § 820.120, should help to ensure that proper labeling is used and, hopefully, decrease the number of recalls due to improper labeling.

FDA agrees with the last comment and has added in § 820.184 "(d) The acceptance records which demonstrate the device is manufactured in accordance with the DMR" to explicitly state the requirement to avoid any confusion.

188. FDA has deleted the requirement for the DHR to be "readily accessible and maintained by a designated individual(s)" because it believes that the objective of that requirement is met through §§ 820.40 *Document controls* and 820.180 *General requirements.*

FDA has also added "device identification" to the requirement under § 820.184(f) because it believes that any identification or control number used should be documented in the DHR to facilitate investigations, as well as corrective and preventive actions. FDA notes that this provision does not add any requirement for identification or traceability not already expressed in §§ 820.60 and 820.65.

iv. Quality System Record (§ 820.186)

189. Several comments stated that the regulation should more closely harmonize with ISO 9001:1994. A few comments stated that the regulation should include the requirements for a quality manual. One comment stated that general quality system procedures and instructions should not be required in the DMR because the DMR is device specific, and many quality system procedures are not tied to a particular device.

FDA agrees in part with these comments and has developed new § 820.186 *Quality system record.* This section separates the procedures and documentation of activities that are not specific to a particular type of device from the device specific records.

v. Complaint Files (§ 820.198)

190. Two comments on proposed § 820.198 *Complaint files* stated that the requirements were very detailed and that much of the language should be placed in a guidance document.

FDA disagrees with the comments. These requirements are essentially the same as the original CGMP requirements under § 820.198, and 18 years of experience with these requirements shows that many manufacturers still do not understand and properly handle complaints. Therefore, FDA believes that the amount of detail in § 820.198 is appropriate and necessary. In an effort to make the requirements more clear, however, the section has been reorganized to better illustrate how complaint information should be handled.

Section 820.198(a) sets forth the general requirement for establishing and maintaining a complaint handling procedure and includes a few items that the procedure needs to address. Section 820.198(b) discusses the initial review and evaluation of the complaints in order to determine if complaints are "valid." It is important to note that this evaluation is not the same as a complaint investigation. The evaluation is performed to determine whether the information is truly a complaint or not and to determine whether the complaint needs to be investigated or not. If the evaluation decision is not to investigate, the justification must be recorded. Section 820.198(c) then describes one subset of complaints that must be investigated, but explains that duplicative investigations are not necessary. In cases where an investigation would be duplicative, a reference to the original investigation is an acceptable justification for not conducting a second investigation. Section 820.198(d) describes another subset of complaints that must be investigated (those that meet the MDR criteria) and the information that is necessary in the record of investigation of those types of complaints. Section 820.198(e) sets out the type of information that must be recorded whenever complaints are investigated. The information described in § 820.198 (e)(1) through (e)(5) would most likely be attained earlier in order to perform the evaluation in § 820.198(b). This information need not be duplicated in the investigation report as long as the complaint and investigation report can be properly identified and tied together. Section 820.198 (e)(1) through (e)(5) are considered to be basic information essential to any complaint investigation. If there is some reason that the information described in § 820.198(e) cannot be obtained, then the manufacturer should document the situation and explain the efforts made to ascertain the information. This will be considered to be acceptable as long as a reasonable and good faith effort was made. For example, a single phone call to a hospital would not be considered by FDA to be a reasonable, good faith effort to obtain information. Section 820.198(f) is the same as § 820.198(d) of the original CGMP, where the manufacturing facility is separate or different from that of the formally designated complaint handling unit. In such cases, it is important that the facility involved in the manufacturing of the device receive or have access to complaint and investigation information. In order to give manufacturers the flexibility of using computer or automated data processing systems, the term "reasonably accessible," from § 820.180, is used. Section 820.198(g) is the complaint recordkeeping requirement for distributors. In order to give manufacturers the same flexibility as described in § 820.198(f), FDA has included "reasonably accessible" in § 820.198(g).

Throughout § 820.198, when there is reference to the MDR regulation or to the types of events that are reportable under the MDR regulation, this section simply refers to events or complaints that "represent an event which is required to be reported to FDA under part 803 or 804 of this chapter."

191. A few comments on § 820.198(a) stated that the section should allow for more than one "formally designated unit" to handle complaints, especially for large corporations where it would not be feasible or beneficial for all divisions to have a single complaint handling unit. A few other comments stated that § 820.198(a)(2) on oral complaints should be deleted because it is too subjective.

FDA disagrees with these comments. Large corporations may have different complaint handling units for different product types or different manufacturing establishments. However, there should be only one formally designated complaint handling unit for each product type or establishment. If a corporation chooses to operate with different complaint handling units for products and/or establishments, the manufacturer must clearly describe and define its corporate complaint handling procedure to ensure consistency throughout the different complaint handling units. A system that would allow multiple interpretations of handling, evaluating, categorizing, investigating, and following up, would be unacceptable. Each manufacturer should establish in its procedures which one group or unit is ultimately responsible for coordinating all complaint handling functions.

FDA also disagrees that the requirement that oral complaints be documented upon receipt should be deleted. A December 1986 General Accounting Office (GAO) report entitled "Medical Devices; Early Warning of Problems Is Hampered by Severe Underreporting," (Ref. 11) showed that approximately 83 percent of the hospitals report complaints orally. FDA believes that these oral complaints must be captured in the complaint handling process.

192. FDA, as noted above, has added to § 820.198(c) the phrase "unless such investigation has already been performed for a similar complaint and another investigation is not necessary" to clarify that duplicative investigations are not required if the manufacturer can show that the same type of failure or nonconformity has already been investigated.

193. Several comments on proposed § 820.198(b), now § 820.198(d), stated that the evaluation of complaints

pertaining to death, injury, or hazard to health should be removed from this section because it is redundant with the MDR regulation. Several other comments on § 820.198(b) stated that complaints pertaining to death, injury, or hazard to health need not be maintained separately, as long as they are identified.

FDA disagrees that the requirements are redundant, but believes that they expressly state what is expected in the handling of this type of complaint information. The requirements have been moved to a separate section, § 820.198(d).

FDA agrees with the second set of comments and has revised the section to permit such complaints to be "clearly identified." This will give a manufacturer flexibility in choosing a means of ensuring that these types of complaints can be immediately recognized and segregated for purposes of prioritizing and meeting other requirements.

FDA has substituted the term "promptly" for the term "immediately" to be more consistent with the new MDR regulation timeframes. FDA has also clarified that § 820.198 (d)(1) through (d)(3) are in addition to the information that must be recorded in § 820.198(e).

194. A few comments on proposed § 820.198 (c) and (d) stated that FDA should make clear that some of the requirements will not always be applicable. For example, the comments stated that a record of corrective action cannot be made if such action is not required, and is not taken.

Where corrective action is not necessary and is not taken, it cannot be documented. The section was revised to make that clear. As stated in the preamble to the proposal (58 FR 61952 at 61968), the manufacturer's procedures should clearly identify when corrective action will be taken.

In addition, FDA combined provisions in § 820.198 (c) through (e) to eliminate redundancy and added the requirement that the records include any device identification, as well as control number used, to facilitate corrective and preventive actions. FDA has also deleted the term "written" in § 820.198(e) to be consistent with FDA's statements on electronic and computer systems.

195. FDA deleted the requirements in proposed § 820.198(f) in response to comments because it agrees that it is not necessary to repeat the requirements of the MDR regulation in the quality system regulation. Section 820.198(a) requires that all complaints be evaluated to determine whether they are subject to

R

the requirements of the MDR regulation under part 803 or 804.

196. A few comments on proposed § 820.198(g), now § 820.198(f), stated that duplicate records are not needed in this age of computer systems, and that the requirement as written would be counterproductive.

FDA agrees with the comments and has rewritten the section to allow the complaints and records of investigation to be reasonably accessible at the formally designated complaint unit and the manufacturing site, where these locations are distinct. A manufacturer's procedures must ensure that the manufacturing site is alerted to complaints concerning devices produced at that site.

197. Several comments on proposed § 820.198(h), now § 820.198(g), stated that the requirement is unnecessary, given that FDA can inspect a foreign manufacturer that imports devices, and is burdensome.

FDA has revised the section to permit the records to be reasonably accessible, similar to § 820.198(f), which should alleviate any burden. However, the agency must have access to these records in the United States.

198. Several comments on proposed § 820.198 (i) and (j) stated that the requirements should be deleted because they are redundant with the MDR requirements in part 803.

FDA disagrees that all of the requirements in § 820.198 (i) and (j) are redundant. The requirement that procedures ensure that complaints are processed uniformly and in a timely manner, and evaluated to determine whether they are reportable under part 803 or 804, has been moved up to § 820.198(a). These are basic requirements for complaint handling. If the complaint is determined to be of the type subject to part 803 or 804, those requirements apply. The requirements of parts 803 and 804 are not repeated in this regulation. FDA has deleted § 820.198(j).

N. Servicing (Subpart N)

199. Numerous comments were received on the servicing requirements that were proposed. Many of these comments dealt with competitive issues between manufacturers that perform or contract out their own servicing and third party service organizations. The comments received, as well as the recommendations from the GMP Advisory Committee, were split on many issues. Therefore in this regulation, FDA has chosen to codify only longstanding requirements for servicing performed by original manufacturers and remanufacturers.

The requirements in § 820.200 are similar to those in ISO 9001:1994, with some supplemental requirements for clarification on monitoring service reports, on the relationship of service reports and complaints, and on the type of information FDA believes is essential in any service report. As described above in the definition section of this preamble, a separate rulemaking will specify and clarify the requirements for third party service organizations.

200. Other comments on proposed § 820.200(a) stated that it is impractical to return a used device to its original specifications because a certain amount of wear and tear should be expected, without detriment to the safety and effectiveness of the device. Several comments on § 820.200(a) stated that the term "records" should be replaced by "reports," to be consistent with ISO 9001.

FDA agrees and has revised the requirements in § 820.200(a) to be similar to the requirements in ISO 9001:1994 as recommended by comments at the GMP Advisory Committee meeting to require that the servicing instructions and procedures ensure that the device will meet "specified requirements" for the device's intended use. FDA is aware that with use and age, a device may be serviced to function as intended, but may not meet original specifications.

FDA agrees with the comments and has modified the language in § 820.200(b), (c), and (d) to use the term "service reports."

201. A few comments on proposed § 820.200(b), "Service report evaluation," questioned whether full corrective action was necessary for every service report and whether service calls need to be handled as complaints only when there is a death, injury, or hazard to safety.

FDA has rewritten this section into § 820.200(b) and (c) to clarify the agency's intent and to use terms consistent with those used in § 820.198. Section 820.200(b) now states that "Each manufacturer shall analyze service reports with appropriate statistical methodology in accordance with § 820.100." Full corrective action may not be required for every service report. However, if the analysis of a service report indicates a high risk to health, or that the frequency of servicing is higher than expected, the remainder of the corrective and preventive action elements are applicable, in accordance with the corrective and preventive action procedures established under § 820.100.

Section 820.200(c) provides that when a service report "represents an event

which must be reported to FDA under part 803 or 804 of this chapter," it is automatically considered by FDA to be a complaint that must be handled according to § 820.198. FDA emphasizes that this provision is not intended to limit "complaints" to MDR reportable events.

202. FDA has also added in § 820.200(d) the requirements for recording the name of the device, any device identification(s) and control number(s) used, as well as test and inspection data, because FDA believes such documentation in the service report will facilitate investigations. This additional documentation provision does not add any requirement for identification or traceability not already expressed in §§ 820.60 and 820.65. Therefore, § 820.200(d) as amended focuses on the type of information that should be captured on the service report instead of where the information should be sent.

O. Statistical Techniques (Subpart O)

203. FDA amended § 820.250(a) to be consistent with the requirements in ISO 9001:1994, section 4.20.

204. Several comments on § 820.250(b) stated that the provision as written seems to require the use of sampling plans, and that every manufacturer does not necessarily use sampling plans. Another comment stated that sampling plans are not often used during reviews of nonconformities, quality audits, or complaints, and that these examples should, therefore, be deleted. Two other comments questioned the meaning of "regularly reviewed."

FDA's intent was not to require the use of sampling plans, but to require that where they are used, they should be written and valid. Section 820.250 was revised to make that clear. Sampling plans are not always required, but any time sampling plans are used, they must be based on a valid statistical rationale. Further, FDA acknowledges that the most common use of sampling plans is during receiving acceptance, and has deleted the examples. FDA has also clarified the review requirement by stating "to ensure that when changes occur the sampling plans are reviewed."

VI. Summary of Changes From the July 1995 Working Draft to the Final Rule and Rationale

Note: Minor changes to improve grammar, readability, and clarity, as well as changes in terminology and organization for the sake of consistency throughout the regulation, are not listed.

A. Section 820.1   Scope

1. Inserted sentence, "If a manufacturer engages in only some operations subject to the requirements in this part, and not in others, that manufacturer need only comply with those requirements applicable to the operations in which it is engaged" for further clarification of the scope in response to many comments.

2. Amended sentence on component manufacturers to read, "This regulation does not apply to manufacturers of components or parts of finished devices, but such manufacturers are encouraged to use appropriate provisions of this regulation as guidance" as a result of the many written comments and oral testimony at the August and September 1995 meetings.

3. Inserted sentence on how to interpret the phrase "where appropriate" in the regulation, as recommended by the GMP Advisory Committee. This sentence is consistent with International Organization for Standards (ISO)/CD 13485—"Application of Quality Systems to Medical Devices."

B. Section 820.3   Definitions

4. Amended the definition of *Complaint* by inserting "after it is released for distribution" in response to comments for clarification and to harmonize with ISO/CD 13485.

5. Amended the definition of *Component* by deleting "packaging" for clarification that every piece of packaging is not necessarily a component, only the materials that are part of the "*finished, packaged, and labeled device.*"

6. Amended the definition of *Design output* to clarify its relationship with the Device Master Record.

7. Amended the definition of *Design review* to delete "and propose the development of solutions" in order to allow the manufacturer the flexibility to determine whom the appropriate person(s) is to propose solutions.

8. Deleted the definition of *End of life* in response to the many written comments and oral testimony at the August and September 1995 meetings.

9. Amended the definition of *Manufacturer* to delete component manufacturers and to remove the terms "*servicer*" and "*refurbisher.*" The obligations of servicers and refurbishers will be addressed in a separate rulemaking later this year. The terms "*installation*" and "*remanufacturing*" were added to codify longstanding FDA policy and interpretations of the original CGMP regulation.

10. Amended the definition of *Manufacturing material* in response to comments requesting clarification and separation of examples.

11. Deleted the definition of *Record* to avoid confusion. *Record* will continue to be defined by the act and case law.

12. Removed the definition of *Refurbisher* for reasons discussed in paragraph 28, section V.A. of this document.

13. Inserted the definition of *Remanufacturer* for reasons discussed in paragraph 28, section V.A. of this document, and made the language consistent with that of the 510(k) provision and the PMA amendment/supplement requirements.

14. Changed the term *Reprocessing* to *Rework* and adopted a definition consistent with ISO 8402 Quality Management and Assurance Vocabulary Standard in response to comments for closer harmonization of terminology.

15. Removed the definition of *Servicing*, and *Servicer* which was proposed to the GMP Advisory Committee, for reasons discussed above.

16. Amended the definition of *Validation* as recommended by the GMP Advisory Committee for further clarity by delineating the terms validation, process validation, and design validation.

17. Amended the definition of *Verification* for further clarity in response to comments and to more closely harmonize with ISO 8402.

C. Section 820.5   Quality System

18. Deleted the requirements in § 820.5(a) and (b) because these requirements are now found in § 820.20.

D. Section 820.20   Management Responsibility

19. Moved the requirements from § 820.186 and rewrote into new § 820.20(d) and (e) for clarity, better organization, and closer harmonization with ISO/CD 13485.

E. Section 820.25   Personnel

20. Inserted the phrase, "establish procedures for identifying training needs" in § 820.25(b) in response to comments to add this requirement and to harmonize with the requirement in ISO/CD 13485.

21. Deleted the sentence in § 820.25 on understanding the "CGMP requirements applicable to their job function" to provide manufacturers with the flexibility to appropriately train personnel.

F. Section 820.30   Design Controls

22. Amended the requirements in *Design and development planning* for clarity and to more closely harmonize with ISO/CD 13485.

23. In § 820.30(c), inserted the sentence, "The procedures shall include a mechanism for addressing incomplete, ambiguous, or conflicting requirements" in response to comments to add this requirement and to harmonize with the requirement in ISO/CD 13485.

24. In § 820.30(d), deleted the sentence, "Design output procedures shall ensure that design output meets the design input requirements" because this was redundant with the requirement in § 820.30(f) *Design verification.*

25. Amended § 820.30(e) *Design review* to clarify that the procedures shall ensure that an independent person is included in design reviews.

26. Section 820.30(f) *Design verification and validation* was split into two paragraphs, (f) *Design verification* and (g) *Design validation* and the requirements were separated between the two paragraphs, in response to many written comments and oral testimony at the August and September 1995 meetings and to improve clarity and consistency with ISO/CD 13485.

27. Amended the requirement for § 820.30(i) *Design changes* to add the phrase "before their implementation" due to an inadvertent omission in the July 1995 Working Draft.

G. Section 820.50   Purchasing Controls

28. Deleted the last two sentences in § 820.50(b) and inserted "Purchasing data shall be approved in accordance with § 820.40" because the last two sentences were redundant with the requirements in § 820.40.

H. Section 820.65   Traceability

29. Substituted the definition of critical device from the original CGMP for the phrase "where necessary to ensure the protection of the public health," in response to many comments requesting clarification as to when traceability is necessary.

30. Added "where appropriate" for the traceability of components in response to the recommendation of the GMP Advisory Committee, the written comments, and to harmonize with ISO/CD 13485.

I. Section 820.70   Production and Process Controls

31. Inserted "identified and approved" in § 820.70(a)(5) before "representative samples" to clarify that the samples have to be established and deemed appropriate before they are used as a standard.

32. Substituted in § 820.70(b) "where appropriate validated according to § 820.75" for "unless inspection and test

R

fully verifies the results of the changes'' because it was redundant with the requirements set forth in § 820.75.

33. Amended the requirement in § 820.70(c) to apply only "Where environmental conditions could reasonably be expected to have an adverse effect on product quality," in response to comments and to be consistent with the original CGMP requirements.

34. Amended the requirements in § 820.70(d) and (e) to include "could reasonably be expected to have an adverse effect on product quality" to consistently qualify when these provisions are appropriate.

35. Amended the requirement in § 820.70(h) to apply only "Where a manufacturing material could reasonably be expected to have an adverse effect on product quality," in response to comments and to be consistent with the original CGMP requirements.

36. Rearranged the wording in § 820.70(i) to clarify "automated data processing systems."

J. Section 820.72 Inspection, Measuring, and Test Equipment

37. Renumbered § 820.84 as § 820.72 for better organization because *Inspection, measuring, and test equipment* requirements are more appropriate under Subpart G— Production and Process Controls than under Subpart H—Acceptance Activities.

38. Section 820.72(b) "Calibration standards" and (c) "Calibration records" were reorganized as paragraphs(1) and (2), respectively under paragraph (b) "Calibration."

39. Amended § 820.72(b) to include provisions for remedial action to "reestablish the limits and to evaluate whether there was any adverse effect on the device's quality" in response to comments which questioned whether this was adequately covered under § 820.100.

40. Section 820.84(d), "Maintenance," is reorganized into § 820.72(a) "Control of inspection, measuring, and test equipment" and "test software" is deleted because it is considered to be covered under "electronic inspection and test equipment" in the general requirement.

K. Section 820.75 Process Validation

41. Section 820.75(a) is amended for clarity. The phrase "with a high degree of assurance" was deleted from the definition of "Validation" and added as a requirement under process validation.

42. Section 820.75(b)(2) was amended to state "where appropriate, the

individual(s) performing the process or the major equipment used" in response to comments requesting that flexibility be given to the manufacturer to determine when these items needed to be documented.

43. Section 820.75 (c) and (d) were redesignated as paragraphs (b)(1) and (b)(2) for better organization and flow.

44. Section 820.75(c) was added to address comments and concerns on when revalidation activities were necessary.

L. Section 820.80 Receiving, In-process, and Finished Device Acceptance

45. Section 820.80(c) was amended to add "where appropriate" to reinforce the discussion in the preamble that in-process testing is not always necessary depending upon the type of device and the manufacturing set-up.

M. Section 820.90 Nonconforming Product

46. Amended the requirement in § 820.90(a) to include, "The evaluation of nonconformance shall include a determination of the need for an investigation * * *. The evaluation and any investigation shall be documented." in response to many written comments and oral testimony at the August and September 1995 meetings on whether every nonconformance had to be investigated.

47. Amended the requirement in § 820.90(b)(1) to read, "Documentation shall include the justification for use of nonconforming product" in response to several comments confused about the meaning of the term "concession."

48. In § 820.90(b)(2), substituted the term "rework" for the term "reprocessing" for reasons described in the definitions section.

49. Deleted the sentence, "Reprocessed product shall be clearly identified during reprocessing, and shall be subjected to reevaluation" in § 820.90(b)(2) because the requirement was redundant with the requirements in §§ 820.60 *Identification* and 820.86 *Acceptance status.*

N. Section 820.100 Corrective and Preventive Action

50. Amended § 820.100(a)(7) to clarify what information is to be submitted to management for review.

O. Section 820.120 Device Labeling

51. Inserted "where appropriate" before "use" in § 820.120(a) because every device may not have a label directly affixed to the device itself (e.g. implantable devices).

52. Inserted the sentence, "The label and labeling used for each production unit, lot, or batch shall be documented in the DHR" into § 820.120(d) in response to comments questioning whether the labeling used should be recorded in the device master record or the device history record.

P. Section 820.160 Distribution

53. Inserted the requirement in § 820.160 "that purchase orders are reviewed to ensure that ambiguities and errors are resolved before devices are released for distribution" in response to the GHTF comments and other EU comments that the regulation did not address the requirements in ISO 9001, section 4.3, "Contract Review."

Q. Section 820.170 Installation

54. Amended the installation requirements for clarity and deleted the last sentence in § 820.170(b), "The results of the installation inspection shall be made available to FDA upon request" because this sentence is redundant with the requirements in § 820.180 for all records.

R. Section 820.181 Device Master Record (DMR)

55. In § 820.181 deleted the phrase "dated, and signature of the qualified individual(s) designated by the manufacturer" and inserted "and approved in accordance with § 820.40" to be consistent with the requirements already in § 820.40.

56. In § 820.181 deleted the phrase "and software source code for customized software" because comments stated that this was already covered with the requirement for "software specifications."

S. Section 820.186 Quality System Record (QSR)

57. Amended the requirement in § 820.186 by adding the sentence,

The QSR shall include, or refer to the location of, procedures and the documentation of activities required by this part that are not specific to a particular type of device(s), including but not limited to the records required by § 820.20. Each manufacturer shall ensure that the QSR is prepared and approved in accordance with § 820.40.

Deleted the requirements in § 820.186(a) through (d) because those requirements are now found in § 820.20. This change was in response to comments and suggestions made by the GHTF for further harmonization with ISO/CD 13485 and for clarity.

T. Section 820.198 Complaint Files

58. In § 820.198 deleted the terminology "pertaining to death,

injury, or any hazard to safety'' throughout this section and inserted ''an event which must be reported to the FDA under part 803 or 804 of this chapter'' to reference the MDR regulation.

59. Added the phrase ''unless such investigation has already been performed for a similar complaint and another investigation is not necessary'' in § 820.198(c) in response to comments which thought a second investigation was always mandated by this requirement.

60. Amended § 820.198(d) by changing the word ''immediately'' to ''promptly'' to be consistent with the new MDR regulation. Added, ''In addition to the information required by § 820.198(e),'' to clarify that an investigation under § 820.198(d) was to include requirements under paragraphs (d)(1) through (d)(3) and under paragraphs (e)(1) through (e)(8).

61. Substituted the phrase ''*reasonably accessible*'' for ''*concurrently maintained*'' in § 820.198 (f) and (g) as recommended by the GMP Advisory Committee to clarify FDA's intent of allowing these records to be available in other media forms besides the hard copies which were previously required.

U. Section 820.200   Servicing

62. Amended § 820.200(a) to adopt language consistent with ISO/CD 13485, which was suggested at the GMP Advisory Committee meeting, in order to clarify the requirement and further harmonize.

63. Deleted the last two sentences in § 820.200(a) on providing information to third party servicers since this industry will be addressed in a separate rulemaking, as discussed above.

64. Section 820.200(d) was amended for clarity and to focus on the service report and what type of information should be captured on the report instead of where the information should be sent.

V. Section 820.250   Statistical Techniques

65. Amended § 820.250(b) by inserting the phrase, ''to ensure that when changes occur the sampling plans are reviewed'' in response to comments for clarification on when the plans needed to be reviewed.

VII. Environmental Impact

The agency has determined under 21 CFR 25.24(a)(8) and (a)(10) that this action is of a type that does not individually or cumulatively have a significant effect on the human environment. Therefore, neither an environmental assessment nor an environmental impact statement is required.

VIII. Intergovernmental Partnership

The agency has analyzed this rulemaking in accordance with the principles and criteria set forth in Executive Order 12875, ''Enhancing the Intergovernmental Partnership'' and in the Unfunded Mandates Reform Act of 1995 (Pub. L. 104–4). Executive Order 12875 states that no agency or executive department shall issue any regulation that is not required by statute and that creates a mandate upon a State, local, or tribal government unless the Federal Government supplies funds necessary to comply with the mandate, or the agency provides the Office of Management and Budget (OMB) a description of the agency's consultation with affected State, local, and tribal governments, the nature of their concerns, any written communications submitted to the agency by such units of government, and the agency's position supporting the need to issue the regulation containing the mandate. Executive Order 12875 does not apply to this final rule because the regulatory requirements are not generally applicable to government facilities but to finished device manufacturers. The agency notes, however, that the membership of the advisory committee established to review this regulation and make recommendations to the agency on the feasibility and reasonableness of the regulation (GMP Advisory Committee) must include three members who are officers or employees of any State or local government or of the Federal Government, and that in 1995 this committee included two State government representatives and one Federal Government representative.

The agency has also examined the consistency of this final rule with the Unfunded Mandates Reform Act of 1995. The Unfunded Mandates Reform Act requires (in section 202) that agencies prepare an assessment of anticipated costs and benefits before proposing any rule that may result in an annual expenditure by State, local, and tribal governments, in the aggregate, or by the private sector, of $100 million (adjusted annually for inflation). FDA believes that the private sector expenditures for this rule fall below $100 million annually but nonetheless, due to uncertainties of these estimates, the agency has prepared for the private sector an assessment of anticipated costs and benefits for the 1993 proposed rule and this final rule as described in section IX. of this document.

IX. Economic Impact

A. Summary

FDA has examined the impacts of the final rule under Executive Order 12866 and the Regulatory Flexibility Act (Pub. L. 96–354). Executive Order 12866 directs agencies to assess all costs and benefits of available regulatory alternatives and, when regulation is necessary, to select regulatory approaches that maximize net benefits (including potential economic, environmental, public health and safety, and other advantages; distributive impacts; and equity). The agency believes that this final rule is consistent with the regulatory philosophy and principles identified in the Executive Order. As explained in detail below, FDA finds that this final rule has an estimated total annual incremental cost of $81.9 million to the U.S. industry and an estimated average annual benefit of from $180 million to $220 million in lives saved and is economically significant under Executive Order 12866. Consequently, the agency has completed this full regulatory flexibility analysis which demonstrates that this rule is consistent with the principles set forth in the Executive Order and the Regulatory Flexibility Act, and also with the Unfunded Mandates Reform Act as described in section VIII. of this document. This analysis, together with the preamble published in the Federal Register and supporting analysis and materials, constitutes a final regulatory flexibility analysis. In addition, this document has been reviewed by OMB as an economically significant regulatory action under Executive Order 12866.

The detailed data for this analysis were developed by Eastern Research Group, Inc. (ERG), under contract to FDA and their two reports: ''Economic Analysis of the Proposed Revisions to the Good Manufacturing Practices Regulation for Medical Devices,'' and ''Addendum to the Final Report'' are on file at the Dockets Management Branch (HFA–305), Food and Drug Administration, 12420 Parklawn Dr., rm. 1–23, Rockville, MD 20857.

The objective of this rule is to reduce the number of fatalities and injuries attributable to defective medical devices. FDA finds that private market incentives do not adequately reduce the risk of design-related device failures because neither physicians nor consumers have all of the information needed to make adequate judgments of product quality and legal tort remedies are slow, inefficient, and extremely costly.

The changes to the CGMP regulation will require manufacturers to extend

R

their quality systems to include several new areas, such as design and purchasing, and to clarify or expand selected existing requirements. Several of the changes to the regulation make it more consistent with ISO 9001:1994 quality standards. The rule will affect all medical device establishments engaged in the design, manufacture, contract sterilization, and packaging of medical devices.

This analysis presents the costs and benefits of the final CGMP rule and reflects the differences between the proposed and final regulation. The complete methodology and preliminary economic analysis was presented in the November 1993 ERG report, "Economic Analysis of Proposed Revisions to the Good Manufacturing Practices Regulation for Medical Devices". While the proposed rule covered component manufacturers, the cost of compliance for such manufacturers was inadvertently omitted from the November 1993 ERG report. However, FDA has decided not to cover component manufacturers, therefore most of the preliminary analysis remains valid (e.g., estimates of labor and resource requirements, level of compliance, and number of firms remain the same for the final analysis, except where noted).

Based on the ERG study, the total annual incremental costs to the U.S. industry of the final CGMP regulation are estimated to be about $81.9 million. These costs are more than offset, however, by benefits to public health and by economic benefits to the medical device industry. FDA estimates that the benefits to public health will include 36 to 44 fewer deaths and 484 to 677 fewer serious injuries per year, which are attributed to design-related device failures. Studies on the value of a statistical-life have reported estimates ranging from $1.6 million to $8.5 million.[1] Assuming an economic value of $5 million per fatality avoided, the monetary value of saving 36 to 44 lives each year will be $180 to $220 million. Therefore, the value of the public health

benefits of preventing deaths alone easily exceeds the cost of compliance even without estimating benefits from a reduced number of serious injuries. Moreover, additional economic benefits to medical device establishments will result from cost savings due to fewer design-related product recalls, better product quality, and greater productivity. In addition, medical device establishments exporting to the EU will greatly benefit from the harmonization of the CGMP regulation with the ISO 9001:1994 quality standards. Because the EU is adopting ISO 9001:1994 as a basis for its medical device manufacturing quality system, the harmonization of the two quality requirements will eliminate the need for device manufacturers to maintain different quality systems for each market.

FDA supports the international harmonization of standards and regulations governing medical devices and the eventual mutual recognition of CGMP inspections between major device markets. While full achievement of this goal is still in the future, the harmonization of quality standards is an important first step.

FDA believes in a step wise approach toward harmonization and eventual mutual recognition. For CGMP inspections or Quality System Conformity Assessments, these goals comprise four basic steps. First, the harmonization of quality system requirements is a fundamental building block of all future work in this area. FDA believes that by working with the GHTF, specifically Study Group #3 of the GHTF, it has developed a final rule that incorporates the harmonized quality system requirements which are recognized around the world. Second is the harmonization of regulatory auditing or compliance inspections. This work is currently underway in the GHTF in Study Group #4, which has developed one draft document entitled "Guidelines For Regulatory Auditing Quality Systems of Medical Device Manufacturers," expected to be

finalized in 1997. The third step is for harmonization of the policy, interpretation, and regulatory consequences of noncompliance with the quality system requirements in this rule and in counterpart requirements of other countries. Underlying these activities is an ongoing need for confidence building between the parties working towards mutual recognition. FDA believes that this regulation will provide a sound foundation for the goal of mutual recognition of inspections, a goal that will benefit industry, as well as the agency. The Health Industry Manufacturers Association has stated that reciprocity for quality assurance inspections could save the medical device industry millions of dollars as well as provide significant savings to governments.[2]

For individual establishments, the economic impact of the regulation will depend on a number of factors, such as the level of current compliance, the type of activities performed at the establishment, and the nature of the product. On average, the smaller establishments will bear a relatively greater economic burden.

B. Industry Profile

Firms in the medical device industry are heterogeneous. They vary in size, product type, product and process technology, and rate of new product introductions. There are over 7,000 medical device establishments involved in the production of approximately 4,000 different types of devices (Table 1). Sixty-two percent of these establishments are very small (fewer than 20 employees), while 27 percent are of medium-size (20 to 99 employees), 7 percent are large (100 to 249 employees), and 4 percent are very large (250 or more employees). These size categories were developed to reflect size categories within the medical device industry and differ from the Small Business Administration definition. Under the Small Business Administration definition, over 98% of all establishments would be small.

TABLE 1.—DISTRIBUTION OF AFFECTED ESTABLISHMENTS BY EMPLOYMENT SIZE

Type of establishment	Total [1]	Employment size [2]			
		Small (1–19)	Medium (20–99)	Large (100–249)	Very large (≥250)
Design and Production Manufacturer	5,415	3,323	1,414	415	265
Contract manufacturer	419	257	109	32	20
Specification developer	541	352	162	27	0
Repacker/relabeler	828	538	248	41	0

[1] Fisher, A.; Chestnut, L.; and Violette, D. (1989). "The Value of Reducing Risks of Death: A Note on New Evidence." *Journal of Policy Analysis and Management,* 8 (pp. 88–100).

[2] Gilmartin, R.V. (1992). "The Benefits of Cooperation for Industry and Regulators Alike: A Global Perspective." Presented at the Third Annual Global Medical Device Conference, October 2.

TABLE 1.—DISTRIBUTION OF AFFECTED ESTABLISHMENTS BY EMPLOYMENT SIZE—Continued

Type of establishment	Total [1]	Employment size [2]			
		Small (1–19)	Medium (20–99)	Large (100–249)	Very large (≥250)
Contract sterilizer	34	22	10	2	0
Total	7,237	4,492	1,943	517	285

[1] Based on data from FDA's Registration and Listing Branch, 1992, adjusted to reflect 13 percent not required to register and 6 percent exempt from CGMP requirements.
[2] ERG (1993), Section 3.

C. Comments to November, 1993 Proposed Changes to the CGMP Regulation

A small percentage of the public comments on the November 1993 proposed regulation addressed the economic impact analysis. The majority of these comments made very general, nonspecific observations and therefore cannot be addressed directly. Many of these comments stated that FDA underestimated the regulatory burden that the proposed CGMP regulation would place on medical device manufacturers. Others stated that their companies would expend more than the per establishment estimated costs; some discussed the hiring of additional personnel to address the compliance requirements.

In developing the cost estimates for the 1993 proposal, ERG attempted to describe the labor hours (and associated costs) needed to achieve an acceptable minimum level of compliance with each requirement. These estimates took into account the incremental labor and capital resources that would be needed to progress from the existing compliance level to the new level required by the proposal. For individual establishments, the economic impact of the CGMP regulation would depend on a number of factors, such as the level of current compliance, the type of activities performed, and the nature of the product. Not surprisingly, those establishments that currently undertake relatively few of the activities to be required would incur greater compliance costs than the averages presented.

In the final rule, FDA has eliminated or modified several requirements to give medical device establishments greater flexibility in selecting compliance methods. In general, the words "where appropriate" were added to many requirements to make them less prescriptive and allow establishments to determine if or when they are appropriate for their product. For example, in §820.65 *Traceability,* the final requirement allows the

manufacturer to identify which components require traceability. In addition, many procedures may not need to be changed, only documented. To further minimize compliance costs, FDA intends to provide additional guidance materials. The DSMA currently offers guidance materials and regional seminars on CGMP matters.

1. Health Industry Manufacturers Association (HIMA)

HIMA commented that FDA understated the costs for personnel training, maintenance of new systems, documentation revisions, and operational costs.

ERG agrees that it did not fully address the initial training requirements in the cost analysis for the proposed CGMP regulation. New costs for initial training were included in the cost analysis for the final CGMP regulation. However, the existing CGMP regulation requires periodic training of personnel. Therefore no incremental costs for periodic training were estimated.

ERG did not change its cost estimate for quality system maintenance and procedure revisions. Estimates were made for the incremental compliance costs associated with an annual review of each new procedure, but these procedures would be revised only sporadically and probable estimates of their future costs would be small and could not be reasonably quantified.

ERG recognized that companies will incur incremental costs to use new procedures. Although a separate estimate of these operational costs was not made, they were incorporated into the estimates of the individual requirements where applicable.

2. Other General Comments

Some manufacturers of low-risk devices and some that have never experienced a product recall or MDR event questioned the merit and benefits of applying design controls to all products. In the proposed and final CGMP regulation, FDA exempted almost all class I devices because the public health benefits gained did not exceed

the costs of implementation. However, FDA believes that all class II and III devices should be covered because their failure could adversely affect public health. Even firms with excellent past records put their consumers at future risk if their design systems are inadequate. ERG estimates that strict compliance to the final CGMP regulation will avert about 43 deaths and over 600 serious injuries per year. In addition, the literature on quality systems consistently states that firms implementing such systems, which begin with design controls, report cost savings in the long-run.

A number of comments argued that the proposed CGMP regulation would slow product innovation and increase health care costs. FDA believes that the gains from improvements in quality control and greater efficiencies will lessen the impact on both innovation and health care costs and will not lower the innovation rate for products with significant medical benefit. Manufacturers will also avoid the costs of most design-related medical device recalls. ERG estimated that design-related recalls cost industry approximately $40 million per year. Health care spending overall will also decrease as deaths, injuries and malfunctions from medical device failures decrease.

Some comments suggested that the proposed CGMP regulation would hurt the domestic medical device industry's competitiveness and encourage companies to move their operations to foreign countries. FDA has sought to harmonize the final CGMP regulation with ISO 9001:1994 and ISO/CD 13485. Some comments had stated they would like to see even greater harmonization in the final regulation. The harmonization of regulatory requirements will benefit medical device establishments because they will be able to maintain a single regulatory compliance program. The harmonization of CGMP requirements is also a first step in developing mutual recognition agreements between U.S. and foreign governments. An FDA sponsored survey of innovative medical device companies found that nearly 65 percent of them sold their products outside the United States, including 40 percent of the small and 70 percent of the medium-sized companies.[3] Thus, a majority of firms should benefit from harmonization efforts. Since foreign firms exporting their products to the United States must comply with the U.S. CGMP regulation, they will incur essentially the same incremental costs to comply with the final CGMP regulation as domestic establishments.

3. Small Business Concerns

Some comments representing small businesses were concerned about the increase in procedural and documentation requirements. The procedures and paperwork requirements will be simpler for small medical device establishments relative to larger firms. Further, small businesses can reduce compliance costs by using FDA guidance and training materials, industry-generated guidance, and other technical assistance that is available. FDA is preparing an extensive range of technical support regarding the final CGMP regulation, including guidance documents, workshops, and other materials and presentations.

Several small businesses argued that the regulatory costs fall disproportionately on small business, hindering industry growth. The regulatory requirements apply equally to whoever is designing and developing new devices. However, the vast majority of firms are small and medium in size and these firms are least likely to have such design control procedures already in place. As a result, their incremental costs may be higher. Nevertheless, because procedures reflect the complexity of the processes they guide, small and medium-sized establishments should incur proportionately lower gross compliance costs for those activities than larger establishments.

4. Section 820.22 Quality audit

Some comments believed that requiring quality audits to be performed by individuals without direct responsibility for the matters being audited poses a severe burden for small business. This requirement is already present in the original CGMP regulation and thus was not addressed in the economic analysis of the final regulation.

5. Section 820.25 Personnel

Comments stated that the requirement to maintain files on consultants was onerous and interfered with manufacturers' selection processes. FDA modified this requirement and moved it to § 820.50 *Purchasing,* in the final CGMP regulation. Companies will now be required to verify that consultants meet specified requirements and define the type and extent of control they will exercise over them. The incremental compliance costs were judged to be negligible.

6. Section 820.30 Design control

Comments believed that the requirement stipulating that devices be sampled from three production runs before a device is released for routine distribution was too prescriptive and burdensome. FDA has modified the requirement in the final rule to require design validation of initial production units, lots, or batches, or their equivalent. This modification should give manufacturers greater flexibility in implementing this requirement.

Some comments from small businesses were critical of the requirement that independent personnel perform design reviews and stated that they will have to hire outside engineers for this task. In the final rule FDA allows greater flexibility and states that the independent personnel can be individual(s) who do not have direct responsibility for the design stage being reviewed. Thus, staff personnel (including engineers working on other components of the device and nonengineering personnel) can perform design reviews.

7. Section 820.40 Document control

Some comments believed that the cost of implementing documentation systems and other paperwork was understated. However, ERG's estimates included the incremental compliance costs for formalizing a written document control procedure and ERG considered paperwork requirements in its estimation. The final rule also extends document control requirements to the design phase and cost estimates for these requirements were added to the economic assessment.

Most companies consider document control procedures to be essential and have realized some benefits from such procedures, typically in the form of efficiency gains and avoided documentation mixups. These potential benefits were not quantified.

8. Section 820.50 Purchasing control

Comments questioned the need to establish the quality of materials purchased from long-established suppliers or from new suppliers of small quantities of components. Historical records, however, even for suppliers of small quantities, can be used to assess a supplier's quality. Supplier audits are not mandated in the CGMP regulation, but may be a useful tool in assessing a supplier's capabilities. Cost estimates for auditing from one- half to four new suppliers per year for small to very large establishments were included in the economic assessment.

9. Section 820.80 Receiving, in-process, and finished device acceptance

One comment believed that requiring manufacturers to retain the quantitative results of testing was excessive. The final rule stipulates that "the results" of acceptance activities are to be recorded, but does not specify that all quantitative results must be recorded. Because this requirement is consistent with current industry practices, incremental costs were not assigned to this section.

10. Section 820.90 Nonconforming product

Comments noted that identifying a product as "reprocessed" has a negative impact on sales. (FDA now uses the term "reworked".) This language was revised in the final rule to clarify that reworked devices need to be identified as such at the manufacturing facility to avoid mixups. No costs were estimated for this requirement.

D. Industry Costs

ERG estimated the total annual incremental cost of the final rule at $81.9 million. This includes $9.5 million in one-time costs that were annualized over 5 years at a 10 percent discount rate. Table 2 lists the most costly of the new requirements.

Costs were based on the incremental tasks each manufacturer must perform to achieve compliance. ERG retained most of the methodology and data from the proposed rule to estimate the costs of the final rule. Where applicable, costs were estimated for additional or changed final requirements. Also, the distribution of costs across establishment size was modified to reflect new information on the rate of product innovation.[4] The rates of innovation per year used for this analysis are: 0.4 percent for small, 1.3 percent for medium-sized, 2.6 percent for large, and 6.5 percent for very large establishments.

---

[3] ERG (1994). *FDA Survey of Establishments Introducing New Medical Devices.* (Task Order 3, Contract No. 223–91–8100.)

[4] ERG (1994). *FDA Survey of Establishments Introducing New Medical Devices.* (Task Order 3, Contract No. 223–91–8100).

TABLE 2.—TOTAL COMPLIANCE COSTS, BY MOST COSTLY INCREMENTAL TASKS

[$ millions]

Incremental tasks	One-time annualized [1]	Annual		Total annualized
		Labor	Nonlabor	
Design Controls:				
Design Verification	NA	18.2	27.4	45.6
Design Review	NA	6.2	NA	6.2
Design Changes	NA	4.0	NA	4.0
Design and Development Planning	NA	1.2	NA	1.2
Other:				
Quality Audit	0.5	4.7	NA	5.2
Evaluation of Suppliers and Contractors	0.6	1.9	0.9	3.4
Management Review	NA	2.2	NA	2.2
Purchasing Data	NA	1.1	NA	1.1
All Remaining	8.4	4.6	0.0	13.0
Total for Final Regulation	9.5	44.1	28.3	81.9

[1] One-time costs annualized over 5 years at discount rate of 10 percent.
NA=Not Applicable.
Note: Totals may not add due to rounding.
Source: ERG (1996), Section 4.

The great majority of costs for all size establishments will be associated with the establishment of design controls for new products. Therefore, the more innovative establishments will experience greater compliance costs than the less innovative establishments. The estimated annual design control costs total $57.5 million, which represents 70 percent of the total annual incremental costs of compliance. The most costly task within the design control category is design verification ($45.6 million), which includes design validation. Other costly tasks are design review ($6.2 million), which encompasses conducting and documenting design reviews; design changes ($4.0 million), which includes documenting and maintaining design change procedures; and design and development planning ($1.2 million), which includes documenting and maintaining plans for device design and development. The requirement for extending the quality system audit ($5.2 million) and the evaluation of suppliers and contractors ($3.4 million) are also relatively high cost items.

The estimated total cost of compliance for the final rule ($81.9 million) is $2.6 million less than the estimated cost of the November 1993 proposed rule ($84.5 million). Some cost increases were due to added requirements for increased documentation. However, these cost increases were offset partly by a decrease of $0.5 million from the modification of some requirements (e.g. §§ 820.65 *Traceability* and 820.160 *Distribution*). The remaining changes resulted from changes in assumptions or new information about cost and compliance rates in design control and supplier audits and from new information regarding product innovation rates across establishment size.

The projected average cost per establishment (see Table 3) varies substantially across industry sectors and establishment size categories. As expected, the average incremental costs are largest for establishments that design medical devices: design and production manufacturers and specification developers. For these two sectors, the average per establishment costs are $15,994 for design and production manufacturers and $14,767 for specification developers. Actual per establishment costs will vary substantially depending on the product type, design complexity, innovation rate, and level of design control currently in place. The average incremental costs for the other three sectors are significantly lower: $3,554 for contract manufacturer, $1,995 for repacker/relabeler, and $2,040 for contract sterilizer.

TABLE 3.—AVERAGE TOTAL ANNUALIZED [1] COSTS PER ESTABLISHMENT BY TYPE AND SIZE

[Dollars]

Establishment type	Small (1–19)	Medium (20–99)	Large (100–249)	Very large (≥250)	All
Design and Production Manufacturer	11,085	25,800	22,748	12,258	15,994
Specification Developer	9,927	24,052	20,583	NA	14,767
Contract Manufacturer	2,357	4,027	5,802	10,678	3,554
Repacker/Relabeler	1,471	2,588	3,969	NA	1,995
Contract Sterilizer	1,491	2,621	3,999	NA	2,400

[1] One-time costs annualized over 5 years at a discount rate of 10 percent.
NA=Not Applicable.
Source: ERG (1996), Section 6.

Because average current compliance rates tend to vary directly with establishment size and there are relatively few large and very large establishments (7 and 4 percent of all medical device establishments, respectively), the largest share of the costs are incurred by small establishments, $35.2 million (43 percent) and medium-size establishments, $34.5 million (42 percent), while the smallest share is incurred by very large establishments, $3.4 million (4 percent) (see Table 4).

TABLE 4.—TOTAL ANNUALIZED COSTS BY SIZE CATEGORY

[$ millions]

Establishment size	One-time annualized [1]	Annual		Total annualized
		Labor	Nonlabor	
Small (1–19)	4.9	18.2	12.1	35.2
Medium (20–99)	3.0	18.2	13.3	34.5
Large (100–249)	1.0	5.1	2.8	8.8
Very large (≥250)	0.7	2.6	0.1	3.4
All establishments	9.5	44.1	28.3	81.9

[1] One-time costs annualized over five years at discount rate of 10 percent.
Note: Totals may not add due to rounding.
Source: ERG (1996), Section 4.

E. Benefits From Proposed Changes to the CGMP Regulation

ERG used the methodology and data from the proposed rule to estimate the benefits of the final CGMP regulation. Adjustments to the number and distribution of MDR's were made based on updated numbers of closed cases. Also, more reliable estimates of industry savings from avoided design-related recalls were incorporated.

The changes to the CGMP regulation will provide public health benefits to medical device users and economic benefits to the medical device industry. Based on its review of medical device recalls over the 4-year period 1988 to 1991, FDA has estimated that 30 percent of all medical device product recalls are due to inadequate design controls. It is extremely difficult to judge how many

of these recalls could reasonably have been avoided, but ERG judged that a majority would have been prevented if manufacturers had fully implemented the CGMP design control requirements.

1. Public Health Benefits

ERG used the MDR database to estimate the public health benefits of the final CGMP regulation. There were over 41,600 MDR's submitted to FDA in 1991; 97 percent of these MDR's are closed (i.e., a review of the case is completed). Of these closed cases, FDA determined that 9.3 percent of the fatalities and 12.4 percent of the serious injuries were due to device failures. The bulk of the remaining incidents were due to user problems, but also include cases where cause could not be clearly established. To estimate the total

number of deaths and serious injuries for 1991 by cause, the 1988–1991 averages of device recalls were used. To estimate the number of deaths and serious injuries due to design-related causes, ERG assumed that the percent of MDR's that were design-related was the same as that for recalls (30 percent).[5] Based on these assumptions, medical devices contributed to an estimated 49 fatalities and 663 serious injuries in 1991 due to design-related problems in class II and III devices (see Table 5). To correct for the substantial under reporting of MDR's, ERG made an upward adjustment in the number of MDR's of 20 percent for fatalities and 40 percent for serious injuries. The number of estimated fatalities adjusted for underreporting of MDR's would be 59, with 929 serious injuries.

TABLE 5.—NUMBER OF DESIGN-RELATED REPORTS AND ESTIMATED AVOIDED DEATHS AND SERIOUS INJURIES

	Fatalities			Serious Injuries		
	Class II	Class III	Total	Class II	Class III	Total
Number in 1991	555	475	1,030	4,391	11,794	16,185
Device-related	105	59	164	330	1,881	2,211
Design-related [1]	32	18	49	99	564	663
Number avoided	23	13	36	72	412	484
Adjusted number of design-related MDR's [2]	38	21	59	139	790	929
Adjusted Number avoided	28	15	43	101	576	677

[1] Assumes 30 percent of device-related MDR's are design-related, based on FDA recall data.
[2] Total number of fatalities and injuries increased by 20 and 40 percent, respectively, to adjust for under-reporting.
Source: ERG (1996), Section 5.

To develop an approximate idea of the preventability of these incidents, ERG convened a panel of industrial engineers and regulatory specialists with extensive experience in the design of medical devices. The panel examined a random sample of 100 design-related medical device recalls and judged

whether implementation of design controls could have prevented the recall. ERG found that the expected value of their judgments implied that proper design controls would have prevented about 73 percent of these recalls. Assuming the same preventability ratio for design-related

MDR events, ERG calculated that the proposal would prevent about 36 to 43 deaths and 484 to 677 serious injuries per year, depending on the degree of MDR underreporting.

To verify the reasonableness of the estimates, FDA examined an alternative method of estimating the number of

R

[5] There is no code in the MDR database to identify design-related events.

fatalities caused by design-related failures. For this calculation, 3 years of design-related recalls were assumed linked to MDR fatalities that occurred for these devices 1 year before or 3 months after the date of the recall. This approach, which provides a conservative estimate because not all relevant fatalities and subsequent MDR's would occur during this limited time period, found that about 60 deaths per year were due to design-related device failures. If 73 percent of such incidents could be avoided through compliance with the proposed CGMP regulation, 44 deaths per year would be prevented.

These estimates of the public health benefits from fewer design-related deaths and serious injuries represent FDA's best projections, given the limitations and uncertainties of the data and assumptions. The above numbers, however, do not capture the quality of life losses to patients who experience less severe injuries than those reported in MDR's, who experience anxiety as a result of treatment with an unreliable medical device, or who experience inconvenience and additional medical costs because of device failure.

Medical device malfunctions are substantially more numerous than deaths or injuries from device failures and also represent a cost to society. Malfunctions represent a loss of product and an inconvenience to users and/or patients. Additionally, medical device malfunctions burden medical personnel with additional tasks, such as repeating treatments, replacing devices, returning and seeking reimbursement for failed devices, and providing reports on the circumstances of medical device failures. No attempt was made to quantify these additional costs.

2. Industry Benefits

The medical device industry would gain substantial economic benefits from the proposed changes to the CGMP regulation in three ways: Cost savings from fewer recalls, productivity gains from improved designs, and efficiency gains for export-oriented manufacturers who would now need to comply with only one set of quality standards.

An average of 359 medical device recall events per year were reported to FDA over the period 1988 to 1991. As stated above, FDA estimates that design-related deficiencies contributed to 30 percent of those recall events annually. Applying the 73 percent recall preventability factor, ERG projects that there would be 67 fewer recalls of class II and III devices each year under the final CGMP regulation (see Table 6). Based on data from a recent survey of

recall costs, 67 fewer recalls implies that the industry would avoid roughly $29 million worth of recall expenses per year by complying with the final CGMP regulation.[6]

TABLE 6.—NUMBER OF AVOIDED DE-SIGN-RELATED RECALL EVENTS BY CLASS OF DEVICE

[FY 1988–FY 1991]

Device class	Average number of design-related recall events[1]	Number of avoid-ed de-sign-relat-ed recall events[2]
I	15	NA
II	80	58
III	12	9
All Devices	107	67

[1] Office of Compliance and Surveillance, CDRH.
[2] ERG estimates based on random sample of 100 design-related recalls.
Source: ERG (1996), Section 5.

ERG also found that the design control requirements in the final CGMP regulation would require manufacturers to integrate their design and production operations and that most industry experts believe that this change would lead to better quality products, more efficient engineering, lower manufacturing costs, and reduced product development time. These savings, however, could not be quantified.

Still another benefit of the revised regulation relates to the harmonization of the final CGMP regulation with the ISO 9001:1994 international standard. This change would especially benefit export-oriented establishments, because they would need to meet only one set of quality standards. ERG could not derive quantitative measures of this benefit. However, 65 percent of innovative medical device companies export their products, thus a majority should benefit from harmonization of CGMP regulation between major trading partners.[7]

F. Economic and Small Business Impact

The ability of medical device establishments to pass on the added cost of the final regulation will determine the economic impact to the industry. The diversity of medical devices

[6] Design-related medical device recalls cost the industry approximately $40 million annually. (Eastern Research Group, Inc. (1994). FDA Survey of Medical Device Recall Costs. (Task Order 3, Contract Number 223–91–8100).

[7] ERG (1994). FDA Survey of Establishments Introducing New Medical Devices. (Task Order 3, Contract No. 223–91–8100.)

precludes any easy characterization of their product markets. Under the current medical care system, however, the demand for many medical devices tends to be price inelastic because they are often prescribed by physicians and frequently paid for by third parties. Thus, small price increases have not typically prompted significant declines in industry sales. Nonetheless, competitive pressures have increased substantially under new health care cost-containment measures. Therefore, to examine the potential effect of the costs of compliance on the industry's competitive structure, ERG calculated the maximum impact on industry average prices and products, using extreme scenarios. Financial data characterizing the scope of FDA-regulated medical device establishments are not available. To make estimates of the regulatory impact on price and profits, ERG used a combination of census and Dun and Bradstreet data (see ERG (1993) for methodology). ERG assumed that the firms characterized in these data sources had the same size and product distribution, and introduced new products at the same rate as the population of FDA-regulated establishments. While the validity of these assumptions is uncertain, it was the only data available to measure regulatory impact. ERG presents two extreme scenarios, the first reflects the magnitude of the potential impact on product prices if all costs were passed forward. The second demonstrates the maximum drop in profits if no costs were passed forward. In reality, some combination of these scenarios will occur.

Based on the assumption that all costs of compliance are passed through to the end user, with no loss in sales and no offset for avoided recalls or other industry productivity gains, ERG found that the average increase in the price of medical devices would be less than 0.13 percent. Estimated price increases ranged from 0.04 percent for X-Ray Apparatus and Tubes (SIC 3844) to 0.34 percent for Dental Equipment and Supplies (SIC 3843) (see Table 7). The maximum price increase was calculated using aggregate compliance costs as a percentage of the value of shipments. The price increases calculated by size of establishment suggest that small establishments will be under greater pressure to increase prices. The cost of compliance represented an average of 1.36 percent of the value of shipments for small establishments and 0.01 percent for very large establishments. These differences in impacts by size reflect the finding that small

R

establishments have lower current compliance than large establishments.

To estimate the potential impact of compliance costs on medical device industry profits, ERG calculated after-tax compliance costs as a percentage of after-tax income for each medical device SIC (see Table 7). Again, no adjustments were made for avoided recalls or expected productivity gains. If manufacturers have no ability to increase prices to offset the increase in compliance costs, this estimate represents an upper bound of the potential effect on entity income. Under these circumstances, the medical device sectors could incur reductions in income ranging from about 0.81 percent (SIC 3845, Electromedical Equipment) to about 4.27 percent (SIC 3843, Dental Equipment and Supplies). ERG concluded that such impacts may affect some establishments' decisions to develop new products where expected profits are marginal or highly uncertain, but judged that the level of incremental costs imposed by this regulation would not substantially lower the innovation rate especially for products with significant medical benefits.

TABLE 7.—MAXIMUM POTENTIAL IMPACT ON PRICE OR PROFITS BY INDUSTRY AND EMPLOYMENT SIZE

	Total annualized compliance costs as a percentage of shipments	After-tax compliance costs as a percentage of after-tax income
Industry:		
3841 Surgical and medical instruments	0.12	2.00
3842 Surgical appliance and supplies	0.14	1.78
3843 Dental equipment and supplies	0.34	4.27
3844 x-ray apparatus and tubes	0.04	0.88
3845 Electromedical equipment	0.05	0.81
3851 Ophthalmic goods	0.24	3.54
All	0.13	1.87
Establishment size:		
Small (1–19)	1.36	NA
Medium (20–99) ...	0.35	NA
Large (100–249) ...	0.09	NA
Very large (≥250) ...	0.01	NA
All	0.13	NA

NA = not available.
Source: ERG (1996), Section 6.

The Regulatory Flexibility Act requires agencies to analyze regulatory options that would minimize any significant impact of a rule on small entities. This section together with other discussions in this preamble and supporting analysis and materials constitute the agency's regulatory flexibility analysis. A description of the projected reporting, recordkeeping, and compliance requirements including the type of professional skills required is included in the ERG economic analysis reports that are referenced above and on file at the Dockets Management Branch (address above). In accordance with the Regulatory Flexibility Act, FDA has considered the effect of this action on small businesses and has determined that there will be a significant impact on a substantial number of small businesses. Almost all medical device establishments are classified as small under the Small Business Administrations definition of size.[8] The incremental costs are greatest for establishments that design medical devices and that currently have lower levels of compliance with the new design control requirements. These requirements account for 70 percent of the total incremental costs of the final rule but affect only design and production manufacturers and specification developers (82 percent of the total affected establishments). Other sectors of the industry will incur substantially lower costs (see Table 3).

The actual added cost per establishment will vary by the establishment's current level of compliance, complexity of product design, product type, and rate of product innovation. As indicated in Table 3, the average medium-size and large manufacturers of devices will incur greater compliance costs ($25,800 and $22,748 per establishment, respectively) relative to small and very large establishments ($11,085 and $12,258, respectively). However, the potential impact on product price (measured as a percent of the value of shipments) is greatest for small (1.36 percent) and medium-size (0.35 percent) establishments. Large and very large establishments will incur only a 0.09 percent and 0.01 percent increase, respectively, due to much larger values of shipments and higher rates of compliance with the final rule. Smaller establishments producing differentiated products or marketing to niche markets

---

[8] The Small Business Administrations definition is by the employment size at the company level. Detailed demographic and financial data is not available by company size, therefore FDA used establishment data. FDA does not know the impact on companies.

may not be at a disadvantage because of their ability to pass on the added cost of compliance. However, those smaller establishments that compete with larger establishments based on price alone would suffer a drop in profits if they currently operate at lower levels of compliance than their competitors.

FDA believes that actual per establishment compliance costs will be lower than estimated for the following reasons: First, the final CGMP regulation closely parallels the ISO 9001:1994 quality standards, which have been adopted as the quality standard for the EU and are becoming the international quality standards for medical devices. Close to 65 percent of domestic medical device manufacturers export their products and generate approximately one-third of their sales from exports.[9] Compliance with the quality control requirements is necessary for firms to maintain international competitiveness and in fact many U.S. medical device manufacturers have become ISO certified since the 1993 publication of the proposed CGMP regulation and the EU implementation of unified regulatory requirements.

Second, the FDA has extended the effective date of the final rule to June 1, 1997, and has chosen not to take regulatory action for an additional year on the design control requirements. This revised effective date will also reduce the cost of implementation estimated for the 1993 proposal where the proposed effective date was only 180 days after date of publication. The extension will give manufacturers a longer time to implement the new requirements, allowing the costs to be spread over almost a 2-year period as compared to 180 days. June 1998 coincides with the implementation of the EU's Inactive Medical Device Directive. Therefore, the economic impact of complying with the new quality system regulation will be shared with the economic impact of complying with the new EU Medical Device Directive for any manufacturer who also produces devices for sale in the EU, lessening the direct impact of the new quality system regulation.

Third, ERG estimates of the number of labor hours needed for design controls assume that many establishments have little or no formal system in place. Once an establishment has developed a system, minor modifications to an establishment's existing product (for which many 510(k) applications and PMA supplements are submitted) may be less costly than ERG assumed.

---

[9] ERG (1994). *FDA Survey of Establishments Introducing New Medical Devices.* (Task Order 3, Contract No. 223–91–8100.)

Finally, cost estimates assume that establishments will use in-house expertise or hired consultants for all compliance activities. In fact, FDA and trade publications have disseminated much of the information that would be needed by the firms. FDA has taken many steps specifically to assist small businesses in complying with this final rule. The two stage implementation of the regulation was a concerted effort to reduce the regulatory burden on small businesses. Stage 1 was set up to be a 1 year training and cooperative phase for the entire medical device community. FDA and industry would be participating in a number of cooperative efforts as well as joint training exercises. Most importantly, FDA would be evaluating design controls and providing industry with feedback in the nature of a report. During this time, to truly allow it to be a learning experience for both the device manufacturers and the FDA investigators, there would be no regulatory actions taken as a result of these evaluations and reports. The biggest benefactor of the two stage implementation would clearly be small businesses.

Further, several guidances have been prepared by FDA for this regulation as a whole, as well as on subject matters that are significant in this final rule. FDA plans to release the following three guidances within 60 days after the final rule is published: (1) DSMA's "Medical Device Quality Systems Manual: A Small Entity Compliance Guide," which includes discussion on the entire regulation plus multiple examples of procedures and forms that can be adopted and modified by manufacturers; (2) "Design Control Guidance For Medical Device Manufacturers," which is intended to assist manufacturers in understanding the intent of the design control requirements. Assistance is provided by interpreting the language of the regulation and explaining the underlying concepts in practical terms; and (3) "Do It By Design: An Introduction to Human Factors in Medical Devices," which contains background information about human factors as a discipline, descriptions and illustrations of device problems, and a discussion of human factors principles and methods as a part of the design control system. FDA also plans to release the following guidances after publication of this final rule: (1) A guidance on "Validation," which will include discussions on design validation, computer validation, and process validation; and (2) a draft of the "Design Control Inspectional Strategy,"

which will be the questions that FDA investigators will be asking when assuring compliance with the design control requirements.

FDA is also prepared to release shortly after publication of this final rule a 4 hour series of videotapes discussing the Quality System Regulation. The videotapes will also be accompanied by a guidebook entitled "The FDA and World Wide Quality System Requirements Guidebook For Medical Devices." This guidebook will contain the entire Quality System Regulation from FDA, the entire text of ISO 9001:1994, FDA guidance from the regulation's preamble, and guidance on quality systems from the GHTF.

FDA has also tentatively scheduled two teleconferences. The first teleconference, which would be to discuss the Quality System Regulation and answer questions that have come up from manufacturers beginning to implement the regulation, is tentatively scheduled for December 1996. A second teleconference is tentatively scheduled for April/May of 1997 and will specifically address design controls and the final Design Control Inspectional Strategy. FDA is also exploring the possibility of conducting regional workshops in May of 1997 to further discuss the design control requirements and their implementation.

In addition to these activities, FDA and DSMA will continue to provide guidance and workshops that can help small business with their compliance activities, and will continue to participate in industry association workshops, conferences, and meetings. While all of the above-mentioned activities will be available to all manufacturers, small manufacturers will benefit the most from these FDA activities without having to pay substantial costs, as most of the guidance and written material will be available on the world wide web, and the teleconferences and other workshops sponsored or cosponsored by FDA will be of nominal cost.

Finally, as described elsewhere in this preamble, FDA intends to conduct a midcourse review of the new design control requirements during the transition year (June 1997 to June 1998). Specifically, the results of the first several months of design control inspections will be reviewed by early 1998, and any midcourse adjustments to the inspectional strategy will be instituted and made public by the Spring of 1998. Also during this midcourse review FDA will evaluate the information gathered at that point and determine if the design control requirements as written in this final rule

are appropriate to obtain the goals expressed in this preamble. Any necessary adjustments or proposed revisions will be published in the Federal Register and comments will be solicited as necessary during the spring of 1998. This implementation strategy is responsive to requests by industry for FDA to harmonize the quality system regulation's implementation with the mandatory date for implementation of the EU's Medical Device Directive, which is June 1998. However, if during the midcourse review of stage one it is determined that the industry and/or FDA needs more time to fully implement the design control requirements, FDA will publish that decision in the Spring of 1998 prior to the June 1, 1998, regulatory implementation date.

Small businesses will also benefit in that FDA considered but rejected applying design requirements to all class I devices, because the added benefits to public health were not great enough to offset the increased burden on industry. Two requirements were eliminated or modified in the final rule that decreased the burden on industry: The applicability of the CGMP regulation to component suppliers was removed, and § 820.65 *Traceability* was limited to traceability of components where necessary to assure the protection of public health. These changes will particularly aid small businesses. In addition, revisions were made to many requirements in the final rule to make it less prescriptive and to allow establishments greater flexibility in implementing the requirements. Cost savings from these changes were not estimated.

In addition, revisions were made to many requirements in the final rule to make it less comprehensive in scope, less prescriptive and to allow establishments greater flexibility in implementing the requirements. Cost savings from these changes were not estimated. Based on the above, the agency has determined that the current rule represents the least burdensome alternative that meets the public health goal of reducing deaths and serious injuries attributable to defective medical devices.

In summary, FDA concludes that the estimated $81.9 million annual incremental cost to comply with the final CGMP regulation is likely an upward bound figure and that it would be substantially offset by significant savings from avoided recalls and more importantly, the avoidance of deaths and serious injuries due to design-related device failures. FDA's estimate of public health benefits includes the

R

prevention of 36 to 44 deaths and 484 to 677 serious injuries annually. Establishing design controls will also result in better designed and higher quality devices and fewer device failures. This quality improvement will in turn reduce the inconvenience and expense of repetitive treatments or diagnoses. The agency also believes the actual cost to comply with the final rule will be lower than estimated because the industry compliance baselines used to estimate costs are from 1993. Since that time, market pressures have induced many firms that export to the EU to become ISO 9001:1994 certified. These firms would now be in compliance with most of FDA's final CGMP regulation. Further, FDA has provided continued education efforts over the past 15 years, to mitigate industry costs.

IX. Paperwork Reduction Act of 1995

This final rule contains information collections that are subject to review by OMB under the Paperwork Reduction Act of 1995 (Pub. L. 104–13). The title, description and respondents of the information collection are shown below with an estimate of the annual incremental increase in the recordkeeping burden that respondents must undertake to achieve compliance with the final regulation.

Title: Medical Devices, Quality System Regulations, Current Good Manufacturing Practice Requirements.

Description: This final quality system regulation amends and revises the current good manufacturing practice requirements for medical devices, set out at 21 CFR part 820. This final regulation replaces quality assurance program requirements with quality system requirements; adds design and purchasing controls; modifies the critical device requirements; revises certain existing requirements, such as validation and management responsibility, to clarify the intent of the requirements; and harmonizes the CGMP regulations for medical devices with quality system specifications in ISO 9001:1994 ''Quality Systems-Model for Quality Assurance in Design, Development, Production, Installation and Servicing.''

Description of Respondents: Business or other for-profit and small businesses or organizations.

CFR section	Number of record-keepers	Annual frequency of recordkeeping	Total annual records	Hours per record-keeper	Total hours	Total operating and maintenance costs
820.20(a)	7,237	1	7,237	10.96	79,386	
820.20(b)	7,237	1	7,237	4.88	35,285	
820.20(c)	7,237	1	7,237	10.28	74,364	
820.20(d)	7,237	1	7,237	16.49	119,305	
820.20(e)	7,237	1	7,237	16.49	119,305	
820.22(a)	7,237	1	7,237	52.03	376,507	
820.25(b)	7,237	1	7,237	21.13	152,896	
820.30(a)(1)	7,237	1	7,237	2.92	21,162	
820.30(b)	7,237	1	7,237	9.91	71,718	
820.30(c)	7,237	1	7,237	2.92	21,162	
820.30(d)	7,237	1	7,237	2.92	21,162	
820.30(e)	7,237	1	7,237	38.98	282,115	
820.30(f)	7,237	1	7,237	62.37	451,342	$27,359,420
820.30(g)	7,237	1	7,237	62.37	451,342	
820.30(h)	7,237	1	7,237	5.56	40,236	
820.30(i)	7,237	1	7,237	28.77	208,173	
820.30(j)	7,237	1	7,237	4.40	31,848	
820.40	7,237	1	7,237	11.76	85,081	
820.40(b)	7,237	1	7,237			
820.50 (a)(1) to (a)(3)	7,237	1	7,237	31.12	225,240	898,500
820.50(b)	7,237	1	7,237	10.04	72,679	
820.60	7,237	1	7,237	0.54	3,914	
820.65	7,237	1	7,237			
820.70 (a)(1) to (a)(5)	7,237	1	7,237			
820.70 (b)–(c)	7,237	1	7,237			
820.70(d)	7,237	1	7,237	3.09	22,335	
820.70(e)	7,237	1	7,237			
820.70 (g)(1) to (g)(3)	7,237	1	7,237			
820.70(h)	7,237	1	7,237			
820.70(i)	7,237	1	7,237	9.41	68,092	
829.72(a)	7,237	1	7,237	5.83	42,165	
820.72 (b)(1) to (b)(3)	7,237	1	7,237			
820.75(a)	7,237	1	7,23	72.79	20,172	
820.75(b)	7,237	1	7,237			
820.75(b)(2)	7,237	1	7,237	0.15	1,096	
820.75(c)	7,237	1	7,237	0.15	1,096	
820.80 (a)–(e)	7,237	1	7,237			
820.86	7,237	1	7,237			
820.90(a)	7,237	1	7,237	6.11	44,217	
820.90 (b)(1) to (b)(2)	7,237	1	7,237	6.11	44,217	
820.100 (a)(1) to (a)(7)	7,237	1	7,237	20.06	145,144	
820.100(b)	7,237	1	7,237			
820.120	7,237	1	7,237			
820.120(b)	7,237	1	7,237			
820.120(d)	7,237	1	7,237			
820.130	7,237	1	7,237			
820.140	7,237	1	7,237	9.45	68,418	
820.150 (a)–(b)	7,237	1	7,237	9.45	68,418	
820.160 (a)–(b)	7,237	1	7,237			

R

CFR section	Number of record-keepers	Annual frequency of recordkeeping	Total annual records	Hours per record-keeper	Total hours	Total operating and maintenance costs
820.170 (a)–(b)	7,237	1	7,237			
820.180	7,237	1	7,237			
820.181 (a)–(e)	7,237	1	7,237			
820.184 (a)–(f)	7,237	1	7,237			
820.186	7,237	1	7,237			
820.198 (a)–(c)	7,237	1	7,237	3.71	26,850	
820.200(a) and 820.200(d)	7,237	1	7,237	4.35	31,459	
820.250	7,237	1	7,237			
Totals	7,237	1	7,237	487.50	3,527,901	28,257,920

[1] Incremental increase in hours and costs to achieve compliance with additional requirements.
Note: Totals may not add due to rounding

Under OMB information collection 0910–0073, which expired on June 30, 1995, there were 375,266 burden hours approved for recordkeeping requirements currently contained in part 820 to include 114,882 burden hours as a one time start up expenditure for 750 new firms. The additional requirements contained in this final rule will add 3,527,901 burden hours to the burden, resulting in a total annual recordkeeping burden of 3,903,167 hours. The 3,527,901 burden hours includes 1,433,579 burden hours for a one time start up expenditure for 7,237 manufacturers and 2,094,321 burden hours expended annually by 7,237 manufacturers.

The final rule estimate of recordkeeping burden includes about 9.6 times as many manufacturers with a one time start up expenditure, due to the addition of the design control requirements, than did FDA's estimate of the manufacturers that would have had a one time start up expenditure under the old regulation. Further the recordkeeping burden hour calculations for the new regulation were done under contract using a more complex methodology involving the estimated noncompliance ratio for small, medium, large, and very large manufacturers (as defined above) times the number of manufacturers in each category and factors in a rate of product innovation for new products, including 510(k) devices. This methodology is more precise than the methodology previously utilized. Therefore, it is very difficult to directly compare the total burden hours in this final rule as compared to the estimated burden hours filed for the old regulation which expired June 1995.

Approximately 85 percent of the additional burden hours for the final rule are from the following four subparts of part 820: (1) Subpart B—Quality System Requirements; (2) Subpart C—Design Controls; (3) Subpart E—Purchasing Controls; and (4) Subpart J—

Corrective and Preventive Action. Over 45 percent of the 3,527,901 burden hours are attributed directly to the addition of design control requirements. The recordkeeping burden hours for design control are significant because of the nature of the new requirements, as well as in response to numerous comments on the 1993 and 1995 proposals. The comments requested that the regulation focus on procedures required under design control as compared to prescriptive requirements on the design activities. The quality system requirements, as well as the corrective and preventive action requirements combined are approximately 31 percent of the additional recordkeeping burden hours and were in response to two major issues: (1) Most importantly, FDA had identified these two areas as two of the top four deficiencies found during inspections of the medical device industry, across all sizes of manufacturers; and (2) numerous comments requested harmonization with the ISO 9000 series standards. The involvement of management with executive responsibility, the concept of a total quality system which is a closed feedback loop system, and the practice of using that closed loop system in taking appropriate corrective and preventive action is paramount in ensuring that safe and effective medical devices are available to the public. The purchasing control requirements and the respective recordkeeping burden are approximately 8 percent of the additional recordkeeping burden. Purchasing requirements were the overwhelming choice of the medical device industry as compared to the option of the final rule encompassing component manufacturers. See the discussion in section V.7. of this document.

It is important to note that small manufacturers may comply with this final rule with less procedures and paperwork than larger manufacturers of

the same product because the structure and interfaces for a small manufacturer often require less documentation and paperwork.

Although the November 23, 1993, proposed rule provided a 90 day comment period under the Paperwork Reduction Act of 1980, and this final rule incorporates the comments received, as required by 44 U.S.C. section 3507(d), FDA is providing additional opportunities for public comment under the Paperwork Reduction Act of 1995, which applies to this final rule and was enacted after the expiration of the comment period.

Therefore, the agency solicits public comment on the information collection requirements in order to: (1) Evaluate whether the proposed collection of information is necessary for the proper performance of the functions of the agency, including whether the information will have practical utility; (2) evaluate the accuracy of the agency's estimate of the burden of the proposed collection of information, including the validity of the methodology and assumptions used; (3) enhance the quality, utility, and clarity of the information to be collected; and (4) minimize the burden of the collection of information on those who are to respond, including through the use of appropriate automated, electronic, mechanical, or other technological collection techniques or other forms of information technology, e.g., permitting electronic submission of responses.

Individuals and organizations may submit comments on the information collection requirements by December 6, 1996, and should direct comments to FDA's Dockets Management Branch (address above).

Prior to the effective date of this final rule, FDA will publish a notice in the Federal Register when the information collection requirements in this rule are submitted for OMB approval, and again when OMB makes a decision to approve, modify, or disapprove the

R

information collection requirements. Persons are not required to respond to a collection of information unless it displays a currently valid OMB control number.

X. Congressional Review

This final rule has been determined to be a major rule for purposes of 5 U.S.C. 801 *et seq.*, Subtitle E of the Small Business Regulatory Enforcement Fairness Act of 1996 (Pub. L. 104–121). FDA is submitting the information and reports as required by that statute.

XI. References

The following references have been placed on display in the Dockets Management Branch and may be seen by interested persons between 9 a.m. and 4 p.m., Monday through Friday.

1. "Device Recalls: A Study of Quality Problems," FDA, Center for Devices and Radiological Health, Rockville, MD 20857, HHS Publication FDA 90–4235, January 1990.

2. "FDA Medical Device Regulation From Premarket Review to Recall," Office of Inspector General, Washington, DC, HHS Publication OEI 09–90–00040, February 1991.

3. "Software Related Recalls for Fiscal Years FY 83—FY 91," FDA, Center for Devices and Radiological Health, Rockville, MD 20857, May 1992.

4. ISO 9001:1994 "Quality Systems—Model for Quality Assurance in Design, Development, Production, Installation, and Servicing."

5. ISO draft revision of ISO/CD 13485 "Quality Systems—Medical Devices—Supplementary Requirements to ISO 9001."

6. Federal Register notice entitled "Medical Devices; Current Good Manufacturing Practices (CGMP) Regulations Document; Suggested Changes; Availability," November 30, 1990 (55 FR 49644).

7. Federal Register notice entitled "Medical Devices; Current Good Manufacturing Practice (CGMP) Regulations; Proposed Revisions; Request for Comments," November 23, 1993 (55 FR 61952).

8. Federal Register notice entitled "Medical Devices; Working Draft of the Current Good Manufacturing Practice (CGMP) Final Rule; Notice of Availability; Request for Comments; Public Meeting," July 24, 1995 (60 FR 37856).

9. European Standard (EN) 46001 "Quality Systems—Medical Devices—Particular Requirements for the Application of EN 29001."

10. "Guidelines on General Principles of Process Validation," Center for Drugs and Biologics, and Center for Devices and Radiological Health, FDA, Rockville, MD 20857, May 11, 1987.

11. "Medical Devices; Early Warning of Problems Is Hampered by Severe Underreporting," United States General Accounting Office, Washington, DC, GAO/PEMD–87–1.

List of Subjects

21 CFR Part 808

Intergovernmental relations, Medical devices.

21 CFR Part 812

Health records, Medical devices, Medical research, Reporting and recordkeeping requirements.

21 CFR Part 820

Medical devices, Reporting and recordkeeping requirements.

Therefore, under the Federal Food, Drug, and Cosmetic Act and under authority delegated to the Commissioner of Food and Drugs, 21 CFR parts 808, 812, and 820 are amended as follows:

PART 808—EXEMPTIONS FROM FEDERAL PREEMPTION OF STATE AND LOCAL MEDICAL DEVICE REQUIREMENTS

1. The authority citation for 21 CFR part 808 is revised to read as follows:

Authority: Secs. 520, 521, 701 of the Federal Food, Drug, and Cosmetic Act (21 U.S.C. 360j, 360k, 371).

2. Section 808.1 is amended by adding new paragraph (d)(10) to read as follows:

§ 808.1 Scope.

* * * * *

(d) * * *

(10) Part 820 of this chapter (21 CFR part 820) (CGMP requirements) does not preempt remedies created by States or Territories of the United States, the District of Columbia, or the Commonwealth of Puerto Rico.

* * * * *

PART 812—INVESTIGATIONAL DEVICE EXEMPTIONS

3. The authority citation for 21 CFR part 812 is revised to read as follows:

Authority: Secs. 301, 501, 502, 503, 505, 506, 507, 510, 513–516, 518–520, 701, 702, 704, 721, 801, 803 of the Federal Food, Drug, and Cosmetic Act (21 U.S.C. 331, 351, 352, 353, 355, 356, 357, 360, 360c–360f, 360h–360j, 371, 372, 374, 379e, 381, 383); secs. 215, 301, 351, 354–360F of the Public Health Service Act (42 U.S.C. 216, 241, 262, 263b–263n).

4. Section 812.1 *Scope* is amended by revising the fourth sentence of paragraph (a) to read as follows:

§ 812.1 Scope.

(a) * * * An IDE approved under § 812.30 or considered approved under § 812.2(b) exempts a device from the requirements of the following sections of the Federal Food, Drug, and Cosmetic Act (the act) and regulations issued thereunder: Misbranding under section

502 of the act, registration, listing, and premarket notification under section 510, performance standards under section 514, premarket approval under section 515, a banned device regulation under section 516, records and reports under section 519, restricted device requirements under section 520(e), good manufacturing practice requirements under section 520(f) except for the requirements found in § 820.30, if applicable (unless the sponsor states an intention to comply with these requirements under § 812.20(b)(3) or § 812.140(b)(4)(v)) and color additive requirements under section 721.

* * * * *

5. Part 820 is revised to read as follows:

PART 820—QUALITY SYSTEM REGULATION

Authority: Secs. 501, 502, 510, 513, 514, 515, 518, 519, 520, 522, 701, 704, 801, 803 of the Federal Food, Drug, and Cosmetic Act (21 U.S.C. 351, 352, 360, 360c, 360d, 360e, 360h, 360i, 360j, 360l, 371, 374, 381, 383).

Subpart A—General Provisions

§ 820.1 Scope.

(a) *Applicability.*

(1) Current good manufacturing practice (CGMP) requirements are set forth in this quality system regulation. The requirements in this part govern the methods used in, and the facilities and controls used for, the design, manufacture, packaging, labeling, storage, installation, and servicing of all finished devices intended for human use. The requirements in this part are intended to ensure that finished devices will be safe and effective and otherwise in compliance with the Federal Food, Drug, and Cosmetic Act (the act). This part establishes basic requirements applicable to manufacturers of finished medical devices. If a manufacturer engages in only some operations subject to the requirements in this part, and not in others, that manufacturer need only comply with those requirements applicable to the operations in which it is engaged. With respect to class I devices, design controls apply only to those devices listed in § 820.30(a)(2). This regulation does not apply to manufacturers of components or parts of finished devices, but such manufacturers are encouraged to use appropriate provisions of this regulation as guidance. Manufacturers of human blood and blood components are not subject to this part, but are subject to part 606 of this chapter.

(2) The provisions of this part shall be applicable to any finished device as defined in this part, intended for human use, that is manufactured, imported, or offered for import in any State or Territory of the United States, the District of Columbia, or the Commonwealth of Puerto Rico.

(3) In this regulation the term "where appropriate" is used several times. When a requirement is qualified by "where appropriate," it is deemed to be "appropriate" unless the manufacturer can document justification otherwise. A requirement is "appropriate" if nonimplementation could reasonably be expected to result in the product not meeting its specified requirements or the manufacturer not being able to carry out any necessary corrective action.

(b) *Limitations.* The quality system regulation in this part supplements regulations in other parts of this chapter except where explicitly stated otherwise. In the event that it is impossible to comply with all applicable regulations, both in this part and in other parts of this chapter, the regulations specifically applicable to the device in question shall supersede any other generally applicable requirements.

(c) *Authority.* Part 820 is established and issued under authority of sections 501, 502, 510, 513, 514, 515, 518, 519, 520, 522, 701, 704, 801, 803 of the act (21 U.S.C. 351, 352, 360, 360c, 360d, 360e, 360h, 360i, 360j, 360l, 371, 374, 381, 383). The failure to comply with any applicable provision in this part renders a device adulterated under section 501(h) of the act. Such a device, as well as any person responsible for the failure to comply, is subject to regulatory action.

(d) *Foreign manufacturers.* If a manufacturer who offers devices for import into the United States refuses to permit or allow the completion of a Food and Drug Administration (FDA) inspection of the foreign facility for the purpose of determining compliance with this part, it shall appear for purposes of section 801(a) of the act, that the methods used in, and the facilities and controls used for, the design, manufacture, packaging, labeling, storage, installation, or servicing of any devices produced at such facility that are offered for import into the United States do not conform to the requirements of section 520(f) of the act and this part and that the devices manufactured at that facility are adulterated under section 501(h) of the act.

(e) *Exemptions or variances.* (1) Any person who wishes to petition for an exemption or variance from any device quality system requirement is subject to the requirements of section 520(f)(2) of the act. Petitions for an exemption or variance shall be submitted according to the procedures set forth in § 10.30 of this chapter, the FDA's administrative procedures. Guidance is available from the Center for Devices and Radiological Health, Division of Small Manufacturers Assistance, (HFZ–220), 1350 Piccard Dr., Rockville, MD 20850, U.S.A., telephone 1–800–638–2041 or 1–301–443–6597, FAX 301–443–8818.

(2) FDA may initiate and grant a variance from any device quality system requirement when the agency determines that such variance is in the best interest of the public health. Such variance will remain in effect only so long as there remains a public health need for the device and the device would not likely be made sufficiently available without the variance.

§ 820.3 Definitions.

(a) *Act* means the Federal Food, Drug, and Cosmetic Act, as amended (secs. 201–903, 52 Stat. 1040 *et seq.*, as amended (21 U.S.C. 321–394)). All definitions in section 201 of the act shall apply to the regulations in this part.

(b) *Complaint* means any written, electronic, or oral communication that alleges deficiencies related to the identity, quality, durability, reliability, safety, effectiveness, or performance of a device after it is released for distribution.

(c) *Component* means any raw material, substance, piece, part, software, firmware, labeling, or assembly which is intended to be included as part of the finished, packaged, and labeled device.

(d) *Control number* means any distinctive symbols, such as a distinctive combination of letters or numbers, or both, from which the history of the manufacturing, packaging, labeling, and distribution of a unit, lot, or batch of finished devices can be determined.

(e) *Design history file (DHF)* means a compilation of records which describes the design history of a finished device.

(f) *Design input* means the physical and performance requirements of a device that are used as a basis for device design.

(g) *Design output* means the results of a design effort at each design phase and at the end of the total design effort. The finished design output is the basis for the device master record. The total finished design output consists of the device, its packaging and labeling, and the device master record.

(h) *Design review* means a documented, comprehensive, systematic examination of a design to evaluate the adequacy of the design requirements, to evaluate the capability of the design to meet these requirements, and to identify problems.

(i) *Device history record (DHR)* means a compilation of records containing the production history of a finished device.

(j) *Device master record (DMR)* means a compilation of records containing the procedures and specifications for a finished device.

R

(k) *Establish* means define, document (in writing or electronically), and implement.

(l) *Finished device* means any device or accessory to any device that is suitable for use or capable of functioning, whether or not it is packaged, labeled, or sterilized.

(m) *Lot or batch* means one or more components or finished devices that consist of a single type, model, class, size, composition, or software version that are manufactured under essentially the same conditions and that are intended to have uniform characteristics and quality within specified limits.

(n) *Management with executive responsibility* means those senior employees of a manufacturer who have the authority to establish or make changes to the manufacturer's quality policy and quality system.

(o) *Manufacturer* means any person who designs, manufactures, fabricates, assembles, or processes a finished device. Manufacturer includes but is not limited to those who perform the functions of contract sterilization, installation, relabeling, remanufacturing, repacking, or specification development, and initial distributors of foreign entities performing these functions.

(p) *Manufacturing material* means any material or substance used in or used to facilitate the manufacturing process, a concomitant constituent, or a byproduct constituent produced during the manufacturing process, which is present in or on the finished device as a residue or impurity not by design or intent of the manufacturer.

(q) *Nonconformity* means the nonfulfillment of a specified requirement.

(r) *Product* means components, manufacturing materials, in- process devices, finished devices, and returned devices.

(s) *Quality* means the totality of features and characteristics that bear on the ability of a device to satisfy fitness-for-use, including safety and performance.

(t) *Quality audit* means a systematic, independent examination of a manufacturer's quality system that is performed at defined intervals and at sufficient frequency to determine whether both quality system activities and the results of such activities comply with quality system procedures, that these procedures are implemented effectively, and that these procedures are suitable to achieve quality system objectives.

(u) *Quality policy* means the overall intentions and direction of an organization with respect to quality, as established by management with executive responsibility.

(v) *Quality system* means the organizational structure, responsibilities, procedures, processes, and resources for implementing quality management.

(w) *Remanufacturer* means any person who processes, conditions, renovates, repackages, restores, or does any other act to a finished device that significantly changes the finished device's performance or safety specifications, or intended use.

(x) *Rework* means action taken on a nonconforming product so that it will fulfill the specified DMR requirements before it is released for distribution.

(y) *Specification* means any requirement with which a product, process, service, or other activity must conform.

(z) *Validation* means confirmation by examination and provision of objective evidence that the particular requirements for a specific intended use can be consistently fulfilled.

(1) *Process validation* means establishing by objective evidence that a process consistently produces a result or product meeting its predetermined specifications.

(2) *Design validation* means establishing by objective evidence that device specifications conform with user needs and intended use(s).

(aa) *Verification* means confirmation by examination and provision of objective evidence that specified requirements have been fulfilled.

§ 820.5   Quality system.

Each manufacturer shall establish and maintain a quality system that is appropriate for the specific medical device(s) designed or manufactured, and that meets the requirements of this part.

Subpart B—Quality System Requirements

§ 820.20   Management responsibility.

(a) *Quality policy.* Management with executive responsibility shall establish its policy and objectives for, and commitment to, quality. Management with executive responsibility shall ensure that the quality policy is understood, implemented, and maintained at all levels of the organization.

(b) *Organization.* Each manufacturer shall establish and maintain an adequate organizational structure to ensure that devices are designed and produced in accordance with the requirements of this part.

(1) *Responsibility and authority.* Each manufacturer shall establish the appropriate responsibility, authority, and interrelation of all personnel who manage, perform, and assess work affecting quality, and provide the independence and authority necessary to perform these tasks.

(2) *Resources.* Each manufacturer shall provide adequate resources, including the assignment of trained personnel, for management, performance of work, and assessment activities, including internal quality audits, to meet the requirements of this part.

(3) *Management representative.* Management with executive responsibility shall appoint, and document such appointment of, a member of management who, irrespective of other responsibilities, shall have established authority over and responsibility for:

(i) Ensuring that quality system requirements are effectively established and effectively maintained in accordance with this part; and

(ii) Reporting on the performance of the quality system to management with executive responsibility for review.

(c) *Management review.* Management with executive responsibility shall review the suitability and effectiveness of the quality system at defined intervals and with sufficient frequency according to established procedures to ensure that the quality system satisfies the requirements of this part and the manufacturer's established quality policy and objectives. The dates and results of quality system reviews shall be documented.

(d) *Quality planning.* Each manufacturer shall establish a quality plan which defines the quality practices, resources, and activities relevant to devices that are designed and manufactured. The manufacturer shall establish how the requirements for quality will be met.

(e) *Quality system procedures.* Each manufacturer shall establish quality system procedures and instructions. An outline of the structure of the documentation used in the quality system shall be established where appropriate.

§ 820.22   Quality audit.

Each manufacturer shall establish procedures for quality audits and conduct such audits to assure that the quality system is in compliance with the established quality system requirements and to determine the effectiveness of the quality system. Quality audits shall be conducted by individuals who do not have direct responsibility for the matters being audited. Corrective action(s), including a reaudit of deficient matters, shall be taken when necessary. A report of the results of each quality audit, and reaudit(s) where taken, shall be made and such reports shall be reviewed by management having responsibility for the matters audited. The dates and results of quality audits and reaudits shall be documented.

§ 820.25   Personnel.

(a) *General.* Each manufacturer shall have sufficient personnel with the necessary education, background, training, and experience to assure that all activities required by this part are correctly performed.

(b) *Training.* Each manufacturer shall establish procedures for identifying training needs and ensure that all personnel are trained to adequately perform their assigned responsibilities. Training shall be documented.

(1) As part of their training, personnel shall be made aware of device defects which may occur from the improper performance of their specific jobs.

(2) Personnel who perform verification and validation activities shall be made aware of defects and errors that may be encountered as part of their job functions.

Subpart C—Design Controls

§ 820.30   Design controls.

(a) *General.* (1) Each manufacturer of any class III or class II device, and the class I devices listed in paragraph (a)(2) of this section, shall establish and maintain procedures to control the design of the device in order to ensure that specified design requirements are met.

(2) The following class I devices are subject to design controls:

(i) Devices automated with computer software; and

(ii) The devices listed in the following chart.

Section	Device
868.6810	Catheter, Tracheobronchial Suction.
878.4460	Glove, Surgeon's.
880.6760	Restraint, Protective.
892.5650	System, Applicator, Radionuclide, Manual.
892.5740	Source, Radionuclide Teletherapy.

(b) *Design and development planning.* Each manufacturer shall establish and maintain plans that describe or reference the design and development activities and define responsibility for implementation. The plans shall identify and describe the interfaces with different groups or activities that provide, or result in, input to the design and development process. The plans shall be reviewed, updated, and approved as design and development evolves.

(c) *Design input.* Each manufacturer shall establish and maintain procedures to ensure that the design requirements relating to a device are appropriate and address the intended use of the device, including the needs of the user and patient. The procedures shall include a mechanism for addressing incomplete, ambiguous, or conflicting requirements. The design input requirements shall be documented and shall be reviewed and approved by a designated individual(s). The approval, including the date and signature of the individual(s) approving the requirements, shall be documented.

(d) *Design output.* Each manufacturer shall establish and maintain procedures for defining and documenting design output in terms that allow an adequate evaluation of conformance to design input requirements. Design output procedures shall contain or make reference to acceptance criteria and shall ensure that those design outputs that are essential for the proper functioning of the device are identified. Design output shall be documented, reviewed, and approved before release. The approval, including the date and signature of the individual(s) approving the output, shall be documented.

(e) *Design review.* Each manufacturer shall establish and maintain procedures to ensure that formal documented reviews of the design results are planned and conducted at appropriate stages of the device's design development. The procedures shall ensure that participants at each design review include representatives of all functions concerned with the design stage being reviewed and an individual(s) who does not have direct responsibility for the design stage being reviewed, as well as any specialists needed. The results of a design review, including identification of the design, the date, and the individual(s) performing the review, shall be documented in the design history file (the DHF).

(f) *Design verification.* Each manufacturer shall establish and maintain procedures for verifying the device design. Design verification shall confirm that the design output meets the design input requirements. The results of the design verification, including identification of the design, method(s), the date, and the individual(s) performing the verification, shall be documented in the DHF.

(g) *Design validation.* Each manufacturer shall establish and maintain procedures for validating the device design. Design validation shall be performed under defined operating conditions on initial production units, lots, or batches, or their equivalents. Design validation shall ensure that devices conform to defined user needs and intended uses and shall include testing of production units under actual or simulated use conditions. Design validation shall include software validation and risk analysis, where appropriate. The results of the design validation, including identification of the design, method(s), the date, and the individual(s) performing the validation, shall be documented in the DHF.

(h) *Design transfer.* Each manufacturer shall establish and maintain procedures to ensure that the device design is correctly translated into production specifications.

(i) *Design changes.* Each manufacturer shall establish and maintain procedures for the identification, documentation, validation or where appropriate verification, review, and approval of design changes before their implementation.

(j) *Design history file.* Each manufacturer shall establish and maintain a DHF for each type of device. The DHF shall contain or reference the records necessary to demonstrate that the design was developed in accordance with the approved design plan and the requirements of this part.

Subpart D—Document Controls

§ 820.40   Document controls.

Each manufacturer shall establish and maintain procedures to control all documents that are required by this part. The procedures shall provide for the following:

(a) *Document approval and distribution.* Each manufacturer shall designate an individual(s) to review for adequacy and approve prior to issuance all documents established to meet the requirements of this part. The approval, including the date and signature of the individual(s) approving the document, shall be documented. Documents established to meet the requirements of this part shall be available at all locations for which they are designated, used, or otherwise necessary, and all obsolete documents shall be promptly removed from all points of use or otherwise prevented from unintended use.

(b) *Document changes.* Changes to documents shall be reviewed and approved by an individual(s) in the same function or organization that performed the original review and approval, unless specifically designated otherwise. Approved changes shall be

R

communicated to the appropriate personnel in a timely manner. Each manufacturer shall maintain records of changes to documents. Change records shall include a description of the change, identification of the affected documents, the signature of the approving individual(s), the approval date, and when the change becomes effective.

Subpart E—Purchasing Controls

§ 820.50 Purchasing controls.

Each manufacturer shall establish and maintain procedures to ensure that all purchased or otherwise received product and services conform to specified requirements.

(a) *Evaluation of suppliers, contractors, and consultants.* Each manufacturer shall establish and maintain the requirements, including quality requirements, that must be met by suppliers, contractors, and consultants. Each manufacturer shall:

(1) Evaluate and select potential suppliers, contractors, and consultants on the basis of their ability to meet specified requirements, including quality requirements. The evaluation shall be documented.

(2) Define the type and extent of control to be exercised over the product, services, suppliers, contractors, and consultants, based on the evaluation results.

(3) Establish and maintain records of acceptable suppliers, contractors, and consultants.

(b) *Purchasing data.* Each manufacturer shall establish and maintain data that clearly describe or reference the specified requirements, including quality requirements, for purchased or otherwise received product and services. Purchasing documents shall include, where possible, an agreement that the suppliers, contractors, and consultants agree to notify the manufacturer of changes in the product or service so that manufacturers may determine whether the changes may affect the quality of a finished device. Purchasing data shall be approved in accordance with § 820.40.

Subpart F—Identification and Traceability

§ 820.60 Identification.

Each manufacturer shall establish and maintain procedures for identifying product during all stages of receipt, production, distribution, and installation to prevent mixups.

§ 820.65 Traceability.

Each manufacturer of a device that is intended for surgical implant into the body or to support or sustain life and whose failure to perform when properly used in accordance with instructions for use provided in the labeling can be reasonably expected to result in a significant injury to the user shall establish and maintain procedures for identifying with a control number each unit, lot, or batch of finished devices and where appropriate components. The procedures shall facilitate corrective action. Such identification shall be documented in the DHR.

Subpart G—Production and Process Controls

§ 820.70 Production and process controls.

(a) *General.* Each manufacturer shall develop, conduct, control, and monitor production processes to ensure that a device conforms to its specifications. Where deviations from device specifications could occur as a result of the manufacturing process, the manufacturer shall establish and maintain process control procedures that describe any process controls necessary to ensure conformance to specifications. Where process controls are needed they shall include:

(1) Documented instructions, standard operating procedures (SOP's), and methods that define and control the manner of production;

(2) Monitoring and control of process parameters and component and device characteristics during production;

(3) Compliance with specified reference standards or codes;

(4) The approval of processes and process equipment; and

(5) Criteria for workmanship which shall be expressed in documented standards or by means of identified and approved representative samples.

(b) *Production and process changes.* Each manufacturer shall establish and maintain procedures for changes to a specification, method, process, or procedure. Such changes shall be verified or where appropriate validated according to § 820.75, before implementation and these activities shall be documented. Changes shall be approved in accordance with § 820.40.

(c) *Environmental control.* Where environmental conditions could reasonably be expected to have an adverse effect on product quality, the manufacturer shall establish and maintain procedures to adequately control these environmental conditions. Environmental control system(s) shall be periodically inspected to verify that the system, including necessary

equipment, is adequate and functioning properly. These activities shall be documented and reviewed.

(d) *Personnel.* Each manufacturer shall establish and maintain requirements for the health, cleanliness, personal practices, and clothing of personnel if contact between such personnel and product or environment could reasonably be expected to have an adverse effect on product quality. The manufacturer shall ensure that maintenance and other personnel who are required to work temporarily under special environmental conditions are appropriately trained or supervised by a trained individual.

(e) *Contamination control.* Each manufacturer shall establish and maintain procedures to prevent contamination of equipment or product by substances that could reasonably be expected to have an adverse effect on product quality.

(f) *Buildings.* Buildings shall be of suitable design and contain sufficient space to perform necessary operations, prevent mixups, and assure orderly handling.

(g) *Equipment.* Each manufacturer shall ensure that all equipment used in the manufacturing process meets specified requirements and is appropriately designed, constructed, placed, and installed to facilitate maintenance, adjustment, cleaning, and use.

(1) *Maintenance schedule.* Each manufacturer shall establish and maintain schedules for the adjustment, cleaning, and other maintenance of equipment to ensure that manufacturing specifications are met. Maintenance activities, including the date and individual(s) performing the maintenance activities, shall be documented.

(2) *Inspection.* Each manufacturer shall conduct periodic inspections in accordance with established procedures to ensure adherence to applicable equipment maintenance schedules. The inspections, including the date and individual(s) conducting the inspections, shall be documented.

(3) *Adjustment.* Each manufacturer shall ensure that any inherent limitations or allowable tolerances are visibly posted on or near equipment requiring periodic adjustments or are readily available to personnel performing these adjustments.

(h) *Manufacturing material.* Where a manufacturing material could reasonably be expected to have an adverse effect on product quality, the manufacturer shall establish and maintain procedures for the use and removal of such manufacturing material to ensure that it is removed or limited to an amount that does not adversely affect the device's quality. The removal or reduction of such manufacturing material shall be documented.

(i) *Automated processes.* When computers or automated data processing systems are used as part of production or the quality system, the manufacturer shall validate computer software for its intended use according to an established protocol. All software changes shall be validated before approval and issuance. These validation activities and results shall be documented.

§ 820.72 Inspection, measuring, and test equipment.

(a) *Control of inspection, measuring, and test equipment.* Each manufacturer shall ensure that all inspection, measuring, and test equipment, including mechanical, automated, or electronic inspection and test equipment, is suitable for its intended purposes and is capable of producing valid results. Each manufacturer shall establish and maintain procedures to ensure that equipment is routinely calibrated, inspected, checked, and maintained. The procedures shall include provisions for handling, preservation, and storage of equipment, so that its accuracy and fitness for use are maintained. These activities shall be documented.

(b) *Calibration.* Calibration procedures shall include specific directions and limits for accuracy and precision. When accuracy and precision limits are not met, there shall be provisions for remedial action to reestablish the limits and to evaluate whether there was any adverse effect on the device's quality. These activities shall be documented.

(1) *Calibration standards.* Calibration standards used for inspection, measuring, and test equipment shall be traceable to national or international standards. If national or international standards are not practical or available, the manufacturer shall use an independent reproducible standard. If no applicable standard exists, the manufacturer shall establish and maintain an in-house standard.

(2) *Calibration records.* The equipment identification, calibration dates, the individual performing each calibration, and the next calibration date shall be documented. These records shall be displayed on or near each piece of equipment or shall be readily available to the personnel using such equipment and to the individuals responsible for calibrating the equipment.

§ 820.75 Process validation.

(a) Where the results of a process cannot be fully verified by subsequent inspection and test, the process shall be validated with a high degree of assurance and approved according to established procedures. The validation activities and results, including the date and signature of the individual(s) approving the validation and where appropriate the major equipment validated, shall be documented.

(b) Each manufacturer shall establish and maintain procedures for monitoring and control of process parameters for validated processes to ensure that the specified requirements continue to be met.

(1) Each manufacturer shall ensure that validated processes are performed by qualified individual(s).

(2) For validated processes, the monitoring and control methods and data, the date performed, and, where appropriate, the individual(s) performing the process or the major equipment used shall be documented.

(c) When changes or process deviations occur, the manufacturer shall review and evaluate the process and perform revalidation where appropriate. These activities shall be documented.

Subpart H—Acceptance Activities

§ 820.80 Receiving, in-process, and finished device acceptance.

(a) *General.* Each manufacturer shall establish and maintain procedures for acceptance activities. Acceptance activities include inspections, tests, or other verification activities.

(b) *Receiving acceptance activities.* Each manufacturer shall establish and maintain procedures for acceptance of incoming product. Incoming product shall be inspected, tested, or otherwise verified as conforming to specified requirements. Acceptance or rejection shall be documented.

(c) *In-process acceptance activities.* Each manufacturer shall establish and maintain acceptance procedures, where appropriate, to ensure that specified requirements for in-process product are met. Such procedures shall ensure that in-process product is controlled until the required inspection and tests or other verification activities have been completed, or necessary approvals are received, and are documented.

(d) *Final acceptance activities.* Each manufacturer shall establish and maintain procedures for finished device acceptance to ensure that each production run, lot, or batch of finished devices meets acceptance criteria. Finished devices shall be held in quarantine or otherwise adequately

controlled until released. Finished devices shall not be released for distribution until: (1) The activities required in the DMR are completed; (2) the associated data and documentation is reviewed; (3) the release is authorized by the signature of a designated individual(s); and (4) the authorization is dated.

(e) *Acceptance records.* Each manufacturer shall document acceptance activities required by this part. These records shall include: (1) The acceptance activities performed; (2) the dates acceptance activities are performed; (3) the results; (4) the signature of the individual(s) conducting the acceptance activities; and (5) where appropriate the equipment used. These records shall be part of the DHR.

§ 820.86 Acceptance status.

Each manufacturer shall identify by suitable means the acceptance status of product, to indicate the conformance or nonconformance of product with acceptance criteria. The identification of acceptance status shall be maintained throughout manufacturing, packaging, labeling, installation, and servicing of the product to ensure that only product which has passed the required acceptance activities is distributed, used, or installed.

Subpart I—Nonconforming Product

§ 820.90 Nonconforming product.

(a) *Control of nonconforming product.* Each manufacturer shall establish and maintain procedures to control product that does not conform to specified requirements. The procedures shall address the identification, documentation, evaluation, segregation, and disposition of nonconforming product. The evaluation of nonconformance shall include a determination of the need for an investigation and notification of the persons or organizations responsible for the nonconformance. The evaluation and any investigation shall be documented.

(b) *Nonconformity review and disposition.* (1) Each manufacturer shall establish and maintain procedures that define the responsibility for review and the authority for the disposition of nonconforming product. The procedures shall set forth the review and disposition process. Disposition of nonconforming product shall be documented. Documentation shall include the justification for use of nonconforming product and the signature of the individual(s) authorizing the use.

R

(2) Each manufacturer shall establish and maintain procedures for rework, to include retesting and reevaluation of the nonconforming product after rework, to ensure that the product meets its current approved specifications. Rework and reevaluation activities, including a determination of any adverse effect from the rework upon the product, shall be documented in the DHR.

Subpart J—Corrective and Preventive Action

§ 820.100   Corrective and preventive action.

(a) Each manufacturer shall establish and maintain procedures for implementing corrective and preventive action. The procedures shall include requirements for:

(1) Analyzing processes, work operations, concessions, quality audit reports, quality records, service records, complaints, returned product, and other sources of quality data to identify existing and potential causes of nonconforming product, or other quality problems. Appropriate statistical methodology shall be employed where necessary to detect recurring quality problems;

(2) Investigating the cause of nonconformities relating to product, processes, and the quality system;

(3) Identifying the action(s) needed to correct and prevent recurrence of nonconforming product and other quality problems;

(4) Verifying or validating the corrective and preventive action to ensure that such action is effective and does not adversely affect the finished device;

(5) Implementing and recording changes in methods and procedures needed to correct and prevent identified quality problems;

(6) Ensuring that information related to quality problems or nonconforming product is disseminated to those directly responsible for assuring the quality of such product or the prevention of such problems; and

(7) Submitting relevant information on identified quality problems, as well as corrective and preventive actions, for management review.

(b) All activities required under this section, and their results, shall be documented.

Subpart K—Labeling and Packaging Control

§ 820.120   Device labeling.

Each manufacturer shall establish and maintain procedures to control labeling activities.

(a) *Label integrity.* Labels shall be printed and applied so as to remain legible and affixed during the customary conditions of processing, storage, handling, distribution, and where appropriate use.

(b) *Labeling inspection.* Labeling shall not be released for storage or use until a designated individual(s) has examined the labeling for accuracy including, where applicable, the correct expiration date, control number, storage instructions, handling instructions, and any additional processing instructions. The release, including the date and signature of the individual(s) performing the examination, shall be documented in the DHR.

(c) *Labeling storage.* Each manufacturer shall store labeling in a manner that provides proper identification and is designed to prevent mixups.

(d) *Labeling operations.* Each manufacturer shall control labeling and packaging operations to prevent labeling mixups. The label and labeling used for each production unit, lot, or batch shall be documented in the DHR.

(e) *Control number.* Where a control number is required by § 820.65, that control number shall be on or shall accompany the device through distribution.

§ 820.130   Device packaging.

Each manufacturer shall ensure that device packaging and shipping containers are designed and constructed to protect the device from alteration or damage during the customary conditions of processing, storage, handling, and distribution.

Subpart L—Handling, Storage, Distribution, and Installation

§ 820.140   Handling.

Each manufacturer shall establish and maintain procedures to ensure that mixups, damage, deterioration, contamination, or other adverse effects to product do not occur during handling.

§ 820.150   Storage.

(a) Each manufacturer shall establish and maintain procedures for the control of storage areas and stock rooms for product to prevent mixups, damage, deterioration, contamination, or other adverse effects pending use or distribution and to ensure that no obsolete, rejected, or deteriorated product is used or distributed. When the quality of product deteriorates over time, it shall be stored in a manner to facilitate proper stock rotation, and its condition shall be assessed as appropriate.

(b) Each manufacturer shall establish and maintain procedures that describe the methods for authorizing receipt from and dispatch to storage areas and stock rooms.

§ 820.160   Distribution.

(a) Each manufacturer shall establish and maintain procedures for control and distribution of finished devices to ensure that only those devices approved for release are distributed and that purchase orders are reviewed to ensure that ambiguities and errors are resolved before devices are released for distribution. Where a device's fitness for use or quality deteriorates over time, the procedures shall ensure that expired devices or devices deteriorated beyond acceptable fitness for use are not distributed.

(b) Each manufacturer shall maintain distribution records which include or refer to the location of:

(1) The name and address of the initial consignee;

(2) The identification and quantity of devices shipped;

(3) The date shipped; and

(4) Any control number(s) used.

§ 820.170   Installation.

(a) Each manufacturer of a device requiring installation shall establish and maintain adequate installation and inspection instructions, and where appropriate test procedures. Instructions and procedures shall include directions for ensuring proper installation so that the device will perform as intended after installation. The manufacturer shall distribute the instructions and procedures with the device or otherwise make them available to the person(s) installing the device.

(b) The person installing the device shall ensure that the installation, inspection, and any required testing are performed in accordance with the manufacturer's instructions and procedures and shall document the inspection and any test results to demonstrate proper installation.

Subpart M—Records

§ 820.180   General requirements.

All records required by this part shall be maintained at the manufacturing establishment or other location that is reasonably accessible to responsible officials of the manufacturer and to employees of FDA designated to perform inspections. Such records, including those not stored at the inspected establishment, shall be made readily available for review and copying by FDA employee(s). Such records shall be legible and shall be stored to minimize deterioration and to prevent loss. Those records stored in automated data processing systems shall be backed up.

(a) *Confidentiality.* Records deemed confidential by the manufacturer may be marked to aid FDA in determining whether information may be disclosed under the public information regulation in part 20 of this chapter.

(b) *Record retention period.* All records required by this part shall be retained for a period of time equivalent to the design and expected life of the device, but in no case less than 2 years from the date of release for commercial distribution by the manufacturer.

(c) *Exceptions.* This section does not apply to the reports required by § 820.20(c) Management review, § 820.22 Quality audits, and supplier audit reports used to meet the requirements of § 820.50(a) Evaluation of suppliers, contractors, and consultants, but does apply to procedures established under these provisions. Upon request of a designated employee of FDA, an employee in management with executive responsibility shall certify in writing that the management reviews and quality audits required under this part, and supplier audits where applicable, have been performed and documented, the dates on which they were performed, and that any required corrective action has been undertaken.

§ 820.181   Device master record.

Each manufacturer shall maintain device master records (DMR's). Each manufacturer shall ensure that each DMR is prepared and approved in accordance with § 820.40. The DMR for each type of device shall include, or refer to the location of, the following information:

(a) Device specifications including appropriate drawings, composition, formulation, component specifications, and software specifications;

(b) Production process specifications including the appropriate equipment specifications, production methods, production procedures, and production environment specifications;

(c) Quality assurance procedures and specifications including acceptance criteria and the quality assurance equipment to be used;

(d) Packaging and labeling specifications, including methods and processes used; and

(e) Installation, maintenance, and servicing procedures and methods.

§ 820.184   Device history record.

Each manufacturer shall maintain device history records (DHR's). Each manufacturer shall establish and maintain procedures to ensure that DHR's for each batch, lot, or unit are maintained to demonstrate that the device is manufactured in accordance with the DMR and the requirements of this part. The DHR shall include, or refer to the location of, the following information:

(a) The dates of manufacture;

(b) The quantity manufactured;

(c) The quantity released for distribution;

(d) The acceptance records which demonstrate the device is manufactured in accordance with the DMR;

(e) The primary identification label and labeling used for each production unit; and

(f) Any device identification(s) and control number(s) used.

§ 820.186   Quality system record.

Each manufacturer shall maintain a quality system record (QSR). The QSR shall include, or refer to the location of, procedures and the documentation of activities required by this part that are not specific to a particular type of device(s), including, but not limited to, the records required by § 820.20. Each manufacturer shall ensure that the QSR is prepared and approved in accordance with § 820.40.

§ 820.198   Complaint files.

(a) Each manufacturer shall maintain complaint files. Each manufacturer shall establish and maintain procedures for receiving, reviewing, and evaluating complaints by a formally designated unit. Such procedures shall ensure that:

(1) All complaints are processed in a uniform and timely manner;

(2) Oral complaints are documented upon receipt; and

(3) Complaints are evaluated to determine whether the complaint represents an event which is required to be reported to FDA under part 803 or 804 of this chapter, Medical Device Reporting.

(b) Each manufacturer shall review and evaluate all complaints to determine whether an investigation is necessary. When no investigation is made, the manufacturer shall maintain a record that includes the reason no investigation was made and the name of the individual responsible for the decision not to investigate.

(c) Any complaint involving the possible failure of a device, labeling, or packaging to meet any of its specifications shall be reviewed, evaluated, and investigated, unless such investigation has already been performed for a similar complaint and another investigation is not necessary.

(d) Any complaint that represents an event which must be reported to FDA under part 803 or 804 of this chapter shall be promptly reviewed, evaluated, and investigated by a designated individual(s) and shall be maintained in a separate portion of the complaint files or otherwise clearly identified. In addition to the information required by § 820.198(e), records of investigation under this paragraph shall include a determination of:

(1) Whether the device failed to meet specifications;

(2) Whether the device was being used for treatment or diagnosis; and

(3) The relationship, if any, of the device to the reported incident or adverse event.

(e) When an investigation is made under this section, a record of the investigation shall be maintained by the formally designated unit identified in paragraph (a) of this section. The record of investigation shall include:

(1) The name of the device;

(2) The date the complaint was received;

(3) Any device identification(s) and control number(s) used;

(4) The name, address, and phone number of the complainant;

(5) The nature and details of the complaint;

(6) The dates and results of the investigation;

(7) Any corrective action taken; and

(8) Any reply to the complainant.

(f) When the manufacturer's formally designated complaint unit is located at a site separate from the manufacturing establishment, the investigated complaint(s) and the record(s) of investigation shall be reasonably accessible to the manufacturing establishment.

(g) If a manufacturer's formally designated complaint unit is located outside of the United States, records required by this section shall be reasonably accessible in the United States at either:

(1) A location in the United States where the manufacturer's records are regularly kept; or

(2) The location of the initial distributor.

Subpart N—Servicing

§ 820.200   Servicing.

(a) Where servicing is a specified requirement, each manufacturer shall establish and maintain instructions and procedures for performing and verifying that the servicing meets the specified requirements.

(b) Each manufacturer shall analyze service reports with appropriate

R

statistical methodology in accordance with § 820.100.

(c) Each manufacturer who receives a service report that represents an event which must be reported to FDA under part 803 or 804 of this chapter shall automatically consider the report a complaint and shall process it in accordance with the requirements of § 820.198.

(d) Service reports shall be documented and shall include:

(1) The name of the device serviced;

(2) Any device identification(s) and control number(s) used;

(3) The date of service;

(4) The individual(s) servicing the device;

(5) The service performed; and

(6) The test and inspection data.

Subpart O—Statistical Techniques

§ 820.250   Statistical techniques.

(a) Where appropriate, each manufacturer shall establish and maintain procedures for identifying valid statistical techniques required for establishing, controlling, and verifying the acceptability of process capability and product characteristics.

(b) Sampling plans, when used, shall be written and based on a valid statistical rationale. Each manufacturer shall establish and maintain procedures to ensure that sampling methods are adequate for their intended use and to ensure that when changes occur the sampling plans are reviewed. These activities shall be documented.

Dated: October 1, 1996.

David A. Kessler,

Commissioner of Food and Drugs.

Donna E. Shalala,

Secretary of Health and Human Services.

[FR Doc. 96–25720 Filed 10–3–96; 11:22 am]

BILLING CODE 4160–01–P

R

APPENDIX D – INDEX

APPENDIX D. INDEX

Bold italic entries represent the major sections of the Quality System regulation. **Bold** page numbers represent the primary description or reference. Page numbers 526xx are the Federal Register pages of the Final Rule for the Quality System regulation, which can be found in Appendix C.

QUICK REFERENCE TABS